SECOND EDITION

Focus on Science 8

Frank J. Flanagan   Sandra J. Hague

 D.C. Heath Canada Ltd.

ISBN 0-669-95279-6

Developmental Editors: Tom Shields Creative & Editorial Services/Jean Bullard
Stylistic and Copy Editor: Louise Oborne
Production Editor: Louise Oborne
Photo Researchers: Sandra LaFortune/ Hilary Forrest

Design: Peter Maher
Illustration: Catherine Farley/Nick Owocki/ Peter Van Gulik/Jenny Duda

Typesetting: Compeer Typographic Services Limited
Colour Separation: Passage Productions Inc.
Cover Photo: The Wave by Alexander Wyse; photographed by Peter Paterson

Canadian Cataloguing in Publication Data

Flanagan, Frank J.
    Focus on science 8

2nd ed.
For use in schools.
Includes index.
ISBN 0-669-95279-6

1. Science — Juvenile literature. I. Hague, Sandra J. II. Title.

Q161.2.F53 1989   500   C89-093004-X

Printed and bound in Canada
1 2 3 4 5 6 MMT 94 93 92 91 90 89

Acknowledgements

The writing and preparation of a textbook is a complex task that involves the expertise and personal commitment of many people. We would like to thank D.C. Heath Canada for its continued support, and in particular the following members of senior management: Robert H. Ross (President) and William McLean (Director of Marketing). Ron Cornelius (Editorial Program Manager) and Stephanie Cox (Production Manager) are to be commended for managing the development and publication of this textbook.

We would especially like to emphasize the editing of Tom Shields, Jean Bullard, and Louise Oborne. Laura Jones, who helped to manage the production of the book, is also deserving of praise.

The visual quality of the book is due to the efforts of Birgitte Nielsen (Photographer), Sandra LaFortune and Hilary Forrest (Photo Researchers), Peter Maher (Designer), and the illustrators: Peter Van Gulik, Nick Owocki, Catherine Farley, and Jenny Duda.

Frank Flanagan would like to extend his warmest appreciation to his family—Ann, Lynne, and Paul—for their love and support.

Sandi Hague would like to thank her family—Murray, Lisa, and Leslie — for their support and understanding during the development of the manuscript.

Many teachers also made significant contributions by commenting on the content of the manuscript during its development. We extend our sincere appreciation to George Findlay, Brian Smith, Kent Weatherilt, John Pettit, Caroline Toffolo, and Richard Plantus for their thoughtful reviews.

This textbook is the second edition of *Focus on Science: Exploring the Physical World* and *Focus on Science: Exploring the Natural World* by Frank J. Flanagan and Douglas Gough. To address changes in science curricula, this second edition contains a considerable amount of new material, as well as material from the original texts that has been extensively revised.

Table of Contents

4   Soil and Plant Ecology/ 175

Chapter 5   Heat and Temperature/ 231

**Chapter 6
Adaptations/ 291**

Introduction

Focus on Science 8 (Second Edition) has been written to help you become scientifically literate. The twentieth century has been one of great scientific discovery and technological change. The advent of flight and the discovery of penicillin are two examples of human achievement that we often take for granted. More familiar, perhaps, are developments in space-age and medical technology. Because of these advances, humans have been able to live for long periods of time in space, and the detection and treatment of diseases using lasers, MRI scanners, vaccines, bionics, and transplants has improved the quality of our lives. These are examples of the positive impact science has had on our lives.

However, some technological advances, such as the development of the insecticide DDT, have had detrimental effects, especially on our environment. Although the development of nuclear power has revolutionized the energy industry, the impact of accidents like Chernobyl has yet to be determined.

Scientific development is also playing a major role in the job market. Increasingly, career opportunities in computer technology, communications, and research and development will depend on a greater knowledge of science.

Our ability to understand scientific developments and discoveries, and to determine their costs and benefits to society will depend on how well we understand the nature of science. *Focus on Science 8* aims to help you become more aware of the nature of science and the impact it has on your life.

The text is organized into seven chapters. Emphasis is placed on scientific investigation, the development of process skills, and the basic understanding of scientific knowledge. Since science is "doing," the *Investigation* and *Try this!* activities are designed for your participation. These hands-on experiences will increase your knowledge of science and polish your skills in the methods of scientific inquiry. Each chapter contains *Section review questions*, a *Chapter review* with a *Words to know* list, and suggestions for science projects and further scientific investigation.

Focus on Science 8 also includes the following special feature pages that focus on specific science-related themes.

• **SCIENCE IN OUR LIVES:** A brief look at a particular scientific or technological development and how it affects our everyday lives.

• **PEOPLE IN SCIENCE:** Mini-biographies of Canadians and their contributions in the field of science and technology.

• **SCIENCE IN SOCIETY:** An issue-related feature that explores the positive and negative sides of a development in science and technology, and the impact of that development on society or on the natural environment. Critical thinking and debates are encouraged in the activity included in each feature.

• **SCIENCE-RELATED CAREER:** An interview with a professional whose occupation requires a science education or is influenced by science and technology.

The authors of *Focus on Science 8* hope that you will enjoy this science course and its many hands-on investigations. Have fun and be sure to follow the safety reminders that appear in red throughout the text.

F.J.F.
S.J.H.

Focus on Science 8

SECOND EDITION

1

Investigating Living Things

Karen was kneeling by a shrub near the school's entrance when her friend Josef walked by.

"What are you looking at, Karen?" asked Josef.

"I'm not sure," said Karen. "It's some kind of insect I've never seen before. Do you know what it is, Josef?"

"Let's see," Josef said, kneeling down to look. "I've never seen one like it before either, but it seems to like living on this plant."

"I think we should try to find out what kind of insect it is," said Karen, picking up her science notebook.

"That's a great idea!" said Josef. "If you make notes about what the insect looks like, I'll make a sketch of the location and the plant it is living on. I wonder if there are others like it in the neighbourhood?"

"Let's get the insect guidebook from school," said Karen. "We could use it to help us identify the insect and the place where it usually lives."

By asking questions about how and why living things survive where they do, Karen and Josef are acting in much the same way as biologists do. To investigate these questions, scientists use the process skills of the scientific method. In this chapter, you will also use the scientific method to investigate living things.

3

Scientists investigate nature by using the process skills of the scientific method. Which skills do you think this scientist is using?

1.1 Scientific processes

Scientists lead fascinating lives because they are always investigating things. **Investigation** is a word that means "careful search." A search begins with a problem. Scientists begin their investigation by defining the specific problem they want to explore. A biologist, for example, may want to know how acid rain affects the growth of certain plants. An ecologist, who studies the relationships among living things, might want to know how the loss of these plants could affect the well-being of other things living around them. These scientists research what is already known about the problems they want to investigate. Each uses his or her knowledge to state a hypothesis. A **hypothesis** is an educated guess about what the outcome of an investigation might be. A hypothesis is stated to suggest a relationship between the variables being tested in an experiment.

Defining a problem and stating a hypothesis are just two of the scientific process skills that scientists use in their investigations. They must also design and carry out experiments that will test their hypotheses. During these experiments, scientists examine everything that could relate to their hypotheses. They test and control variables, and they observe and record the results. When an experiment is completed, scientists make **conclusions** based on the observations they have made during the experiment. Sometimes the conclusions scientists make support their hypotheses, and sometimes they do not. When a conclusion does not support the hypothesis, a new hypothesis must be made. Scientists compare their conclusions with those reached by other scientists working on similar problems and hypotheses. From this accumulated knowledge, scientists form **generalizations** that can be tested in new experiments. They also try to find ways to use and apply their conclusions and generalizations.

Experimenting includes important scientific process skills. Combined with defining problems and stating hypotheses, other process skills such as predicting, inferring, reporting, measuring, observing, controlling variables, and classifying are often used.

Does all this make scientists sound as though the work they do is complicated? It is. But most scientists have discovered that investigating, experimenting, and reporting results can

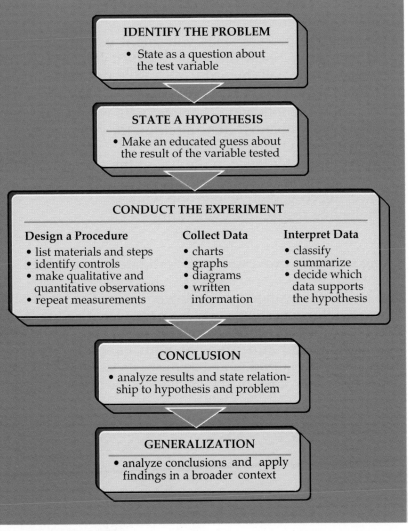

Figure 1–1 Process skills

be challenging, rewarding, and exciting. The investigations in this chapter will help you to discover how challenging and satisfying science can be for you, too.

Try this!

Figure 1–1 shows how various process skills might be used in an investigation. Examine the skills carefully to see how they relate. Then see if you can write answers to the following questions in your notebook.

1. Outline the process skills you might use to conduct an investigation. Show the order in which you would expect to use them. Will the order always be the same? Explain why or why not.

2. Which of the following characteristics would help scientists solve problems? State a reason for your choice.
   a) having an inquiring mind
   b) having confidence in the use of the scientific method to solve problems
   c) being co-operative in group work
   d) having respect for living things

Using scientific processes to investigate living things

You guide your canoe quietly toward a reed-covered shore where wildflowers creep away from the water's edge. A chorus of loons strikes echoes across the misty lake, while a beaver slaps its tail and dives as your canoe approaches. Alarmed by the sound, a moose raises its head from its meal of yellow water lilies in the shallows nearby. Metallic-blue

Which process skills would you use to study how this moose is able to survive in this environment?

Figure 1–2

dragonflies drone around you, making dinner out of the mosquitoes in your path. Nearing the shore, you find a portage that climbs through the forest to the next lake.

People have always been interested in living things such as those in Canada's wilderness. Scientists use the process skills of the scientific method to learn about the nature of living things. See how many of these skills you can use, and how much fun you can have, while exploring living things in Investigation 1. One skill you will need is your ability to use your senses to observe carefully. Another will be your ability to read and to use the knowledge available in guidebooks, for example, to help you identify the things that you observe.

Poison oak

Poison sumac

Poison ivy

Caution: Avoid any plants or animals that you know you are allergic to. Tell your teacher if you have any allergies before you begin this investigation. Avoid poisonous plants such as poison oak, poison sumac, and poison ivy.

Investigation 1   Investigating living things

PURPOSE
To become familiar with the skills that will help you to observe, identify, and record information about living things in their natural environments.

MATERIALS
pencil
paper
clipboard
containers
collecting jars with
  perforated lids

nature guidebooks on plants
  and animals
digging tools such as small
  shovels or garden trowels

PROCEDURE
1. Select one of your classmates to be your partner. Investigate an environment identified by your teacher.
2. Draw a map of the area and chart the route you will take to go there.

Be careful not to harm living ~~~~~~~~natural habi-
~~~~~~insects, worms,
~~~amphibians. Never disturb
or collect endangered species.
If you are unsure, check with
your teacher.

3. Observe and identify as many different kinds of living ~~~ sketch of the landscape to show the type of environment you are investigating.

2. Sketch four or five kinds of living organisms and describe their features in a chart like the one below.

Living Organism	Sketch	Description
Mushroom		
Dragonfly		
.		
.		
.		

3. List the physical conditions of the environment that you explored. For example, was it moist or dry? Was it rocky? Did it have a source of water? Did it have much soil?

CONCLUSIONS

Which process skills did you use most to investigate living things? Which process skills did you use least? What can you conclude about the skills you used?

Discussion questions

1. Do you think it is necessary to use all of the process skills in an investigation? Why or why not?

2. When you use the process skills in an investigation, should you always use them in the same order? Explain your answer.

3. Do you think you could use these skills in non-scientific studies? Explain your answer.

These coins are examples of metalworking.

Figure 1–3 Charles Darwin

Construct a classroom terrarium... ... lected specimens for further investigation. A terrarium is a glass container where land animals and plants can be kept. An aquarium with a clear plastic lid makes an excellent terrarium. Try to duplicate the environment in which you found your specimens as closely as possible. Keep in mind heat, light, temperature, soil, and moisture requirements. You might find some ideas at your school resource centre or library. Observe your specimens carefully for two weeks and record your observations. Afterward, carefully return the specimens to their natural environment.

The growth of scientific knowledge

In order to survive in their environments, people have always investigated nature and living things. Early peoples had to be able to solve problems such as how to keep warm, where to live, which animals were dangerous, and where the best areas were to find edible plants. Later, as humans developed agriculture and began to settle in villages, more discoveries were made about how to grow crops and raise animals for food. By asking questions, and using a trial-and-error method of investigation, people were able to develop metalworking, methods of transportation and record-keeping, and systems of measurement.

The scientific method is a problem-solving system that brings order to a trial-and-error method of discovery. As knowledge about nature increased, people began to study science for its own sake. The processes of the scientific method that you will learn about in this chapter have only been applied consciously to problem solving during the past 500 years. However, our understanding of nature has expanded greatly because of the work of scientists, such as Galileo, Copernicus, and Darwin, who used the scientific method in their research and experiments.

Good scientists are always open-minded about what they observe and the conclusions and generalizations they draw from the experiments they perform. Sometimes a new observation may extend a previous conclusion or generalization. Each conclusion or generalization that is made is based on

The observations that are made during an archaeological dig help scientists to form conclusions about how early peoples lived.

the relationship thought to exist between two or more observations. If a new observation is added, or an old one is altered, then the conclusion or generalization made from the observations must also change. Scientists accept results as valid only when they occur every time an experiment is repeated under identical conditions.

An example will help you to understand this idea. Scientists in the first part of the twentieth century believed that all lobe-finned fish had died out 70 million years ago. They believed this because of the relationship between two major observations: first, fossil records showed no evidence of lobe-finned fish after 70 million years, and second, no one in recorded history had ever seen a lobe-finned fish. Imagine their surprise when one of these ''extinct'' fish was caught

The coelacanth was thought to be extinct until it was rediscovered in the Indian Ocean in 1938.

in the Indian Ocean in 1938. Obviously, certain conclusions and generalizations had to be changed.

Scientific knowledge must never be thought of as absolute truth. It is, rather, the sum of our understanding about how we *think* things in nature work at a particular point in time. As our knowledge changes, so does our understanding. The scientific method has allowed scientific knowledge to grow rapidly. However, scientists continuously revise and update this knowledge as they make new observations. Are you beginning to see why an open and inquiring mind is useful in scientific study? Remember that the most important thing is to ask questions that are worth investigating.

Try this!

Scientists believe that all living things possess these basic characteristics: cells, metabolism, growth, reproduction, movement and locomotion, irritability, and adaptation. Scientists investigate different living organisms to discover how they perform these life functions. Comparing the specific characteristics of different organisms allows scientists to test the validity of their definition of life.

How do humans and birds differ in the ways they carry out their life functions? In what ways are they similar?

You can conduct an investigation of your own by completing the comparison chart below in your notebook. Use your class resource centre and school library. You may want to investigate other living things instead of those listed.

Characteristic	Human	Maple Tree	Spider	Fish
Cellular Nature	• made up of many cells			
Growth	• growth from baby to adult			
Metabolism	• produces heat to keep warm			
Movement and Locomotion	• walks • runs			
Reproduction	• two parents			
Irritability	• nervous system			
Adaptation	• can think and reason			

The life sciences

The scientific method has led to a vast amount of knowledge. But by the late seventeenth century, scientific knowledge had grown so much scientists began to specialize in one area or field of science. This led to the development of scientific fields such as geology, astronomy, chemistry, physics, mathematics, and biology. However, even these fields have been subdivided as scientific knowledge grows. Consider biology, for example. Biology means ''the study of life.'' Today, scientific knowledge about life is so great that biology has been divided up into many smaller fields known as the **life sciences**. These sciences are divided into two main branches: botany (the study of plants) and zoology (the study of animals). Some of the life sciences within these branches are listed in Table 1.1 on page 14.

Why do you think scientists study plants?

Table 1.1 Life sciences

Field	Subject Observed and Studied
Anatomy	• the structure of living things
Bacteriology	• the study of bacteria
Biochemistry	• the chemical processes that occur in living things and their effects
Biophysics	• the physical movements and processes, such as forces and pressures, that living things experience
Cytology	• the cells of living things
Ecology	• living things and their relationship to each other in any particular environment
Genetics	• the characteristics passed on from generation to generation by one species to its offspring
Ornithology	• the study of birds

Section review questions

1. What is an investigation? What do you have to state at the beginning of any investigation?
2. What is a hypothesis? List four other process skills that scientists use in their investigations.
3. How has the use of the scientific method affected the development of scientific knowledge?
4. Why has it been necessary to subdivide the field of biology? What are the two main branches of biology? Why are they called life sciences?
5. Many life scientists need to know about more than one field of science. Biochemists, for example, need to know about biology *and* chemistry. Can you think of any other examples? List other fields that scientists who study the life sciences in Table 1.1 would need to know.

Maud Leonora Menten

Maud Leonora Menten was born in Lambton, Ontario, in 1879. She attended the University of Toronto and became one of its first female graduates in medicine. After publishing some scientific papers, she received several fellowships that allowed her to study further. She became involved in cancer research at the Rockefeller Institute for Medical Research in New York. From there, she travelled to Berlin, Germany, where she continued her experiments.

Together with Dr. Leonor Michaelis, she developed conclusions and generalizations about the behaviour of enzymes. (Enzymes are complex proteins produced in a living cell that can cause chemical changes in other substances.) Their findings about these complex chemicals became widely accepted by the scientific community, resulting in the Michaelis-Menten Equation, which was named in their honour in 1913. This equation led to the expansion of research in the field of biochemistry. Today, it is regarded as fundamental to the study of the chemical nature of living things.

In 1916, Maud Menten received her doctorate in biochemistry at the University of Chicago. She was later appointed a full professor in pathology at the University of Pittsburg. She remained there until her retirement in 1950. During her lifetime, she wrote and published over 70 scientific papers. Most of these papers were related to cancer research.

Modern scientists consider Menten's work to be more important today than it was when it was originally published because more research concerning enzymes is being done. Her dedication is an inspiration to science students everywhere. On July 11, 1979 —the hundredth anniversary of Menten's birth—a plaque was unveiled at Queen's Park in Toronto by the 11th International Congress of Biochemistry. It is a tribute to the great contributions of Maud Leonora Menten.

1.2 Developing scientific process skills

Do you remember the first time you put on a pair of ice skates? A friend may have explained how to lace up the skates and how to glide forward on them, one foot after the other. It probably sounded quite simple at the time. After all, other people were skating around having fun, and they seemed to be moving with no effort at all. So what happened?

Cycling and skating are two skills people can learn. By practising, you can learn the process skills of the scientific method.

Did you know?
You can use the process skills you develop to help you solve problems or make decisions about other things in your life. For example, collecting information and making conclusions based on this data could help you to decide what kind of bicycle to buy or where your family might go on vacation.

How many times did you fall and get up before you could circle the rink for the first time?

Skating is a skill people learn. Skills are abilities that you gain as the result of much practice. It takes lots of practice to skate well, to play the piano, to shoot a basketball, or to write well.

The scientific method is a way of using specific skills to approach a problem in a systematic way. To become skilled at using the scientific method, it is necessary to practise these skills. Let's review and practise these skills. Then you can design your own scientific experiment.

Identify a problem

Scientific investigation starts with a **scientific problem**. The problems that scientists deal with are varied. Some people believe that the most important problems today are related to issues such as the greenhouse effect, pollution of air and water, acid rain, and the use of chemicals to control insects. Because these issues are wide-ranging, scientists try to ask questions to help them narrow the focus of an issue so it can be investigated. For example, what effect does the use of insecticides have on the quality of lake or river water and the fish who live in that environment?

A scientist must then decide whether his or her question is specific enough for a scientific investigation? A question that can be investigated using the scientific method should have the following characteristics.

1. The question should ask how one factor affects another factor.
2. The factors should be easy to identify as variables that can be controlled and tested.
3. The question should enable you to develop a hypothesis and a procedure to test it.

What question would you ask about this bullfrog that might lead you to a scientific investigation?

Try this!

1. Try to decide which of the following questions are most appropriate for scientific investigations. Write your answers in your notebook using this scale.

```
Poor      Fair      Good
0    1    2    3    4    5
L____I____I____I____I____I
```

a) Is the drainage of wetlands necessary for urban expansion?
b) Why is the greenhouse effect a problem?
c) How does the drainage of wetlands affect plants such as duckweed, cattails, and water lilies?
d) How does the intensity of light affect the mass of algae growing in an aquarium?
e) How do ants locate a food source during the winter months?

2. Test your reasons for rating some questions 3 or higher by doing the following.
   a) State the problem to be investigated.
   b) State a hypothesis.
   c) Identify the variable to be tested.
   d) Identify the variables to be controlled.
   Should you revise your ratings?
3. Write a good scientific investigation question for one of the following topics.
   - acid rain
   - nutrition
   - exercise
   - pesticides
   - plants

State a hypothesis

A **hypothesis** is an educated guess about what you expect will happen when you test a variable using the scientific method. A good hypothesis is usually written as a cause/effect statement. For example: An increase in the amount of sunlight will increase the growth of a bean plant. When stating a hypothesis, you should also make sure that it is closely related to the problem of an experiment so you are able to design a procedure to test it.

Try this!

To practise making a hypothesis, write one for each of the following questions.
1. What happens to food if it is left unwrapped in a warm cupboard for several days?
2. How will the absence of water affect the growth of a marigold plant?
3. How does perspiration affect the body temperature of an athlete during a competition?

Design an experiment

A good hypothesis should make a statement about the **variable** to be tested in an experiment. The next step is to design

These students have designed a procedure to help them test the variable in their experiment.

a procedure that will test the variable fairly. To conduct the test fairly, all variables that could affect the outcome, except the one being tested, need to be controlled. Then you must devise a series of steps or a procedure. These steps need to be clearly stated so that someone else could repeat the experiment to test your hypothesis. Each step should clearly identify what is to be measured or observed. Indicate which tests should be repeated to ensure the accuracy of your results.

Try this!

Joel is designing an experiment to investigate how fertilizer affects the growth of bean plants. His hypothesis is that fertilized bean plants will grow faster and larger than bean plants that haven't been fertilized. Based on what you have just read about designing an experiment, analyze the materials list and procedure on page 20. Is everything required to carry out the experiment listed? Are the steps of the procedure clear? What improvements would you make? Rewrite the materials list and the procedure if you think they are incomplete. State reasons for your changes.

MATERIALS
8 bean seeds
8 foam cups
potting soil

PROCEDURE
1. Soak all the bean seeds in water for 24 h.
2. Fill all the foam cups three-quarters full with potting soil.
3. Punch holes in each foam cup.
4. Plant one seed in each cup.
5. Label four foam cups A and four foam cups B.
6. Water the A cups daily. Add fertilizer to the B cups and water daily.
7. Observe the growth of the bean plants for two weeks.

Observe and record

While you are conducting an experiment, you must make careful qualitative and quantitative observations. These observations should be carefully recorded. Your recorded observations make up the data or the information the experiment was designed to investigate.

Scientists make **inferences** and **predictions** based on observations. For example, you might *infer* that a shiny, firm, red apple will be delicious when you bite into it. Your inference is a judgement based on what you have observed.

Which student is making qualitative observations and which one is making quantitative observations? How do you know?

Qualitative and quantitative observations
In scientific inquiry, it is possible to make two basic types of observations: qualitative observations and quantitative observations. **Qualitative observations** are those you make with your senses of sight, sound, smell, touch, and taste. However, you already know that your senses can be fooled. Sometimes things are not as they appear. As a result, qualitative observations alone are usually not precise enough for scientific inquiry.

Scientists also try to make as many quantitative observations as they can. **Quantitative observations** are measured quantities such as length, diameter, mass, or temperature. Observations such as "the flower is 5.0 cm long and 2.3 cm in diameter" are quantitative observations.

Try this!

To compare qualitative and quantitative observations of the physical characteristics of organisms, copy and complete the following two charts.

	Qualitative Observations		
	Specimen		
Physical Characteristic	Lima Bean	Leaf	Earthworm
Shape			
Texture			
Colour			
Odour			

	Quantitative Observations		
	Specimen		
Physical Characteristic	Lima Bean	Leaf	Earthworm
Width			
Length			
Height			
Mass			

What observations would you make about this plant? Would they be qualitative or quantitative observations?

1. Why is it important to make qualitative observations as well as quantitative observations?
2. How does skill in making quantitative observations affect the accuracy of your information about the physical characteristics of living things? Explain why this skill would be important to a biochemist, a veterinarian, and a lab technician.

3. Rank each of the following observations for their accuracy. Write your answers in your notebook using this scale.

| Poor | | Fair | | Good | |
| 0 | 1 | 2 | 3 | 4 | 5 |

a) A sheet of binder paper is smooth, white, 21.5 cm wide, 28 cm long, and has a mass of less than 0.1 g.
b) A fly is a living organism with six legs, four wings, a head, a thorax, and an abdomen.
c) An orange is round, porous, smooth, juicy, and has a circumference of 8 cm.
d) A glass of water is transparent, odourless, and tasteless.

Conduct your own qualitative and quantitative observations of the above items you rated less than 3. How would you improve the accuracy of these observations?

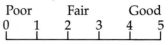

Try this!

1. You use metric measurement every day. Test your knowledge by classifying each of the following according to how you would measure them. Write your answers in a chart like the one below. (Sugar has been done as an example.)
   - load of bricks
   - paperclips
   - swimming-pool water
   - melting ice
   - milk
   - pencil
   - running track
   - photograph
   - soft drink
   - shampoo

Length (mm, cm, m, km)	Volume (mL, L, kL)	Mass (g, kg)	Temperature (°C)
		sugar	

2. State which measuring tool you would use to measure length, volume, mass, temperature, speed, and time.

Recording methods

You are asked to find and record data almost every day at school. In history class, you might research and make short notes about a particular event. In geography class, you may have to sketch a map showing the location of your school and home. You may also use these skills in your science class. But when you record data from a controlled experiment, you should use a chart or a graph. It is a good idea to develop a way to record data before you conduct any experiment.

How is this student recording information?

Try this!

How good are you at thinking of ways to record information?

1. Select one of these investigations and design a chart similar to the ones you have already been using in this chapter to record your data.
   a) Record the daily temperature, pH level, and water level of an aquarium.
   b) Record the amounts of what you eat daily for each of the four basic food groups.
   c) Record your pulse rate after 1, 2, 5, and 10 min of exercise.
2. Develop a circle graph and a bar graph to record the following information about how Lisa spent her weekly allowance of $10.00: a) $2.50 on milk, b) $1.25 on school dance, c) $1.25 on snacks, and d) $5.00 for savings . If Lisa were to continue to spend her allowance in the same way, how much could she expect to save in a four-week period?

Make conclusions

When you have completed the procedure of your experiment and recorded your observations, it is time to make conclusions. **Conclusions** are concise statements based on observations that support or do not support your hypothesis. Conclusions also answer the question stated in the problem. Sometimes you may obtain negative results. Honest reporting of your conclusions under these circumstances is essential. If your experiment can be repeated to produce similar results, your conclusions are valid.

Try this!

State a conclusion based on the following observations. Leslie placed three army caterpillars in a jar containing several poplar twigs and leaves. In a second jar, she placed three caterpillars and a clump of moss. She punched holes in both lids, sealed the jars, and placed them outside on a picnic table. After ten days, she examined the jars and noticed that three cocoons were attached to the bare poplar twigs and three inactive caterpillars were on the moss. Leslie removed the lids and observed the jars each day. One day, she discovered that one jar contained three empty cocoons and the other still contained three inactive caterpillars. What problem was Leslie investigating? What might her hypothesis have been? What can she conclude based on her observations?

You should be ready now to design and carry out your own investigation. Investigation 2 will give you an opportunity to practise your scientific process skills. Remember that properly identifying a problem and stating a hypothesis will help you to decide which variable is to be tested in an experiment, which variable you will expect to change as a result, and which variables are to be controlled.

Did you know?
Germination is when a seed ends its dormant state and develops leaves and a root system.

Investigation 2   An investigation that you design

PROBLEM
How does moisture affect the time marigold seeds take to germinate in a ten-day period?

MATERIALS
marigold seeds
6 pots (75 mm in diameter)
growth medium (1 part perlite,
    1 part vermiculite, 1 part
    coarse sand)
tap water
watering can
masking tape
marker
pencil

MEASURING TOOLS
graduated cylinder
thermometer

PROCEDURE
1. Identify the variable that you will test.
2. Identify all the other variables you will have to control that might affect the time the seeds take to germinate.
3. Describe how you will test the variable you identified in Step 1. (Remember that you should test the variable several times.)
4. Develop a procedure for planting and watering the seeds over a ten-day period.
5. Identify a suitable location in the classroom that will allow you to exercise control over the variables you identified in Step 2.
6. Write down a detailed problem, hypothesis, and procedure. Submit it for your teacher's approval.
7. When your teacher has approved your investigation, conduct your experiment following the procedures you have developed.

Developing a proper procedure is important when you are designing an experiment.

OBSERVATIONS
1. Make written notes about your observations in your notebook. Be sure to include the dates and times when the observations were made.
2. Design a chart to record the information from your observations. You might also use a graph, such as Figure 1–4, to record your information.

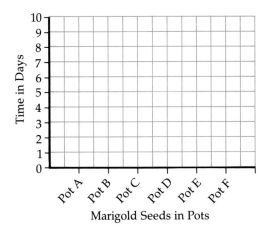

Figure 1–4   The effect of moisture on the germination of marigold seeds

CONCLUSIONS
Based on your observations, what can you conclude about the effect moisture has on the time marigold seeds take to germinate?

Discussion questions

1. State why it is important to identify the variable to be tested and the variables to be controlled.
2. How would you redesign this investigation if you wanted to find out how temperature affected germination?

Make generalizations

Conclusions can lead to new scientific knowledge. Before your experiment can be validated, however, it must be repeated many times by you and by others. Each time it is repeated, the same results must be observed. Then you can compare the observations and conclusions from these experiments. The point of comparison is to find a general rule that will apply whenever the experiment is repeated. This rule is called a **generalization**.

Apply the findings

In Investigation 2, you acquired new knowledge about the effect of moisture on seed germination. If you wanted to grow a vegetable garden, how would you apply this new knowledge to ensure the germination of the seeds you wanted to plant? The new knowledge derived from scientific research is of great importance. The findings of scientists are often applied by others to solve everyday problems. For example, research into the nature of specific diseases has led to the creation of new substances that can prevent or cure illnesses in living things. Current scientific research may lead to the development of cures for crippling diseases such as

The findings of scientific research may lead to the development of new drugs to treat diseases.

meningitis or the deadly AIDS virus. Funding for this scientific research often comes from charities and government agencies. Pharmaceutical companies also invest large amounts of money in scientific research they hope will lead to the development of new health products.

Section review questions

1. What is the scientific method? What is the best way to learn the process skills of the scientific method?
2. In order to investigate a question using the scientific method, what characteristics should the question have?
3. Why is it necessary to control all variables except the test variable in an experiment?
4. What is a hypothesis? Why is a hypothesis important to the design of an experimental procedure?
5. Describe the characteristics of a well-designed procedure.
6. Explain the difference between a qualitative observation and a quantitative observation. State why you think observations are the basis of scientific knowledge.
7. Match the following process skills with their definitions.

conclusion
generalization

inference

• a judgement based on observations
• a concise statement based on observations
• a rule developed from the same results occurring when an experiment is repeated

Did you know?
Natural resistance to disease is called immunity. Resistance that develops in a person as a result of vaccines is known as artificial immunity. Scientists in this century have been able to develop vaccines that have allowed people to develop artificial immunity against many types of flu and other diseases such as tuberculosis, polio, measles, and smallpox. Early in this century, millions of people died as a result of influenza and other epidemics.

The process of science

Scientific discoveries usually result when scientists use the skills of the scientific method in their investigations. But scientists also need to be persistent, to follow hunches, and, sometimes, to have a bit of luck.

Alexander Fleming, a Scottish scientist, spent many years developing scientific process skills in his research. When Fleming was a professor of bacteriology at St. Mary's Hospital in London, England, he conducted research to discover a substance that would destroy bacteria. In 1922, when he was studying a bacterial culture, he decided to test the effect of mucus on the microbes that were breeding in the culture. He made a solution and poured it over the culture. Much to Fleming's surprise, the microbes were immediately destroyed. Based on the results of this and similar experiments, Fleming concluded that secretions from the body contained a substance that destroyed germs naturally.

In 1928, as Fleming was conducting further germ experiments, he discovered that mould from the plant *Penicillium* had blown in through an open window and settled on an uncovered bacterial culture.

The mould that formed destroyed the bacteria. Fleming grew the mould and tested it on other types of bacteria. He found that his experiments using this mould were more effective in killing germs than his earlier experiments with mucus had been.

Today, you know that the drug produced from the chemical substances in the *Penicillium* mould is penicillin. It is one of the most important substances used by doctors to combat bacterial diseases. Fleming had hypothesized that there was some substance in the mould that had killed bacteria. He designed and conducted experiments to investigate this hypothesis. In addition to using the scientific process skills, Fleming kept an open mind and relied on his keen powers of observation. The discovery of penicillin was a discovery made through the process of science.

1.3 Control of variables

In Investigation 2, you had to identify all the variables related to your experiment before you carried it out. You had to decide which variable you wanted to test and which ones you had to control. Do you remember what the test variable was? Why was it necessary to identify the test variable and the control variables before conducting your experiment?

A **variable** is something that can vary, or change, during an experiment. What is tested is an educated guess called a hypothesis. The hypothesis states that if one variable is changed, it may affect another variable as a result. However, in order for the test to be fair, other variables that could affect the test variable must be controlled or not allowed to change.

Try this!

Copy the chart below into your notebook. For each scientific problem, identify the test variable, the variable affected, and the variables to be controlled. Could you design experiments around each problem? What materials would you need for each experiment?

Problem	Tested Variable	Affected Variable	Controls
1. How does coloured light affect the growth of plants?	light	growth rate	moisture light soil . . .
2. How does exercise affect the production of carbon dioxide?			
3. How does temperature affect the growth of yeast?			

Can you think of another scientific problem related to exercise? What variable might you test in an investigation?

Taking control

Being able to identify, control, and test certain variables is one of the most important scientific process skills. Controlling all variables except the test variable is particularly important. When all variables except the test variable are kept constant, any changes that result must be caused by the test variable. Keeping all other variables constant except the test variable is a **control**.

An important issue confronting many countries is the issue of acid rain. Normal rain is slightly acidic and has a pH level of 5.6. Acid rain, however, can be ten or even 100 times more acidic than normal rain. The pH levels of several common substances are shown in Figure 1–5.

Did you know?
The letters "pH" mean "potential hydrogen." They indicate the activity of electrically charged particles of hydrogen in a substance.

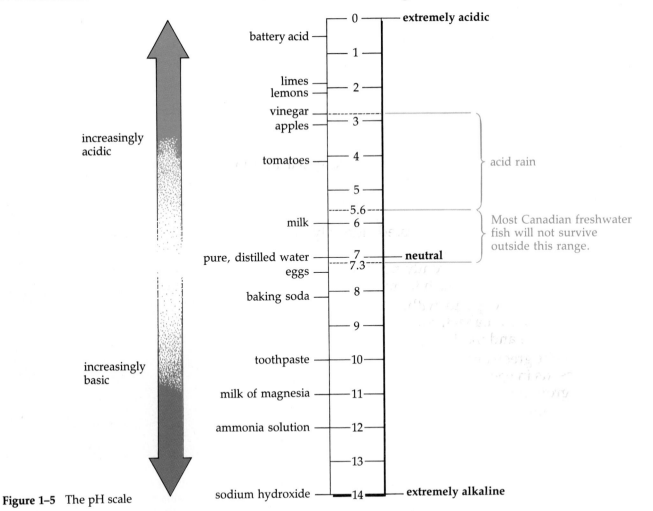

Figure 1–5   The pH scale

increasingly acidic

increasingly basic

battery acid — 0 — **extremely acidic**
— 1 —
limes — 2
lemons —
vinegar — 3
apples —
tomatoes — 4
— 5
-----5.6----
milk — 6
pure, distilled water — 7 — **neutral**
----7.3----
eggs —
baking soda — 8
— 9
toothpaste — 10
milk of magnesia — 11
ammonia solution — 12
— 13
sodium hydroxide — 14 — **extremely alkaline**

acid rain

Most Canadian freshwater fish will not survive outside this range.

Investigation 3   Using controls

PROBLEM
How will acidity affect the time green bean seeds take to
germinate?

MATERIALS   MEASURING TOOLS
12 green bean seeds   four 500-mL beakers
4 foam cups   measuring cup or
4 large beakers   graduated cylinder
growth medium (2 parts potting
    soil, 1 part coarse sand or
    perlite, 1 part vermiculite)
pencil
masking tape
marker
tap water
vinegar
wide-range indicator paper
    and pH scale
aluminum tray

HYPOTHESIS
State how you think increased levels of acidity will affect the
time green bean seeds take to germinate.

PROCEDURE
1. Identify the variable to be tested. Identify the variables
   you will have to control.
2. Use the pencil point to gently poke four or five drainage
   holes in the bottom of each foam cup.
3. Fill four of the cups to within 3 cm of their tops with
   growth medium. Label the cups A, B, C, and D using the
   masking tape and marker.
4. Soak all the green bean seeds in water for 24 h. Then plant
   three seeds in each foam cup. Cover the seeds with 1 cm
   of the growth medium.
5. Label the four beakers A, B, C, and D. Use the measuring
   cup or the graduated cylinder to measure 500 mL of water.
   Pour it into Beaker A. Pour 450 mL of water and 50 mL of
   vinegar into Beaker B. Pour 250 mL of water and 250 mL
   of vinegar into Beaker C. And pour 500 mL of vinegar into
   Beaker D.

6. Test each solution with wide-range indicator paper and record its pH level using the pH scale.
7. Place the four cups containing the green bean seeds on an aluminum tray on a sunny window ledge away from other sources of heat.
8. Once a day for a two-week period, add 20 mL of the solutions in beakers A, B, C, and D to the corresponding cups containing the green bean seeds.

OBSERVATIONS
1. Copy the chart below into your notebook.
2. Record the pH level for each solution.
3. Record the day when each bean seed germinated with an X.

	Beaker A			Beaker B			Beaker C			Beaker D		
	pH level ___			pH level ___			pH level ___			pH level ___		
Time in Days	Cup A (seed #)			Cup B (seed #)			Cup C (seed #)			Cup D (seed #)		
	1	2	3	1	2	3	1	2	3	1	2	3
1												
2												
3												
4												
5												
6												
7												
. . .												
14												

4. Draw a bar graph to record the germination rates of each green bean seed. An example is shown in Figure 1–6.

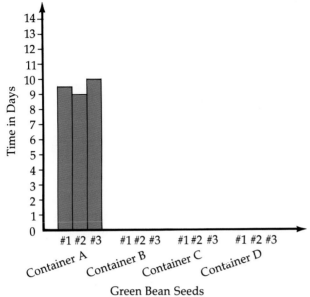

Figure 1–6   The effect of acidity on the germination of green bean seeds

CONCLUSIONS
Based on the information in your chart and graph, state how acidity affects the time green bean seeds take to germinate.

Discussion questions

1. Why was it necessary to use three seeds in each cup? Would your results have been more or less accurate if ten seeds had been used in each cup? Explain your answer.
2. Why was it necessary to carefully measure the acidity of each solution.
3. What generalization could you develop based on your observations and conclusion? How could ecologists apply this knowledge to the problem of acid rain?

In Investigation 3, you probably concluded that acidity (the tested variable) did have an effect on the germination of green bean seeds (the variable that changed as a result). Does this mean that only acidity can affect the germination of green bean seeds? What do you think? You can test your thinking in Investigation 4.

Investigation 4   Testing other variables

PROBLEM
How will different growth mediums affect the germination of green bean seeds?

MATERIALS

9 green bean seeds	masking tape
3 foam cups	marker
pencil	tap water
loam	watering can
clay	aluminum tray
sand	

HYPOTHESIS
State whether green bean seeds will germinate faster in loam, clay, or sand.

PROCEDURE
1. Identify the variable to be tested. Identify the variables to be controlled.
2. Use the pencil point to gently poke four or five drainage holes in the bottom of each foam cup.
3. Fill one of the foam cups within 3 cm of its top with loam. Use the masking tape and marker to label this cup Growth Medium A.
4. Fill the second foam cup to the same level with clay. Label this cup Growth Medium B.
5. Fill the third foam cup to the same level with sand. Label this cup Growth Medium C.
6. Soak all the seeds in water for 24 h. Then plant three seeds in each cup. Cover them with 1 cm of each growth medium, respectively.
7. Place the three cups on an aluminum tray on a sunny window ledge away from other sources of heat.

8. Water the green bean seeds with 20 mL of water daily over a two-week period. Check the cups daily for signs of germination.

OBSERVATIONS
1. Record your observations in a chart like the one below. Place an X in the appropriate row each time you notice that a seed has germinated.

Time in Days	Growth Medium A (seed #)			Growth Medium B (seed #)			Growth Medium C (seed #)		
	1	2	3	1	2	3	1	2	3
1									
2									
3									
4									
5									
6									
7									
8									
9									
10									
11									
12									
13									
14									

2. Determine the average number of days for germination of the seeds in each group.

CONCLUSIONS

Conclude how the germination of green bean seeds is affected by different growth mediums.

Discussion questions

1. Compare your results with those of your classmates. What generalizations can you make as a class? State two ways these findings might be put to use.
2. Hans finds no difference in the time it takes green bean seeds to germinate for the three growth mediums in Investigation 4. As a result, he concludes that the choice of growth medium has no effect on the germination of green bean seeds. What advice would you give him?
3. Your aunt hears about your investigations and decides to start her corn, pea, lettuce, and other garden seeds in the growth medium that gave you the best results. She wants to do this in a room she keeps very warm for this purpose. What would you tell her?

Try this!

State how you would redesign Investigation 4 to test the following growth mediums: perlite, vermiculite, garden soil, and leaf mould. Then set up your experiment at home and test each of these mediums in turn. Based on your results, which medium would you conclude is best for growing green bean seeds? Test other garden seeds as well. Are the results always the same? What can you learn from your results?

Section review questions

1. Explain the difference between a test variable and control variables. Why are controls important?
2. Simone designs and conducts an experiment to test how quickly tomato seeds will germinate when given different amounts of water. During her experiment, she suddenly

realizes that each test group has received different amounts of light. What should she do and why?

3. What might happen if each of Simone's test groups were exposed to different temperatures without her knowledge? Would her conclusions be valid? What would she have to do to make sure they were valid?

1.4 Investigating living things

''Look, Susan!'' René whispered excitedly, his eyes tracking a white-winged bird rising from the top of the spruce forest. Susan's breath caught in the frozen air as she followed René's gaze. With hardly a sound, a snowy owl descended swiftly to the forest floor, its talons poised to kill. A small rodent, too far from its den, shrieked in panic. The great bird grasped its prey, barely touching its wings to the ground, and rose again above the snow-draped boughs. ''A snowy owl, René! That's fantastic!'' Susan said, ''They're usually seen only in the far North. Let's make a note of this and report it to our club.''

Each year, birdwatchers like René and Susan provide a val-

Birdwatchers provide important information about how birds live.

uable service. Although birdwatching is probably an interesting hobby for René and Susan, it is also an important investigation. The sightings that birdwatchers report to organizations like the National Audubon Society of North America tell scientists where particular birds live, how many of them there are, what they eat, and where they migrate.

Information like this can be very useful. If certain birds should disappear from an area, or change their habits, it may mean that something is wrong in their environment. Herring gulls, ospreys, and loons, for example, have disappeared around acidified lakes. These birds eat fish, but acid rain has made it impossible for fish to survive in these waters. As a result, these birds no longer have a food source and have been forced to move to other areas.

Try this!

Visit a park, an empty lot, or a wild area close to where you live. Observe the birds that can be seen in the region over a two-week period. How many different species can you identify? Borrow a pair of field glasses and design a classification key to help you. Record what the birds eat, where they nest, and what their habits are. Can you infer what it is about the area that attracts these birds? Why might some of these birds migrate south in the winter? Make a report to your class about your findings.

The importance of studying living things

Scientists want to know about the habits, characteristics, and habitats of all living things. They believe that each life form has a role to play in the survival of other living things. You already know that all life on Earth depends on green plants, and that green plants are the basis of what is known as the food chain. The food chain is simply the way energy is passed from one living thing to another.

Humans are at the top of most food chains. We depend exclusively on other forms of life to survive. Even living things that some people consider to be unpleasant play important roles in supporting other forms of life. Snakes, for

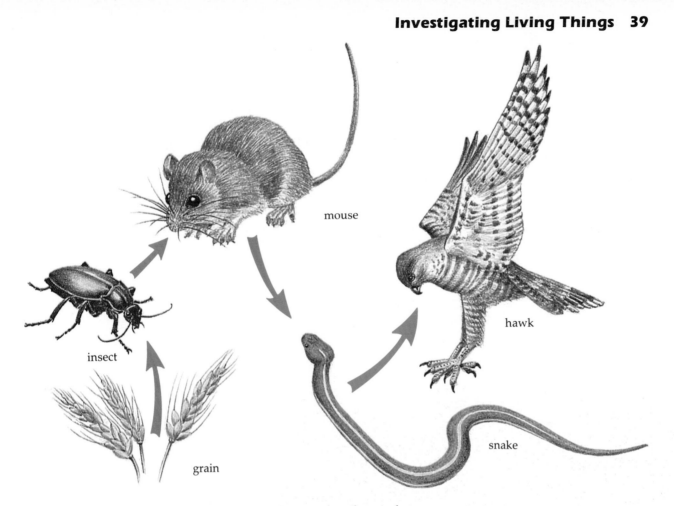

mouse

insect

grain

hawk

snake

Figure 1–7 This is one example of a food chain. Can you describe one that includes humans?

example, eat insects, mice, and other animals that compete with us for grains and other foods. Spiders help to keep plant-eating insects and other pests under control so plants can survive. Earthworms break down organic matter, releasing nutrients into the soil. The fruits, vegetables, and other crops that we grow depend on these living organisms. Without them, some scientists think that the quality of life would deteriorate rapidly. Scientists believe that all life is interdependent.

One small organism that helps to enrich the soil is the mealworm. It lives in damp, dark places in mills, under feed bags, or in grain. Mealworms feed mainly on grains or cereals, but they can often be scavengers.

Try this!

Draw charts like the ones below in your notebook. Use a magnifying glass to observe the structure of several mealworms. Record your observations in your charts. Use a balance and a ruler to measure the mass, length, and the width of several mealworms. Average your results and record these figures in the chart. Look up a description of a mealworm using reference materials or science books. How does your description compare? Which description is more complete? Explain why.

Body Part	Description
Head	
Antenna	
Mouth	
Eyes	
Body Segments	
Legs	

Specimen	Length	Width	Height
1			
2			
3			
Totals			
Averages			

Figure 1–8

_____

Try this!

Observe and describe how a mealworm moves by placing it on a piece of glass and observing it from underneath. Does the mealworm move efficiently on a smooth surface? Trace its pattern of movement on graph paper. What might your observations indicate about where mealworms would prefer to live? State this as a hypothesis and design an experiment that could be used to test your hypothesis.

Remember to wash your hands thoroughly after handling the mealworms.

Mealworms are often studied by biologists to learn about respiration, digestion, and basic body functions. Scientists use mealworms because they are predictable, and they are usually unaffected by artificial conditions. They are clean, odourless, require little care, and are inexpensive. Because mealworms exhibit reasonably consistent behaviours, they are a good species to study. You will learn more about mealworms in Investigation 5. The investigation will also give you an idea of the type of environment mealworms prefer.

Investigation 5   The behaviour of mealworms

PROBLEM
How will mealworms behave in response to various environmental stimuli?

MATERIALS
mealworms in a jar
pencil
masking tape
scissors
test tube
flat-edged tweezers
wire mesh
pen light
whistle
ice cube
cotton swabs
turpentine

MEASURING TOOL
ruler

If you state that mealworms will *not* respond to any of these changes, then such a hypothesis is called a **null hypothesis**.

HYPOTHESIS

State how you think bright light, loud noise, cold temperature, and the odour of turpentine will affect the behaviour of mealworms.

PROCEDURE

1. Choose a partner to perform the investigation with. Cut off one piece of masking tape approximately 100 mm long. Then calibrate the edge of the masking tape in pencil from 0–100 mm.

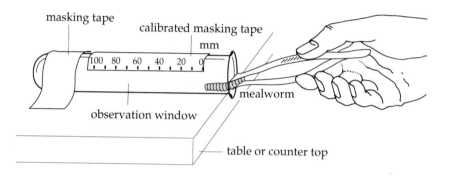

masking tape · calibrated masking tape · mm · 100 80 60 40 20 0 · mealworm · observation window · table or counter top

Figure 1–9

Caution: Be careful not to drop the test tube. Use a dustpan and whisk to sweep up broken glass if you should break anything. Do not use your fingers.

Be careful not to injure the mealworms. A piece of folded paper can be used instead of the tweezers. Wash your hands thoroughly after handling the mealworms.

2. Set the test tube on a level table or counter top with its opening protruding just over the edge. Use masking tape to secure the test tube to the table as in Figure 1–9. Make sure the "0" reading on the calibrated tape is 2 cm from the test-tube opening. Be sure to leave a space along the length of the tube so that you can observe the mealworm.

3. Use the tweezers to pick up a mealworm from the jar. Place it inside the test tube with its tail end just before the "0" mark.

4. Hold a small piece of wire mesh over the test-tube opening to prevent the mealworm from escaping. Ask your partner to shine the pen light at the mealworm while you observe and measure the mealworm's response. (You may need to give the mealworm time to react.)

5. Repeat Step 4 using the whistle. Repeat the step again placing the ice cube over the open end of the test tube. Finally, place a cotton swab soaked in turpentine just inside the test-tube opening. Measure the mealworm's response in each of these three cases.

6. Repeat Steps 4 and 5 using two other mealworms.

OBSERVATIONS

1. Record the distance each mealworm moved in response to each environmental stimulus. Calculate the average response of the three mealworms. Use a bar graph like Figure 1–10 to record your observations.

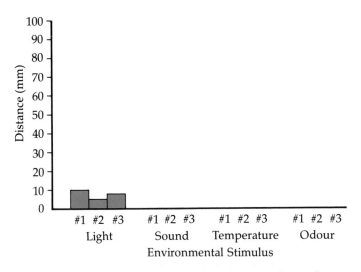

Figure 1–10 The response of mealworms to environmental stimuli

CONCLUSIONS

What conclusions can you make about the ways environmental stimuli affect the behaviour of mealworms?

Discussion questions

1. What generalization can you make about the environment mealworms prefer? How could you use this information to help you maintain an appropriate environment for mealworms?

2. How do you think a mealworm's senses help it to survive? Based on your observations, what do you think is the mealworm's keenest sense?
3. Were there any environmental stimuli that the mealworms did not respond to? Why?
4. Why do quantitative observations and multiple trials make your conclusions more valid?

Section review questions

1. Explain how a food chain demonstrates the interdependence of living things.
2. You have to collect some earthworms for a science project. What sort of experiments could you design to find out what earthworms need to survive?
3. Why do you think it is important to know how to maintain an appropriate environment for all living things? What factors would you have to consider?

1.5 Investigating people

Look around you. What do you see? You probably see desks, chairs, windows, buildings, roads, plants, animals, *and* people. People live practically everywhere on Earth, and are of different sizes, shapes, colours, nationalities, and cultures. People are among the most fascinating of all living things.

Why are humans so interesting? Perhaps it is because we are the most successful, creative, and intelligent species on Earth. But it may be because each of us is unique, so we are curious about the uniqueness of others. You can see this uniqueness yourself just by comparing your fingerprints with those of someone else. Curiosity about ourselves results in useful observations. Many helpful discoveries, such as the braille system, have been made by people who have carefully observed the needs of other people.

Ergonomists are people who analyze how humans and machines interact. By observing the natural shape and movement of the human body, they are able to design tools and machines that promote safety and increase efficiency in working environments.

What kinds of investigations might you conduct about the people in this photograph?

Try this!

How keen a ''people-observer'' are you? Select a classmate to work with, then quickly move out of your partner's sight. While your partner is gone, write down everything you can remember about his or her height, hair and eye colour, clothes, and mannerisms. Don't spend more than 5 min writing down your observations. Then ask your partner to return. How accurate were your observations? What would you pay closer attention to if you repeated this activity?

Gathering, classifying, and reporting

The goal of science is to increase knowledge, which would be impossible without careful observations. However, data from these observations must be gathered, classified, and reported in ways that will allow you to make useful conclusions and generalizations. This is why the charts and graphs you developed in the previous investigations were so useful. They helped you to gather and classify observed data, and to see how the variables you tested related to the variables that changed as a result. In Investigation 6, you will have an opportunity to practise your gathering and classifying skills by making careful observations about the students in your class.

Investigation 6   Gathering and classifying data

PURPOSE
To practise gathering, classifying, and reporting data.

MATERIALS   MEASURING TOOLS
paper   scales
pencil   metre stick
                        measuring tape

PROCEDURE
1. On a sheet of paper, draw a chart like the one on page 47. (It is not necessary to put your name on the paper.)
2. Estimate your mass and height. Then estimate the diameter of your upper right arm. Finally, estimate the length of your right arm from your shoulder to your wrist bone.
3. With the help of a partner, measure your mass and height using the scale and the metre stick. Use the measuring tape to measure the diameter and length of your right arm. Be sure to take three measurements each time and to average your results.
4. Collect the completed charts and count them. This number represents the number of people in your sample group.
5. Divide the charts into piles according to the age each student reported.

Give each student in each age group a number on your graphs. (See Figures 1–11 and 1–12.) Be sure to record each student's measurements accurately on your graphs.

OBSERVATIONS
1. Record your estimated and actual measurements in a chart like the one on page 47. (Remember to include your age.)
2. Draw graphs like Figures 1–11 and 1–12 on page 47. Ask one student to read out each student's height and mass measurements by age group. Record each measurement on the appropriate graph.
3. Average the measurements recorded on each graph by totalling them and dividing by the number of students in your sample group. Record the averaged measurements of your class on the appropriate graph.

	Estimated Measurement (cm)	Actual Measurement (cm)				
		#1	#2	#3	Total	Average
Mass						
Height						
Diameter of Upper Right Arm						
Length of Right Arm						
Age of Student						

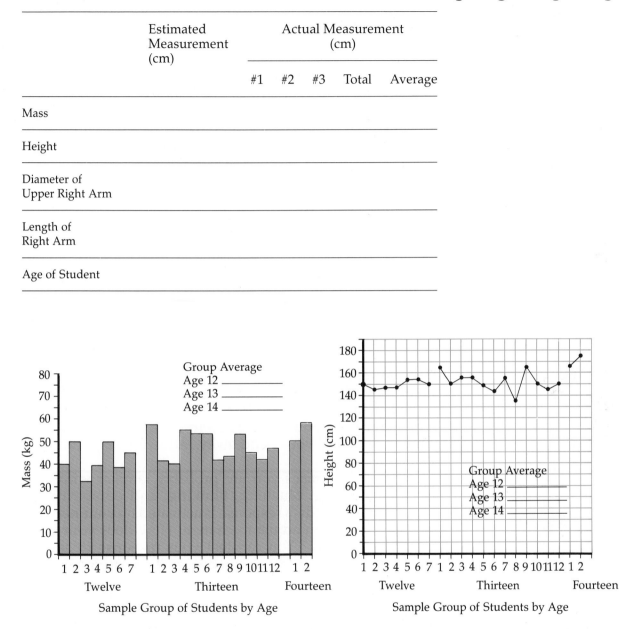

Figure 1–11 Comparison of height and age of grade 8 students

Figure 1–12 Comparison of mass and age of grade 8 students

CONCLUSIONS
What can you conclude about the importance of making quantitative observations and recording data accurately?

Discussion questions

1. How did your estimated measurements compare with your quantitative measurements? What would the class averages have been like if they had been based on estimates alone?

2. What generalizations can you make about the students in your sample group? Why is it important to include enough students in a sample group before you make a generalization?

3. After analyzing your graphs carefully, make a generalization relating age to the average height and mass of the students in your sample group.

4. State two or three ways the average measurements recorded for your sample group might be used by doctors, physical fitness instructors, and health officials.

Figure 1–13   Responding to stimuli

Response to stimuli

Have you ever been startled by a car horn or an ambulance siren? Maybe you've touched a hot stove element by mistake or had your fingers too close to a candle flame. Do you remember how you responded in each case? When you jumped or pulled your hand away, you were responding to a stimulus.

Common responses you are probably familiar with may include shivering, blushing, blinking, and perspiring. In each case, your body's response is activated by your nervous system to help you adjust to change. How does your body respond to stimuli? You can test your response to several stimuli in Investigation 7 and in the *Try this!* activity on page 51.

Investigation 7   Exercise and your pulse

PROBLEM
How does the stimulus of exercise affect your pulse rate?

HYPOTHESIS
Based on what you already know, state how exercise will affect your pulse rate.

MATERIALS
skipping rope

MEASURING TOOL
watch

PROCEDURE
1. Place your right forearm down on your desk with the palm of your hand facing up.
2. Make a loose fist with your left hand. Leave your first and middle fingers extended.
3. Place the two extended fingers over your right wrist just below the base of your right thumb. Use the illustration in Figure 1–14 to help you.
4. Push down gently. There is an artery at this point. The beating you feel under your fingertips is your pulse.
5. Look at the second hand on the watch and count the number of beats you feel in 10 s. Then multiply the number of beats by 6 to obtain the number of beats per minute. For example, 12 beats × 6 = 72 beats per minute. This is your pulse rate when at rest.

Caution: If you have a medical condition, such as a heart murmur or asthma, inform your teacher before doing this investigation.

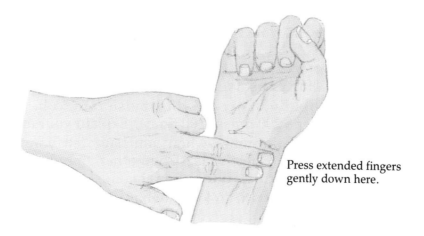

Press extended fingers gently down here.

Figure 1–14

6. Using the skipping rope, skip on the spot for a count of 25, then immediately take your pulse rate. Afterward, allow your pulse rate to return to normal.
7. Repeat Step 6 using a count of 50. Repeat the step again using a count of 100.

OBSERVATIONS
1. Record any qualitative changes that you observed about your body before and after the pulse tests.
2. Record your quantitative observations in a chart like the one below. Average your test results to obtain your active pulse rate.

	Pulse Rate Tests			Active Pulse Rate	
Resting Pulse Rate	25 Skips	50 Skips	100 Skips	Total	Average

CONCLUSIONS
What can you conclude about your body's response to exercise?

Discussion questions

1. Which variable did you test in this investigation? Which variables did you control? How did you control these variables?
2. What factors might account for variations in the pulse rates of different students?
3. What would you expect your pulse rate to be if you skipped rope 200 times? 300 times? Explain your answer.
4. Think about the times when you have felt your heart "pound," then state at least two other stimuli that you believe could affect your pulse rate.
5. Why is it important to know what your normal resting pulse rate is?
6. How do quantitative observations improve your findings? State reasons for your answer.

Did you know?
Your pulse is caused by the rhythmic flow of blood through your arteries. This blood flow is caused by the beating of your heart. The normal resting pulse rate for most people is 72-80 beats per minute.

7. Compare your findings with those of your classmates. Develop a graph to represent class data. What generalizations can you make based on any similarities that you observe? Be sure to consider qualitative findings, too.

Try this!

Design an experiment to test reaction times to various stimuli such as a) a loud noise, b) an ice cube placed down the back, and c) the sudden sight of rubber spiders bouncing in the air. Consider the variables you will need to test and control. Then ask friends or relatives who are in good physical shape to be your test subjects. Take each person's resting pulse rate before telling him or her that you are about to test their reaction to a few stimuli. Tie a blindfold on each subject, then suddenly expose him or her to one of the stimuli. (In the case of visual stimuli, you will have to suddenly remove the blindfold.)

Take each subject's pulse rate again within seconds of his or her exposure to the stimuli. Ask them to remove the blindfold, if they haven't already done so, and notice the difference between their two pulse rates. What other changes did each subject notice?

Caution: Be certain that your subjects are in good physical shape. Don't tell them what the stimuli you will expose them to are, but be sure they understand that they will be in no danger. Do not proceed without their full consent.

Section review questions

1. State three reasons why observing people can be fascinating.
2. Can you make meaningful conclusions and generalizations with random observations? Explain your answer.
3. What is meant by a ''normal'' resting pulse rate? Describe how you might be able to determine what ''normal'' is.
4. Why is it useful to estimate a quantity before you measure it?
5. State at least four ways in which your body can respond to stimuli. Why are these responses important?

Measuring blood pressure

Why does water flow from a tap when you turn the tap on? The answer is pressure. Many centuries ago, scientists discovered that pressure can be applied to a fluid system like the water pipes in your home. Their investigations led them to the scientific principle that pressure is distributed throughout a fluid system.

This conclusion about pressure is now an accepted scientific principle. Like many other principles, it has been applied in a variety of practical ways. The convenience of running water in your home is just one example. Much of the equipment used in plastics and metal-forming plants operates on hydraulics, which is the pressure of fluids in systems. Hydraulic hoists are used to lift cars and trucks for repairs.

One of the most useful applications of pressure has been the development of the sphygmomanometer. This device is used by doctors, nurses, and other health-care professionals to measure blood pressure. Together, your heart and blood vessels form a fluid system to carry life-giving blood throughout your body. As your heart beats, or contracts, blood is pumped under pressure to your cells. Just after each contraction, this pressure

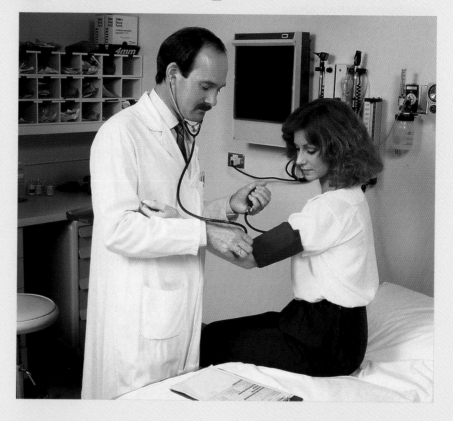

rises to a maximum level known as systolic pressure. Between contractions, it falls to a minimum level known as diastolic pressure.

During a physical examination, the sphygmomanometer is used to measure both systolic and diastolic pressure. A typical reading for teenagers is 120 systolic over 80 diastolic, depending on age and sex. If your doctor tells you that your blood pressure is too high or

too low, it may mean that you have a health problem.

The development of the sphygmomanometer has made it possible for health-care professionals to diagnose several diseases before they become serious. High blood pressure can lead to strokes. This device alerts a doctor to the problem so that a treatment program can be started to control and possibly cure the disease.

1.6 Scientists at work

Scientists endeavour to use their expertise to increase knowledge and understanding, and to find ways to apply this knowledge for the benefit of society. Table 1.2 illustrates some of the major historical advances that have been made in the life sciences. Without these advances, we wouldn't enjoy even the simplest medical care or understand how to breed the best plants and animals. Millions of people would suffer from diseases, such as smallpox, that today can be controlled or cured.

Table 1.2 Historical advances in the life sciences

Date	Discoverer(s)	Advance
10 000 B.C.	Early Peoples	• acquired basic knowledge about nature
3000 B.C.	Egyptians	• studied human anatomy and physiology • conducted primitive surgery
400 B.C.	Hippocrates (Greek)	• roots of modern medicine • developed the idea that diseases have natural causes and that the body can heal itself
350 B.C.	Aristotle (Greek)	• gathered and organized written records on a wide variety of plants and animals
A.D. 77	Pliny the Elder (Roman)	• wrote *Natural History*, an encyclopedia of scientific knowledge
A.D. 1000	Avicenna (Persian)	• wrote *Canon of Medicine*, a medical encyclopedia • accurately described tetanus and meningitis
1543	Andreas (Flemish)	• published *On the Fabric of the Human Body*, a book of human anatomy based on dissection of human cadavers
1628	William Harvey (British)	• discovered blood circulation by scientific experimentation and observation
1665	Robert Hooke (British)	• used a microscope to observe fine structures of plants and animals

Table 1.2 Historical advances in the life sciences

Date	Discoverer(s)	Advance
1753	Carolus Linnaeus (Swedish)	• developed a system for classifying plants and animals • identified many thousands of species
1751–1792	Denis Diderot Jean Alembert (French)	• prepared a 28-volume encyclopedia of philosophy, science, and technology
1796	Edward Jenner (British)	• discovered a vaccine for smallpox
1839	Matthias Schleiden Theodor Schwann (German)	• proposed that all living things are made of cells
1851	Charles Darwin (British)	• proposed theories of evolution based on natural selection and survival of the fittest
1866	Gregor Mendel (Austrian)	• developed the laws of heredity and set the foundation for the study of genetics
1876	Louis Pasteur (French)	• discovered that micro-organisms caused certain diseases
1882	Robert Koch (German)	• discovered the bacteria that causes tuberculosis
1913	Casimir Funk (Polish)	• discovered the importance of vitamins in the human diet
1922	Frederick Grant Banting Charles Best (Canadian)	• discovered insulin and used it to treat diabetes
1928	Alexander Fleming (British)	• discovered penicillin
1953	Jonas Salk (American)	• developed a vaccine for polio
1954	Joseph Murray (American)	• performed kidney transplant successfully
1968	Christiaan Barnard (South African)	• pioneered heart transplants
1984	Dr. R. Gallo (American)	• co-discoverer of the AIDS virus

Try this!

Study Table 1.2 beginning on page 53. Then state the importance of each of the following discoverers: William Harvey, Carolus Linnaeus, Charles Darwin, Louis Pasteur, Jonas Salk, and Frederick Banting. Try to find out who was responsible for these scientific advances: the smallpox vaccine, the laws of heredity, the discovery of penicillin, and the discovery of the bacteria that cause tuberculosis. Write a report on your findings.

Contributions of Canadian scientists

Although Canada is a relatively young country, Canadian scientists have frequently been on the frontier of scientific advancement.

One important Canadian scientist was Dr. Wilder Penfield (1891–1976). He tried to better understand the complexities of the human mind.

Dr. Penfield was the founder and first director of the Montreal Neurological Institute. He wrote numerous medical books and scientific papers that are now used as standard references on the functions of the human brain. He established a surgical treatment for epilepsy called the "Montreal Procedure," and also developed a method to remove brain scars.

Based on his surgical experiences, he produced reports on brain tumors, headaches, memory; motor, sensory, and speech functions, and the relationship between the brain's structure and consciousness.

Many people have benefited from Dr. Penfield's work. The Montreal Neurological Institute has an international reputation for teaching, research, and the treatment of diseases of the central nervous system. Current theories about the differing functions of the right and left hemispheres of the brain are based on Dr. Penfield's discoveries.

Dr. Wilder Penfield

Try this!

Investigate the life and contributions made by a Canadian life scientist. You might investigate Dr. Frederick Banting, Dr.

Charles Best, Sir Charles Saunders, N. Ford-Walker, L. Seminovitch, Murray L. Barr, or Dr. Baldur Stefansson. Check the computer index or card catalogue at a library or resource centre for publications on or by these scientists. Consult the table of contents, bibliography, and index of these publications to help you obtain as much information as possible. Look for films or video cassettes about their work, too. Consider the following points as you prepare your profile.

a) What problem was presented to the scientist?
b) What hypothesis did he or she propose?
c) Identify the scientific processes used by the scientist.
d) Explain what current or future applications have resulted or are likely to result from the scientist's work.
e) Identify highlights in the scientist's career.
f) What personal information can you find?

Organize your profile in point form under headings such as *Personal Information, Education, Career Development, Achievements, Other Scientific Advances,* and *Contributions to Society.*

Section review questions

1. Match the following advances with the people responsible for their discovery.
   a) living things are made of cells   • Jonas Salk
   b) polio   • Egyptians
   c) tuberculosis   • Schleiden and Schwann
   d) studied human anatomy and physiology   • Robert Koch
2. How has society benefited from the work of Dr. Wilder Penfield?
3. Name three other famous Canadian scientists. Explain the work of one of these scientists.

SCIENCE-RELATED CAREER

Meet Marva Gilkes

Marva is a Registered Nurse's Assistant who works as an operating-room technician at Toronto General Hospital. For many years, she has specialized in thoracic surgery, which involves operations on the part of the body between the neck and the abdomen. She is also a member of the heart- and heart-lung-transplant team.

Q. Where did you do your training?
A. I came to Canada from Barbados when I was nineteen and did my R.N.A. training then. At that time, the courses were held at hospitals. Now they are taught at a community college.

Q. Do most operating-room tech-
nicians specialize in certain types of operations?
A. Often they do. There are nine different services at Toronto General, which include ear, nose, and throat surgery, cardiac (heart) surgery, and plastic surgery. I can be assigned to any of these areas, but I tend to work mainly in the thoracic area.

Q. What role do you play on the operating-room team?
A. I usually "scrub," which means I work in the sterile field of the operating room handing over instruments to the surgeon. It's called scrubbing because I must scrub my hands, from my fingers to my elbows, with strong antiseptic soap for about ten minutes before putting on a gown and gloves. This ensures that everything in the operating room is sterile. Once I have scrubbed and put on my gown and gloves, I can go into the sterile field. There I can't touch anything that hasn't been sterilized.

Q. You have scrubbed for some lung-transplant operations. Were those operations especially demanding?
A. Yes, and they were exciting. Four years ago, the only living single-lung transplant in the world was done at Toronto General and I scrubbed for it.

These transplant operations are terrific because they make such a difference. Someone who has been on oxygen twenty-four hours a day, and has been really sick, can be up and walking after the operation.

Q. Describe a common operation.
A. We might do a thoracotomy for a right upper lobectomy, which is the removal of the right upper lobe of the lung to test it for cancer. After I've set up the room, the resident, the doctor, and I will drape the patient who has been anesthetized. Then the doctor makes an incision and uses retractors to open the chest area. I hand him the instruments and anticipate what he'll need. The surgeon then separates the upper lobe of the lung to send it to pathology for testing. What happens next depends on the pathology results.

Q. What do you like about your job?
A. I get a real lift from scrubbing. I really like it. The surgeons in this department are great and it's always exciting.

Q. What is the most difficult part of your job?
A. It's very demanding physically. You stand on your feet for hours and hours. You have to be very careful and on top of things all the time.

Should non-scientists examine hypotheses?

In the 1960s, scientists in Scandinavia began to notice new and disturbing events. Fish were disappearing from lakes where they once were common. Sculptures and buildings that had stood unblemished for centuries were becoming pitted and pocked. What could be wrong?

Dr. Svante Oden, a Swedish soil scientist, hypothesized that these problems were the first visible results of acid rain. He believed that acid rain was formed in the atmosphere when certain polluting emissions combined with water vapour. These emissions were created by burning fuels such as coal, oil, and gasoline. From his research, he inferred that the effects of acid rain could be devastating.

The implication of Dr. Oden's hypothesis was great, but testing it would be difficult. There were many variables that would be difficult to control outside of a laboratory. The suspected sources of the emissions were often hundreds of kilometres away in different countries. Politicians, the public, and industry officials would need to be convinced before taking action. They wanted a great deal of evidence.

Few people outside of Dr. Oden's country paid much attention to his findings. In the 1970s, however, scientists around the world began reporting similar occurrences. Fish populations were decreasing in thousands of lakes and rivers in Ontario, Quebec, and Nova Scotia. Levels of dangerous metals, such as mercury, were rising in many of these same waters. World-famous forests in Germany, Czechoslovakia, and Poland were dying as the result of a mysterious disease. Statues and monuments in Greece were eroding, while car finishes and window glass in the midwestern and northeastern United States became dull.

Concerned citizens and government and industry officials began to investigate acid rain. They sifted through collected data to find possible patterns, causes, and cures. Scientists worked to identify sources of polluting emissions, to monitor their effects, and make this information available. Even though Dr. Oden's hypothesis had not actually been "proved," Canadians and many others have accepted its validity. Scientists and non-scientists alike became convinced that acid rain had to be

stopped. As a result, the governments of Canada's seven most-eastern provinces passed legislation to cut the emissions contributing to acid rain in half by 1994.

Explore the issue

New legislation in Canada should help to reduce acid rain both here and in the United States. But will it be enough? Scientists tell us that 50% of the acid rain that falls in Canada comes from emissions that originate in the United States. Consequently, Canadian governments have asked the United States to pass similar legislation.

Several state governments have approved of Canada's actions and have lobbied the United States Federal Government to pass such legislation. Other states, usually those operating coal mines or industries that burn large quantities of fossil fuels, have lobbied against it. The government of the United States has insisted on the need for more studies, saying that it is not willing to legislate expensive clean-ups until more is known about the causes and distribution of acid rain.

Figure 1–15   The acid rain hypothesis

What do you think the American government should do? Research this issue in groups of three. What knowledge and information should American politicians have before they make any conclusions? What should they understand about the way scientific knowledge is accumulated? Appoint a panel of five "American" judges from your class and present your arguments to them. What are their decisions? What have they based them on? What might the consequences be for American and Canadian manufacturers, forest harvesters, resort operators, and maple-syrup producers? What conclusions can your class make about the importance of non-scientists examining a hypothesis on an issue such as acid rain?

Chapter review

Words to know

Write a brief definition for each of the terms listed below. The location of these terms is indicated by the section number in the brackets.

- conclusions (*Section 1.1/Section 1.2*)
- controls (*Section 1.3*)
- generalizations (*Section 1.1/Section 1.2*)
- hypothesis (*Section 1.1/Section 1.2*)
- inference (*Section 1.2*)
- investigation (*Section 1.1*)
- prediction (*Section 1.2*)
- scientific problem (*Section 1.2*)
- variable (*Section 1.2/Section 1.3*)

Questions

A. Indicate whether each of the following statements is true or false. Explain why the "false" statements are not true.

1. An investigation is a careful search that begins with a problem.
2. A hypothesis is the answer discovered at the end of an investigation.
3. The process skills of the scientific method are always used in the same order.
4. Generalizations are not as important as conclusions.
5. Scientists focus on certain details of a problem while ignoring all the others.
6. The use of the scientific method has greatly increased the growth of knowledge.
7. Scientific knowledge never changes.
8. Skills come only to people with natural talents.
9. Observation is the basis for all scientific knowledge.
10. Sir Alexander Fleming was a British bacteriologist who discovered insulin.

B. Choose the best answer for each of the following.

1. A variable is
   a) something that cannot be controlled
   b) something that must be controlled
   c) something that may change during the course of an experiment
   d) none of the above
2. A control is
   a) a physical restraint placed on an experimental animal
   b) a variable that is not allowed to change while some other variable is tested
   c) a record of experimental results
   d) a list of all the variables in an experiment
3. Observations can be
   a) qualitative or quantitative
   b) qualitative and quantitative
   c) ignored when making generalizations
4. Failure to control all variables other than the test variable during an experiment will mean that

a) your conclusions will only be valid for a limited time
b) your conclusions will only be valid for that one experiment
c) your conclusions will have limited applications
d) your conclusions may not be valid at all

5. Scientists compare results from several experiments in order to develop
   a) conclusions
   b) generalizations
   c) hypotheses

6. An inference is
   a) a judgement based on observations
   b) a foregone conclusion
   c) a generalization about generalizations
   d) an erroneous conclusion that must be changed

7. Non-scientists such as politicians
   a) should never concern themselves with science
   b) play important roles in the actions taken by our society to new scientific data
   c) should not attempt to use scientific data to reach conclusions
   d) all of the above

C. Write full answers for each of the following.

1. A student decides to investigate the effect of moisture on the time marigold seeds take to germinate. Which variable will be tested? Which variables will he or she have to control?

2. Explain why the study of animals is useful to human beings. State at least three reasons.

3. List the major scientific accomplishments of the following scientists
   a) Maud Leonora Menten
   b) Sir Alexander Fleming
   c) Dr. Wilder Penfield

4. State five ways humans respond to environmental stimuli. Give a specific example for each.

5. Why is the measurement of blood pressure important?

Science challenge

1. Use the scientific method to solve a real-life problem such as
   a) choosing from a list of program options for secondary schools
   b) finding a part-time job in the newspaper
   c) purchasing an expensive gift for a friend
   Consider each choice and state its positive and negative aspects. Analyze your data to make an appropriate decision.

2. Write a report about the role of CANSAP (the Canadian Network for Sampling Acid Precipitation) in tracking airborne pollutants. Who uses the data they collect? How is it used?

Science projects

1. Construct a scientific model of an area of North America that is subject to acid rain. Show where polluting emissions originate, how and where they are deposited, and the living and non-living things that are affected. Try to make your model as realistic as possible.

2. Conduct a research investigation for one of the following problems.
   a) How do environmental conditions affect the behaviour of living things? (For example, insects.)
   b) How do antibiotics, such as penicillin, affect the action of viruses that cause diseases such as the common cold or the flu?

3. Examine the issue of animal-care legislation in your community. What provincial legislation exists? Visit the local office of your Humane Society or Society for the Prevention of Cruelty to Animals (SPCA). What is the position of the officials there on using animals for scientific research? How does it compare with the position of doctors, scientists, and politicians in your community? Write a report that outlines the position of each side. Then state and defend your own position.

2

Solutions

High above a busy downtown street, a window washer is suspended in midair against the side of a building. He works from a platform that is secured from the roof of the building by ropes, hooks, and pulleys. By lowering and raising the platform, he moves from window to window, leaving each one clean and bright after he washes it.

Helping him to do his job is a bucket of potent cleaning solution. He makes this cleaning solution by dissolving a specific amount of a special orange powder in warm water. Sponged over each window, this solution works quickly to dissolve a thin film of dirt and grime on the glass. Then he removes the dirty solution with a squeegee. The glass is now clean and will dry quickly.

Like the window washer's cleaning solution, there are many other solutions you and your family use every day. Liquid detergent, cologne, oven cleaner, tea, coffee, soft drinks, and fruit juices are examples of some of these solutions. But what makes these familiar substances solutions? And what do they have in common? You will find out in this chapter.

Caution: Never taste any solution unless you have been given permission by your teacher or another adult.

2.1 Solutions are everywhere

When you mix orange-juice concentrate or fruit-juice crystals with water to make juice for your breakfast, you are making a solution. But what is this solution?

Scientists define a **solution** as a uniform **mixture**, or blend, of two or more substances. By "uniform," scientists mean that the substances are evenly blended with each other throughout the entire mixture. Substances that have the ability to **dissolve**, or blend, evenly in this way are called **solutes**. The substances they dissolve in are called **solvents**.

To remember the difference between a solute and a solvent, think of a glass of water and a salt shaker. If you shake a small amount of salt into the water and then stir it, the salt will dissolve. The salt is the *solute* and the water is the *solvent*. Together they make a solution called salt water. Since you have used only a small amount of salt, the solution is weak or **dilute**. If you add more salt, the solution becomes stronger or **concentrated**. How do you think a dilute solution of salt water would taste compared to the taste of a concentrated solution?

The world's oceans are solutions of mineral salts and water. More than two-thirds of the Earth's surface is covered by

Oceans are solutions of mineral salts and water. Do you think that all oceans contain the same amount of mineral salts? Why?

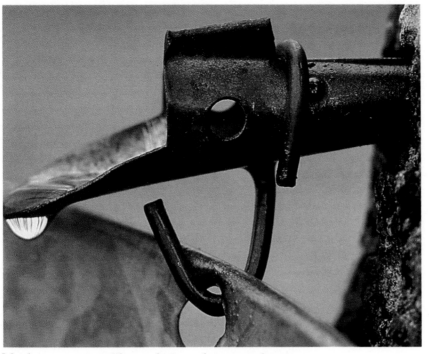

Maple-tree sap is a dilute solution of sugar and water.

Did you know?
The sap that flows from a maple tree is a dilute solution of sugar and water. What do you think will happen to this solution when it is heated to make maple syrup?

them. Oceans are very important to life on Earth, but you and many other animals must have fresh water to live.

Canadians are fortunate to have an abundance of fresh water. In some countries, fresh water is scarce and must be made from sea water that contains salt. One way to remove the salt from sea water is by using the sun's energy to vaporize the water. This vapour is then caught and cooled, causing it to condense to form pure water. The salt that is left behind is mainly sodium chloride or table salt. Besides its use as a seasoning, sodium chloride is also used to manufacture the chlorine used in bleach and the sodium hydroxide used to manufacture soap.

Investigation 1   Salt-water and sugar-water solutions

PURPOSE
To compare dilute and concentrated solutions of salt and water and sugar and water.

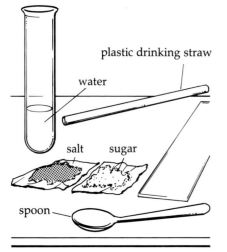

Figure 2–1

Caution: The salt-water and sugar-water solutions in this investigation are examples of "safe" solutions. However, many solutions are extremely poisonous. Never taste solutions without your teacher's permission. If you have diabetes or any other medical condition that might be affected by these solutions, be sure to inform your teacher.

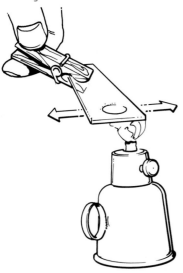

Figure 2–2 Evaporating water

MATERIALS

2 test tubes	tap water
test-tube rack	plastic drinking straw
microscope or	spoon
magnifying glass	alcohol burner
glass slide	matches
salt	clothespin
sugar	safety glasses

PROCEDURE

1. Place a few salt crystals on a clean slide and examine them under the microscope or the magnifying glass. (If the microscope has more than one objective, use the low-power objective for this investigation.)

2. Fill a test tube one-third full with warm tap water. Place it in the test-tube rack. Drop a pinch of salt into the test tube and observe the salt as it dissolves.

3. You have now made a dilute solution of salt and water. Taste a drop of it from the end of a clean plastic drinking straw.

4. Add a small spoonful of salt to the test tube containing the dilute solution. Put your thumb over the end of the test tube and shake it until the salt dissolves. Taste a drop of this concentrated solution.

5. Place a drop of the concentrated solution on a clean slide. Examine it under the microscope or the magnifying glass. Look for salt particles in the solution. Can you see any?

6. Put on your safety glasses. Light the alcohol burner with your teacher's permission. Use the clothespin to hold the slide. Move the slide back and forth over the flame so that the water evaporates slowly.

7. Examine the deposit left on the slide under the microscope or the magnifying glass.

8. Repeat Steps 1–7 using sugar instead of salt. (Use two pinches of sugar in Step 2 and two small spoonfuls of sugar in Step 4.)

OBSERVATIONS

1. Make a sketch of the salt and sugar crystals as they appeared under the microscope or the magnifying glass.

2. Record how the dilute and concentrated solutions of salt and water compared in taste. Then record how the dilute

and concentrated solutions of sugar and water compared in taste.

3. Record what you observed in Step 5.
4. For both concentrated solutions, make a sketch of the deposit left on the slide as it appeared under the microscope or the magnifying glass after the water had evaporated.

CONCLUSIONS

What can you conclude about the properties of dilute and concentrated solutions?

Discussion questions

1. Which materials were used as the solutes and the solvents in this investigation?
2. Explain why the drop of concentrated solution left a deposit on the glass slide after it was heated.
3. Explain why the dilute and concentrated solutions of salt and water did not taste the same.
4. Is it safe to taste all solutions? Explain your answer.
5. What evidence did you find to indicate that the particles in a solution are very small?
6. Scientists believe that the tiny particles in a crystal are arranged in an orderly pattern. What evidence did you find to support this belief?

Not all solutions are safe. In fact, many solutions are actually dangerous. Some solutions are poisonous, and others may be flammable, explosive, or corrosive (see Figure 2–3 on page 68). Look for these symbols on products in your home and learn what they mean. Here are some other rules to remember when working with solutions.

1. Keep all liquids and solids away from your mouth.
2. Always wash your hands after handling any solution.
3. Use safety glasses to protect your eyes when you do experiments involving heat or chemicals.

Caution: Only light the alcohol burner with your teacher's permission. Make sure the burner is on a level, uncluttered surface where it won't be knocked over. Always wear safety glasses when you heat any substance. Tie back long hair and keep your fingers and clothes away from the flame. Heat the slide gently so the glass does not get too hot. Extinguish the flame as soon as you finish using the burner.

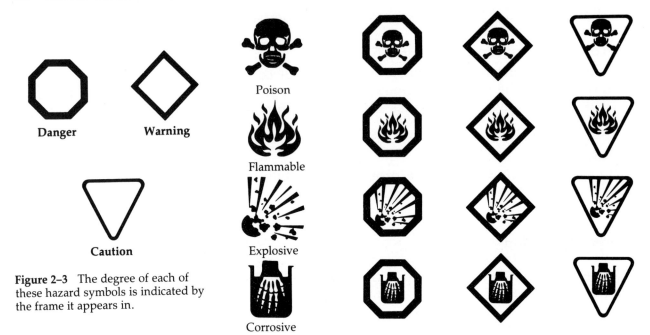

Danger

Warning

Caution

Poison

Flammable

Explosive

Corrosive

Figure 2–3 The degree of each of these hazard symbols is indicated by the frame it appears in.

Figure 2–4

Keep all liquids and solids away from your mouth.

Always wash your hands after handling any solution.

Wear safety glasses to protect your eyes when you do experiments involving heat or chemicals.

Section review questions

1. What is a solution? State an example.
2. When sugar is dissolved in water, which substance is the solute and which substance is the solvent?
3. What other terms are used to describe weak and strong solutions? State an example for each type of solution.
4. List four examples of dangerous solutions found in your home. How do you know they are dangerous? What precautions should be taken when these solutions are used?

Did you know?
Ground water and surface water usually contain a variety of substances in solution. These solutions are essential for plant growth.

Salt in solution in your body

Your body needs a certain amount of salt (sodium chloride) in solution. For example, the "water" in your eyes is actually a solution of salt and water that bathes and protects your eyes. When your body gets too hot from exercising, you start to perspire. Perspiration is a solution of salt and water that cools your body through evaporation. However, too much salt is not healthy. High concentrations of salt in solution in your body can cause high blood pressure, heart disease, liver disease, and kidney disease.

Doctors recommend that you consume only about 2 g of salt each day in your diet. However, researchers estimate that the average Canadian consumes five times this amount daily, or 10 g/d. Doctors recommend cutting back on the use of salt. But cutting back on salt is not easy. Many people are addicted to its taste. The more salt they use on their food, the more they want.

Leslie McCoy is a dietitian from Edmonton. She says that one way to cut back on salt is by taping over half the holes of your salt shaker. You should also try using salt-free foods. Read food labels carefully to see how much salt is contained in each product. Many canned foods are packed in a weak salt-water solution that acts as a preservative. Avoid these products or drain off as much of the salt water as possible. Salt in solution is important to maintain many of your body's functions. But too much can put your health in danger.

2.2 Solutions and mechanical mixtures

In Investigation 1, you observed that when a solid, such as salt, is mixed with a liquid, such as water, a solution results. Salt is **soluble** in water because it dissolves. But are all substances soluble? Do you think that all mixtures form solutions?

Consider a mixture of sand and water. You can mix these two substances by stirring them together in a container. When you stir them, you are performing a mechanical action. When you stop, however, the sand settles to the bottom of the container, and the water and the sand no longer form a mixture. Even while you are stirring, the sand is not mixed uniformly throughout the water because it does not dissolve. In other words, the sand is **insoluble**. A mixture of sand and water is an example of a **mechanical mixture**. You can see that two types of mixtures are possible — solutions and mechanical mixtures.

Did you notice in Investigation 1 that when the sugar or the salt dissolved, they broke down into extremely tiny particles too small to see? In a mechanical mixture, the particles, like the sand particles, are much larger. It is this difference in the size of the particles that makes a solution different from a mechanical mixture. Figure 2–5 on page 72 illustrates some of the other characteristics that distinguish solutions from mechanical mixtures. In Investigation 2, you will use these characteristics to help you classify various mixtures either as solutions or as mechanical mixtures.

When you stir sand and water, you are performing a mechanical action. A mechanical mixture is different from a solution because the particles in a mechanical mixture do not dissolve.

Investigation 2   Solutions and mechanical mixtures

PURPOSE
To distinguish solutions from mechanical mixtures by their properties.

MATERIALS
masking tape
marker
tap water
powdered milk
copper sulphate

MEASURING TOOL
1-mL measuring spoon

Solutions   **Mechanical Mixtures**

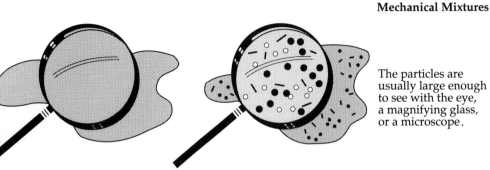

The solute particles cannot be seen even with a magnifying glass or a microscope.

The particles are usually large enough to see with the eye, a magnifying glass, or a microscope.

The solute cannot be separated from the solution by filtering. The particles are so small that they pass through the filter holes.

The particles can usually be separated from the mixture by filtering.

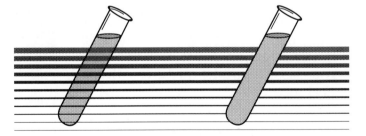

A solution is clear or transparent even when it is coloured.

A mechanical mixture is cloudy; you cannot see clearly through it.

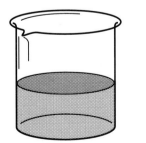

Solute particles do not settle to the bottom of a container or float to the top when a solution is left standing.

The particles of a mechanical mixture will either settle to the bottom of a container or float to the top when the mixture is left standing.

Figure 2–5 The characteristics of solutions and mechanical mixtures

garden soil
instant coffee
4 test tubes
test-tube rack
4 rubber stoppers
paper coffee filters
funnel
beaker
safety glasses
magnifying glass
filmstrip projector or flashlight

PROCEDURE
1. Use the masking tape and marker to number each test tube.
2. Fill each test tube half-full with water. Place each one in the test-tube rack.
3. Put on your safety glasses. Add 1 mL of powdered milk to test tube #1. Add 1 mL of copper sulphate to test tube #2, 1 mL of garden soil to test tube #3, and 1 mL of instant coffee to test tube #4.
4. Place a rubber stopper in each test tube. Shake each test tube and return it to the test-tube rack.
5. Examine each mixture with a magnifying glass. Look for individual particles in each mixture.
6. Turn on the filmstrip projector or the flashlight, then darken the room. Stand to one side of the light. Hold each test tube in turn in front of the light beam. Notice which mixtures are transparent and which are cloudy.
7. Return the test tubes to the test-tube rack. Observe whether any of the mixtures show signs of settling.
8. Try to **filter** each of the mixtures by using a paper coffee filter, the funnel, and the beaker as shown in Figure 2–6. Remember to use a new filter paper and to clean the beaker before filtering each mixture. Your teacher can show you how to make a filter paper from a paper towel if you run out of coffee filters. See Figure 2–7. (Filtering will remove any undissolved particles from each mixture and leave them behind as a **residue** on the filter paper. The liquid that passes through the filter paper is called the **filtrate**.)
9. After filtering, refill each test tube with its corresponding mixture. Make sure that the test tubes have been cleaned thoroughly first.

Caution: Don't look directly into the beam of light from the projector. The very bright light could blind you for a few seconds.

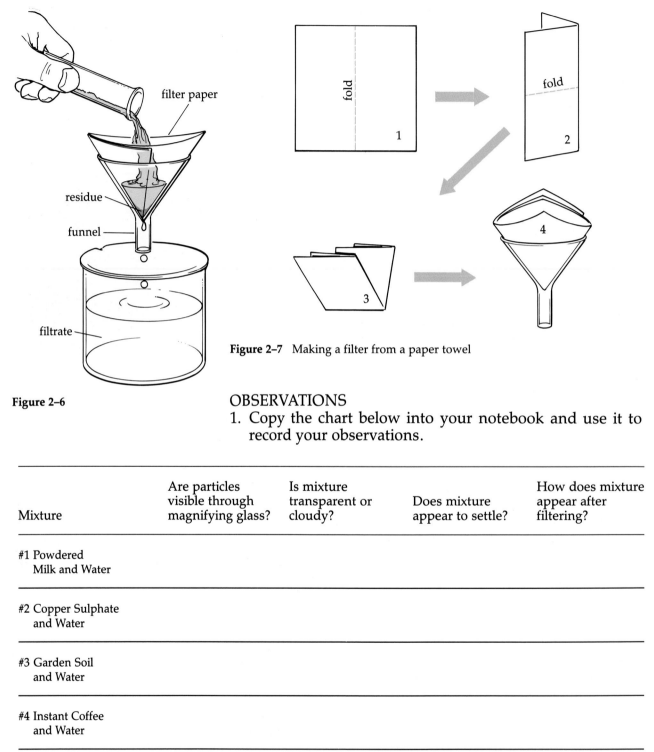

Figure 2–7   Making a filter from a paper towel

Figure 2–6

OBSERVATIONS
1. Copy the chart below into your notebook and use it to record your observations.

Mixture	Are particles visible through magnifying glass?	Is mixture transparent or cloudy?	Does mixture appear to settle?	How does mixture appear after filtering?
#1 Powdered Milk and Water				
#2 Copper Sulphate and Water				
#3 Garden Soil and Water				
#4 Instant Coffee and Water				

Discussion questions

1. Which of the mixtures were solutions? Which were mechanical mixtures? Explain.

2. Based on what you know about solutions and mechanical mixtures, complete the following chart.

Substances Mixed	The mixture will form a:		If it becomes a solution:	
	Solution	Mechanical Mixture	Name the Solute	Name the Solvent
Sugar and Water				
Soil and Water				
Salt and Water				
Pebbles and Water				
Oil and Water				
Instant Tea and Water				
Condensed Soup and Water				
Frozen Orange Juice and Water				
Aspirin and Water				
Iodine (3%) and Alcohol (97%)				

3. State a hypothesis that explains why the solution particles passed through the filters, but the mechanical mixtures did not.

Try this!

In Investigation 2, you observed that the particles in a mechanical mixture can be separated from the mixture by filtering, but the particles of a solution cannot. To find out why, look closely at the structure of a piece of filter paper using a microscope or a magnifying glass. Do you see any open spaces or ''holes'' in the paper? What role do you think these holes have in the filtration process? Make a drawing of the structure of the filter paper as you have observed it under a microscope or a magnifying glass. Use your drawing to help you explain why solution particles cannot be separated from a solution by filtering.

Section review questions

1. State four characteristics of a solution.
2. Why isn't garden soil mixed with water a solution?
3. Is powdered milk mixed with water a solution or a mechanical mixture? Why?
4. Many medicines say ''shake well.'' Explain why.
5. Which has larger particles, a solution or a mechanical mixture? How do you know?

2.3 Other kinds of solutions

A solid dissolved in a liquid is not the only kind of solution. In fact, matter in each of the three states—solid, liquid, and gas—can form solutions with matter in the same state or in each of the other two. In this section, you will learn more about these different kinds of solutions.

Air

Air is a solution of gases dissolved in a gas. It contains about 78% nitrogen, 21% oxygen, slightly less than 1% argon, and traces of carbon dioxide, neon, helium, methane, krypton,

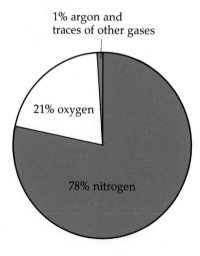

Figure 2–8 Air is a solution of gases.

and water vapour. Nitrogen can be considered the solvent in air, while the other gases are the solutes.

When air is cooled to extremely low temperatures, it turns into a liquid called liquid air. Scientists can separate liquid oxygen and liquid nitrogen from liquid air. The pure oxygen and nitrogen are collected and bottled in tanks under great pressure. Both oxygen and nitrogen have many uses.

Oxygen gas, for example, is used in hospitals to help patients who have breathing problems. It can also be used in a torch to help weld metals together. By itself, pure oxygen will not burn. However, when it is mixed correctly with another gas called acetylene, the resulting solution burns with a very hot flame. The flame is hot enough to melt certain metals and cause them to join, or weld, together.

Of course, your body needs oxygen, too. When you inhale, oxygen gas is absorbed by your lungs, where it is dissolved and carried in your bloodstream. The bloodstream transports oxygen to all of the cells — muscle, nerve, and bone — enabling them to do work. In the process, cells give off another gas — carbon dioxide. This gas also dissolves in the bloodstream and is carried back to the lungs. From the lungs, you exhale carbon dioxide into the atmosphere.

As you have seen, air is composed of a large percentage of nitrogen. Liquid nitrogen has a very cold temperature, which

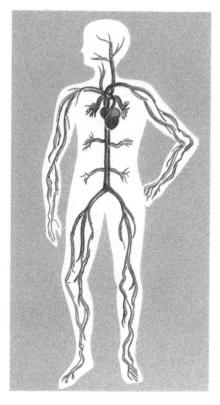

Figure 2–9 The human circulatory system

Why would being able to transport enough oxygen to muscle cells be important to this weight lifter?

Snow tractors like this one are used in polar regions.

ranges between −196°C and −209°C depending on the pressure it is under. Research scientists use liquid nitrogen to test the performance of different materials under extremely cold conditions. These results may influence the design of machinery used in the Earth's polar regions and in space. Some materials behave very strangely at such cold temperatures. For example, when rubber is cooled in liquid nitrogen, it becomes so brittle that it will shatter when it is tapped with a hammer.

Soft drinks

A soft drink is a solution of a gas and solids dissolved in a liquid. Water is the liquid used to make soft drinks, and carbon dioxide is the gas. Sugar and different flavourings are the solids that are used. Can you guess what might cause the hissing sound when you open a soft-drink can or bottle? Why do you think soft drinks are sometimes called "carbonated" beverages?

Why did bubbles form in this glass of water?

Try this!

Is a gas dissolved in ordinary tap water? Here's a test you can perform to find out. Fill a glass half-full with cold tap water. After 1 min, observe the condition of the water. Make a note of your observation. Observe the water again after 2 h. Compare your observations. Did you observe any changes in the water? What can you conclude about the ability of a gas to be dissolved in tap water?

Antifreeze

Antifreeze is a liquid dissolved in another liquid. This solution is used in the cooling systems of many cars and trucks to keep their engine blocks from freezing in the winter or overheating in the summer. It is made by mixing ethylene glycol, which is a liquid, with water. The freezing point of the antifreeze solution can easily be adjusted by using more or less ethylene glycol. In Canada, antifreeze solutions are usually mixed to have freezing points between −40°C and

−60°C. This freezing point is much lower than the freezing point of pure water (0°C) or ethylene glycol (−15.6°C).

Alloys

Alloys are solid solutions of two or more metals. To make an alloy, the metals are melted together in correct proportions and allowed to cool. Mercury is a metal. But it is a liquid at room temperature. Mercury forms a solution, or an alloy, when it is mixed with the metals silver and tin. This solution is used by dentists to fill teeth. Brass is an alloy of copper and zinc. Other alloys include bronze, which is an alloy of copper and tin, and solder, which is an alloy of lead and tin.

Table 2.1 provides examples of other kinds of solutions.

Antifreeze is a solution of two liquids.

Table 2.1   Kinds of solutions

Type of Solute	Type of Solvent	Example of Solution
Solid	Liquid	• salt dissolved in water
Liquid	Liquid	• oil dissolved in gasoline
Gas	Liquid	• carbon dioxide dissolved in water (soft drinks)
Solid	Solid	• zinc dissolved in copper (brass)
Liquid	Solid	• mercury dissolved in silver and tin (dental fillings)
Gas	Solid	• hydrogen dissolved in platinum
Solid	Gas	• moth balls dissolved in air
Liquid	Gas	• perfume dissolved in air
Gas	Gas	• air (mixture of nitrogen, oxygen, and other gases)

Volume changes in solutions

Suppose you were to make a solution of water and alcohol by mixing equal volumes of both substances together. What would you predict the volume of the solution to be? Would it be equal to the sum of the two volumes? You will find out in Investigation 3.

Caution: Alcohol is both poisonous and flammable. Keep it and your solution away from sparks, heat, and open flame. Make sure the room you are working in is well ventilated. Avoid breathing the fumes from the alcohol. Keep it away from your mouth and eyes. Ask your teacher to dispose of your solution when you have completed your investigation.

Investigation 3   Volume changes in a solution of alcohol and water

PROBLEM
What happens to the volume of a solution where equal volumes of alcohol and water are combined?

MATERIALS
alcohol
water

MEASURING TOOLS
two 100-mL graduated
    cylinders

HYPOTHESIS
Make a hypothesis about what change will occur in the volume of a solution where equal volumes of alcohol and water are combined.

PROCEDURE
1. Carefully pour 50 mL of water into one of the graduated cylinders. Be sure to measure from the bottom of the meniscus, just under the surface of the water (see Figure 2–10).

Figure 2–10   When using a graduated cylinder to measure liquids, always measure from the bottom of the liquid's curved surface (the meniscus). If you don't, you will get an inaccurate measurement. Handle the cylinder carefully.

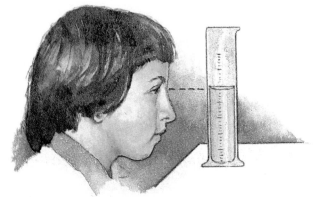

2. Pour 50 mL of alcohol into the other graduated cylinder.
3. Pour all of the liquid from one cylinder into the other cylinder so that the water and alcohol are mixed.
4. Measure the final volume.

OBSERVATIONS
1. Record the total combined volume of the mixture.

CONCLUSIONS
What can you conclude about the combined volume of water and alcohol in solution?

Discussion questions

1. Predict the volumes of water and alcohol if you were able to separate the solution.
2. What should you do before making a general conclusion about volume changes using other liquids in solution?
3. Assume that the liquids water and alcohol are made up of invisible particles with spaces between them (see Figure 2–11). Use this scientific model to explain the change in volume.
4. Do you think the combined mass might be different than the individual masses? Design an experiment to find out.

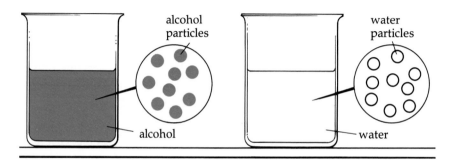

Figure 2–11 A scientific model of alcohol and water

Try this!

Some liquids, like alcohol and water, will mix easily to form a solution. However, some liquids will not. Fill a test tube half-full with water. Pour 5 mL of vegetable oil into the same test tube. Use your thumb as a stopper for the test tube. Shake the test tube back and forth several times. After shaking the test tube, place it in a test-tube rack. Observe what happens. Does the oil dissolve in the water? What do you think happens to the oil that escapes from an oil tanker when it breaks up at sea?

Caution: Commercial and household solvents that evaporate quickly are often extremely dangerous. Watch out for gasoline, acetone, mineral spirits, carbon tetrachloride, and benzene. Glues, nail polishes, spot removers, and paint thinners may contain these solvents. Most of these solvents are highly flammable. Breathing or sniffing them is also dangerous. Gasoline can affect your heart and cause lead poisoning, and carbon tetrachloride is bad for your kidneys and liver. Acetone can penetrate your skin. Products containing these solvents should be used only by adults, in small quantities in a well-ventilated area, away from sparks or flame. Directions for use must always be followed carefully.

House painters use solvents like Varsol and turpentine to thin paints.

Try this!

The freezing point of a solution is lower than that of the solvent. This is why people sprinkle rock salt on icy sidewalks. Some of the salt dissolves into a thin film of water on top of the ice. The ice underneath this film then melts to become part of the solution. More salt dissolves, and the process continues until most of the ice melts. You can watch this process at work. Sprinkle some table salt on one of two ice cubes that you have just removed from your freezer. Watch both ice cubes closely. Which one shows the first sign of melting? Why?

Section review questions

1. What are the two main gases in air? What percentage of air do each of these gases make up?
2. Which two gases are dissolved in the bloodstream? How does each gas get there, and where does it go?
3. How are soft drinks made?
4. How is antifreeze made? How is it used? Why does it work?
5. What is an alloy? State two examples.
6. Why can a student mix 52 mL of water with 50 mL of alcohol in a flask that holds only 100 mL of liquid without any overflow?

2.4 Solvents

You have already seen that a solvent is a substance in which other substances, or solutes, are dissolved. Water is one of the most important solvents because the dissolved minerals it contains are essential to all human, animal, and plant life. Scientists have found that water acts as a solvent for many things. You will learn more about the use of water as a solvent later in this chapter.

Since water will not act as a solvent for everything, other

solvents are used instead. Tincture of iodine is a solution where iodine is mixed with the solvent alcohol. Mineral spirits, or Varsol, is a solvent derived from petroleum. Turpentine is a solvent made from the sap of pine trees. These two solvents are often used to thin paints and to dissolve grease.

Different kinds of solvents are also used in the "dry" cleaning process. In order to remove a stain like grape juice from a fabric, solvents must be used that will dissolve the particles making up the stain. This is exactly how dry cleaning works. Special solvents are used instead of soap and water. But these solvents are not really dry. They evaporate so quickly after a dry-cleaning wash that the clothes feel like they had never been wet.

By acting quickly, you can often remove stains from fabrics before the stains become set. To do this, you need to know which solvents work best on which types of stains. In Investigation 4, you will see how some common solvents, other than water, can be used in this way.

Investigation 4   Dissolving stains from fabrics

PURPOSE
To investigate which solvents work best to dissolve stains from fabrics.

MATERIALS
small glass bowl
popsicle sticks
paper towels
safety glasses

7 lots of white, cotton
fabric; each lot consisting
of four 10-cm x 10-cm
pieces of fabric stained
with one of the following:
  grass clippings
  oil-based paint
  bacon fat
  nail polish
  coffee
  red wine
  chocolate

MEASURING TOOLS
50-mL graduated cylinder
timer

supplies of the following
solvents:
  mineral spirits (Varsol)
  rubbing alcohol (isopropyl)
  baby oil
  vegetable oil

Caution: Mineral spirits and rubbing alcohol are both flammable and poisonous. Before using these substances, read the warnings on the container labels. Make sure the area in which they will be used is well ventilated. Keep both substances away from heat, sparks, and flame. Avoid inhaling the fumes or getting them in your mouth or eyes. Wash both solvents from your skin with soap and water when you have finished the investigation. Ask your teacher to dispose of the used solvents. Solvents that evaporate quickly, like mineral spirits and rubbing alcohol, should be used only in small quantities.

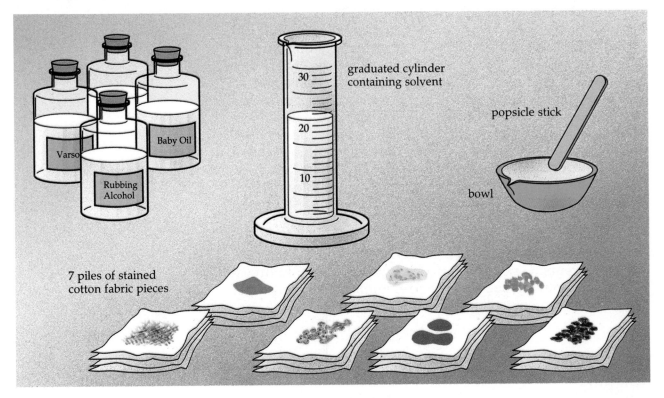

Figure 2–12

PROCEDURE

1. Put on your safety glasses. Measure out 20 mL of mineral spirits using the graduated cylinder. Pour the mineral spirits into the small glass bowl.
2. Place a piece of grass-stained fabric into the mineral spirits. Carefully move the fabric around with a popsicle stick to see if the spirits will dissolve the stain.
3. After soaking the fabric for 2 min, remove it from the bowl. Carefully wring out the mineral spirits so that the excess is caught in the bowl. Spread the fabric on a paper towel to dry.
4. Repeat Steps 2 and 3 with each of the fabric pieces stained with the other six substances.
5. Repeat Steps 1–4 with each of the other three cleaning solvents. Be sure to wash your hands thoroughly when you have finished using the solvents.

OBSERVATIONS

1. Copy the chart on page 85 into your notebook. Use it to record your observations.

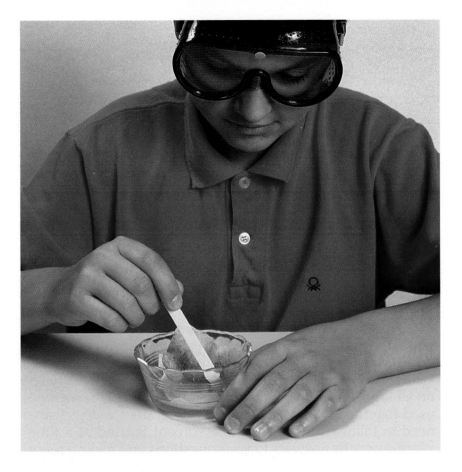

Cleaning Solvent	Stain						
	Grass	Oil-based Paint	Grease	Nail Polish	Coffee	Red Wine	Chocolate
Mineral Spirits							
Rubbing Alcohol							
Baby Oil							
Vegetable Oil							

Discussion questions

1. Which solvent removed more stains than the other solvents? Which solvent removed fewer stains? Which stain was the most stubborn?
2. Why would a dry cleaner need to know the type of fabric a piece of clothing is made of before it is cleaned? Why would a dry cleaner want to know what caused the stain?
3. Why do you think dry-cleaning plants need exhaust fans?
4. Why do you think it might not be safe to use several solvents together at the same time?

Try this!

Visit a dry cleaners to find out what cleaning solvents are used. Prepare a list of questions before you go. For example, you might ask how long the solvents take to remove most stains. Are there stains that require special solvents? Which stains are the hardest to remove? Are the solvents safe to use on all kinds of fabric? Are two or more solvents sometimes used together? What safety precautions does a dry cleaner need to follow if more than one solvent is used at a time? Write down the answers to your questions and make a report to your class.

Section review questions

1. Why must different solvents, other than water, be used to remove certain stains?
2. Explain how solvents remove stains from clothes.
3. Why are some solvents dangerous?
4. Which solvent would you use to
   a) clean oil-based paint from a paint brush?
   b) remove grass stains from a pair of pants?
5. Is dry cleaning really a ''dry'' process? Explain why it is called ''dry'' cleaning.

Solvents in your body

You probably don't think much about eating. It's something you do when you are hungry; when you sit down for breakfast, or lunch, or dinner. But have you ever thought about what happens to the food you eat?

As you chew, your teeth break down food into smaller particles. A digestive juice—a solvent called saliva—is secreted in your mouth. The saliva moistens the particles so they can be swallowed, and dissolves certain nutrients in them, which are mostly starches and sugars. When you swallow, the softened food and nutrients move into your stomach. Different digestive juices go to work to break down the particles further and dissolve other nutrients. The nutrients and the remaining food then pass into your intestines. As they enter the intestines, other digestive juices work to dissolve additional nutrients.

By now your body's various digestive solvents have done all they can to put as many nutrients as possible into solution. These nutrients, consisting of sugars, fats, and proteins, are absorbed from the walls of your intestines and pass into your bloodstream. Your heart pumps the

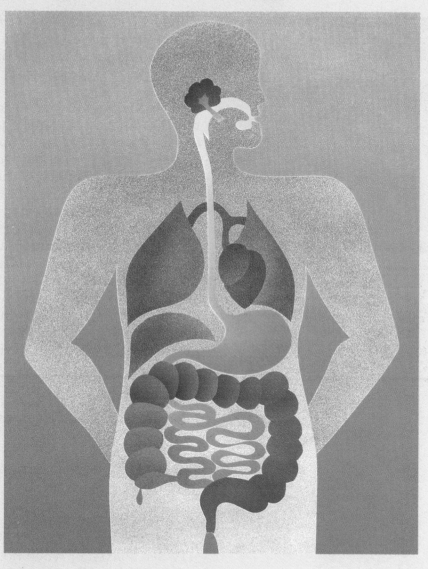

Figure 2–13 The human digestive system

blood to your cells. Here the nutrients, along with oxygen from your lungs, pass into your cells to be used for growth, repair, and respiration.

2.5 The rate of dissolving

Factors affecting the dissolving rates of solids

Knowing the dissolving rates of solids is important to researchers in the drug industry. Can you think of another industry where the same knowledge might be valuable?

The time it takes for a solid to dissolve in a solvent is known as its **rate of dissolving**. Knowing the rate of dissolving is important to the manufacturing process of medicines, dyes, and processed foods such as food colourings and flavoured syrups.

A drug company that makes cough syrup, for example, needs to know how long it will take to combine the ingredients of its product, and wait for them to dissolve, before the cough syrup can be bottled. The company knows that the longer this process takes, the more expensive the product will be for the consumer, and the more people the company may have to employ to carry out the process.

Manufacturers know that to be competitive, they must produce good-quality products as quickly and as inexpensively as possible. To do this, a drug company employs research scientists who try to find ways to make the ingredients of the company's products dissolve faster. These scientists ask questions about the dissolving rates of solids. Will stirring a mixture make a solid dissolve more quickly? Will heating the mixture speed up the dissolving process? Could another solvent instead of water be used to speed up the rate of dissolving?

In Investigation 5, you will ask the same questions to determine the factors that affect the dissolving rate of a solid.

Investigation 5   Factors affecting the dissolving rate of a solid

PURPOSE
To compare the rates at which a solid dissolves.
A) when shaken or when not shaken
B) in cold water or in hot water
C) when broken up or in one piece
D) in water or in alcohol

HYPOTHESIS
State which factors for each test will cause the solid to dissolve the fastest.

MATERIALS

8 sugar cubes	spoon
2 large test tubes	cold tap water
2 rubber stoppers	hot tap water
test-tube rack	alcohol
pail	

PROCEDURE

TEST A
1. Fill the pail with cold tap water. Fill two large test tubes half-full with water from the pail. This will ensure that the temperature of the water in both test tubes is the same.
2. Drop a sugar cube into each test tube and place a rubber stopper in each tube. Place one test tube in the test-tube rack.
3. Shake the other test tube while you hold the stopper with your thumb (see Figure 2–14). Observe both test tubes carefully. Which sugar cube completely dissolves first?
4. Wash and dry each test tube before beginning Test B.

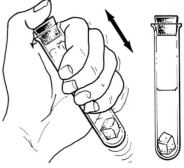

Figure 2–14

TEST B
1. Fill one test tube half-full with cold tap water. Fill the other one half-full with hot tap water.
2. Drop a sugar cube into each test tube and place a rubber stopper in each tube. Place both tubes in the test-tube rack.
3. Observe the sugar cubes as they dissolve. Does one dissolve more quickly than the other? (If you like, you can shake the test tubes, but be sure to shake both equally. Remember to put your thumbs over the tops of the stoppers.)
4. Wash and dry each test tube before beginning Test C.

TEST C
1. Fill both test tubes half-full with cold water from the pail. Place them in the test-tube rack. (The temperature of the water in both test tubes must be the same.)

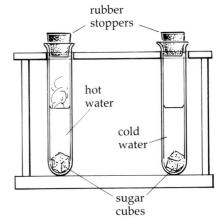

Figure 2–15

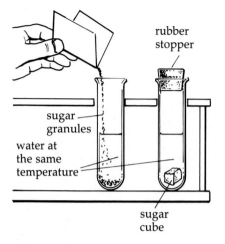

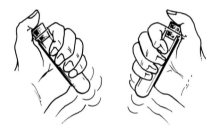

Figure 2–16

Figure 2–17

Caution: Alcohol is very poisonous and extremely flammable. Use it in very small quantities away from heat or an open flame. Make sure you are working in a well-ventilated room. Avoid inhaling the fumes from the alcohol. Keep it away from your mouth and eyes.

2. Use a spoon to break one sugar cube into small pieces on a sheet of paper. Be careful not to lose any of the pieces.
3. Pour the broken cube into one test tube and place the solid cube in the other.
4. Place a stopper in both tubes. Pick up one tube with each hand. Place your thumbs over the stoppers and shake both tubes back and forth 30 times.
5. Check the solid in each test tube to see which dissolves first.
6. Wash and dry each test tube before beginning Test D.

TEST D
1. Fill one test tube half-full with water. Fill the other one half-full with alcohol.
2. Place a stopper in both test tubes. Place your thumbs over the stoppers. Shake both tubes back and forth 30 times.
3. Compare the sugar cube in each test tube. Which one dissolved first?

OBSERVATIONS
1. Record your observations in a chart like the one below.

Test	Observations
A) Shaking or Not Shaking	
B) Hot Water or Cold Water	
C) Broken Pieces or One Piece	
D) Water or Alcohol	

CONCLUSIONS
Write a conclusion for each test based on your observations. How do these conclusions compare with your hypotheses?

Discussion questions

1. What should you do before making a more general conclusion relating to factors affecting the dissolving rates of all solids?

2. The graph in Figure 2–18 shows how raising the temperature of 100 mL of water affects the amounts of three different solid solutes that can be dissolved in it. In other words, the temperature of the solvent is a factor in the dissolving rate of each solid. The dissolving rate of which solid is most affected by the temperature of the solvent? Which solid is least affected?

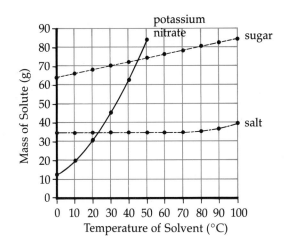

Figure 2–18

Factors affecting the dissolving rates of gases

You already know that gases can dissolve in liquids. Soft drinks and tap water are solutions that contain dissolved gases. Some of the factors that affect the dissolving rates of gases differ from those that affect solids. You can see for yourself what these differences are by carefully observing the rate at which carbon dioxide gas comes out of a liquid solution, such as a soft drink, in which it is already dissolved. You can do this by changing temperature and pressure, as you will in Investigation 6.

Investigation 6   Factors affecting the amount of gas
                  dissolved in a liquid

PURPOSE
To investigate how changes in temperature and pressure
affect the rate at which gas will come out of a solution.

MATERIALS
large bottle   Plasticine
2 dishpans   hot and cold tap water
750-mL bottle of a soft drink   pitcher
1 m of plastic tubing

PROCEDURE
1. Find a partner. Fill the large bottle to the top with cold tap
   water. Fill one of the dishpans two-thirds full with cold
   tap water.
2. Fill the other dishpan one-third full with hot tap water.
   Place it beside the dishpan containing cold tap water on
   a level surface.
3. Put your ear close to the top of a cold bottle of a soft drink
   and listen carefully as you remove the cap. What do you
   hear?

Caution: Make sure that you
do not shake up the contents
of the soft-drink bottle too
much when you are transport-
ing it to school.

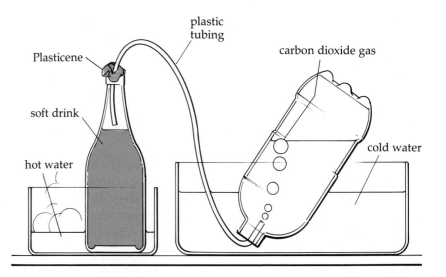

Figure 2–19

4. Insert one end of the plastic tubing into the soft-drink bottle and seal it in place with Plasticine. Then stand the bottle upright in the dishpan of hot water.
5. Place the palm of your hand over the top of the large bottle. With your partner's help, turn the bottle upside down and place its neck below the water level in the dishpan of cold water (see Figure 2–19). Remove your palm from the top of the bottle and insert the free end of the plastic tubing into its neck. Hold the bottle in position and observe what happens.
6. Ask your partner to collect more hot tap water with the pitcher and gradually pour it over the soft-drink bottle. The soft drink will warm up more quickly if your partner shakes the bottle gently. Observe what happens as the soft drink heats up.
7. Disconnect the equipment and taste the soft drink that is left in the bottle.

Caution: Be careful when you are using hot water. Keep your hands and face away from steam that may come from the tap. To prevent spilling the water, do not fill the pitcher completely. Pour the water slowly and gradually into the dishpan containing the soft-drink bottle. Don't pour the hot water directly onto the bottle as it may break.

OBSERVATIONS
1. Describe what you heard when you removed the cap from the soft-drink bottle. Is the pressure inside the bottle higher, lower, or the same as it was before the cap was loosened?
2. Record what you saw when you placed the free end of the plastic tubing into the neck of the large bottle. What did you observe when you heated the soft drink in the bottle?
3. Describe how the soft drink tasted at the end of the investigation.

CONCLUSIONS
State how pressure affects the amount of gas that is dissolved in a soft drink. Based on your observations, what can you conclude about a) the effect of temperature on the amount of gas that will dissolve in water and b) the effect of pressure on the amount of gas that will dissolve in water. State whether water will dissolve more gas or less gas when it is warmed.

Discussion questions

1. Why does a cold soft drink fizz when you pour it into a warm glass?

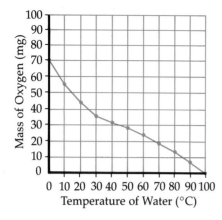

Figure 2–20

2. According to the graph in Figure 2–20, how many milligrams of oxygen will dissolve in 1 L of water at 10°C? If the temperature of the water is raised to 30°C, how much oxygen will dissolve in it at that temperature?

3. A new manufacturing plant is constructed beside a small river. Water at 15°C is pumped from the river to be used in the plant to cool various engines. At 70°C, it is poured back into the river. What effect will this have on the oxygen content of the water downstream from the plant? How do you think this could affect aquatic life?

4. A student fills an aquarium with cold water. After an hour, bubbles appear inside the aquarium against the glass. Explain why this happens.

Try this!

How much gas do you think there is in a 750-mL bottle of a soft drink? Check your estimate by carefully collecting the gas from a cold bottle of a soft drink as you did in Investigation 6. Try shaking the soft drink and using a hot-water bath to collect as much gas as you can. When all the gas is collected, make a mark on the side of the collecting bottle at the level of the gas. Empty the collecting bottle and turn it

right side up. Use a graduated cylinder to measure the amount of water it takes to fill the bottle to the line you have marked on it. This measurement will be the same as the volume of the gas that you collected from the soft drink.

Section review questions

1. What three steps would you take to dissolve a hard candy quickly? Would it dissolve better in alcohol or in water?
2. Refer to the graph in Figure 2–20. If 1 L of water was heated so that its temperature rose from 30°C to 100°C, how many milligrams of oxygen would be given off?
3. Scuba divers who work at considerable depths underwater are careful not to surface too quickly to avoid a condition called the ''bends,'' or decompression sickness. This condition arises when nitrogen bubbles develop in a diver's bloodstream causing severe cramping and breathing difficulty. Explain how and why these bubbles could form.
4. What factors affect the rate at which solids dissolve in a liquid? What factors affect the rate at which gases dissolve in a liquid?

Scuba divers can be affected by decompression sickness if they surface too quickly.

PEOPLE IN SCIENCE

Sir Frederick Grant Banting

Canadian scientist Frederick Banting was born on a farm near Alliston, Ontario, in 1891. In the spring of 1921, Banting and his assistant, Charles Best, performed some important experiments in an attempt to find a cure for diabetes. Earlier, a close friend of Banting's had died because of this serious disease.

The experiments of Banting and Best led to the discovery of insulin, a digestive juice, or solvent, that is secreted into the stomach of healthy people by an organ called the pancreas. People with the most common form of diabetes do not make enough insulin, which is needed to digest sugar, an essential nutrient. As a result, these people have too much sugar dissolved in their blood. High sugar levels can make diabetics feel extremely thirsty, hungry, and tired. If the disease is not treated, diabetics can become thin and weak, or fall into comas that may lead to death.

The first human patient treated with insulin was a 14-year-old boy. The treatment took place at Toronto General Hospital. After taking insulin, the level of sugar in the boy's blood dropped, and his symptoms disappeared.

In 1923, Banting shared the Nobel prize for medicine, and he gave half of his prize money to Best. He gave the remaining money to a research fund. In 1934, he was knighted for his great contribution to science and medicine. Banting died in a plane crash off the coast of Newfoundland in 1941. He was on his way to England to chair a committee on aviation medical research. The loss of this great Canadian scientist, whose hard work and skill had helped to save the lives of millions of diabetics around the world, was a great one.

2.6 Saturated and unsaturated solutions

Have you ever watched the caretakers at your school wash a floor? First, they dip their mops into buckets full of cleaning solution. The mops are very wet, and they drip excess solution as they are pulled from the buckets. The caretakers mop the floor with the solution, allowing it to dissolve dirt. Afterward, they wring out the mops until they are just damp. Then the caretakers mop the floor again to absorb the dirt and the used solution. This process is repeated until the floor is clean.

Do you know why this process works? When the caretakers' mops are dripping, the mops are saturated. This means they *cannot* absorb, or hold, any more liquid. The mops drip and transfer cleaning solution to the floor. When the mops are wrung out, they are damp, or unsaturated. This means that the mops *can* absorb the used cleaning solution and the dirt from the floor.

In the same way that this mop cannot hold any more liquid, saturated solutions cannot dissolve any more solute.

The terms saturated and unsaturated are used in a similar way to describe certain solutions. When a small amount of salt is dissolved in a container of lukewarm water, the resulting dilute solution is an **unsaturated solution**. Unsaturated means that the solution can hold or dissolve more salt. As more salt is added to this solution, it also dissolves in the same amount of water. The solution becomes more and more concentrated. Eventually, a point is reached where no more salt can dissolve. At this point, the solution is a **saturated solution**. The solution has dissolved as much salt as it is capable of holding. Any extra salt that is added will simply settle, undissolved, to the bottom of the container.

Suppose that more water is added to the container and the solution is stirred. What do you think would happen to the undissolved salt? Would it dissolve? Why or why not? Investigation 7 will help you to find out.

Investigation 7   Making saturated and unsaturated salt-water solutions

PURPOSE
To investigate the difference between a saturated and an unsaturated solution.

MATERIALS
pail
tap water
table salt
paper cup
popsicle stick

MEASURING TOOLS
100-mL graduated cylinder
250-mL beaker
balance
1-g mass

HYPOTHESIS
State the effect that an increase in the amount of solute will have on a saturated solution. State the effect an increase in the amount of solvent will have on a saturated solution.

PROCEDURE

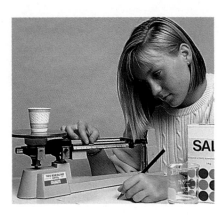

1. Fill a pail with tap water and let it stand overnight to reach room temperature.
2. Measure out 100 mL of water from the pail using the graduated cylinder. Pour 50 mL of water into the beaker.
3. Use the balance to measure the mass of the paper cup. Then put salt into the cup until you have exactly 1 g of salt after subtracting the mass of the cup. Add the salt to the water in the beaker.
4. Use the popsicle stick to stir the solution until all the salt has dissolved.
5. Again measure out 1 g of salt and add it to the beaker. Stir the solution until the salt is completely dissolved.
6. Repeat Steps 4 and 5 until no more salt will dissolve.
7. Pour the remaining 50 mL of water from the graduated cylinder into the saturated solution in the beaker. Stir and observe what happens.
8. Measure out 1 g of salt. Add it to the solution and stir. Repeat this step until no more salt will dissolve in the solution.

OBSERVATIONS
1. Record the number of grams of salt you were able to dissolve in 50 mL of water at the end of Step 6 before the solution became saturated.
2. Record any differences in appearance between the unsaturated solution and the saturated solution.
3. After you added more water to the saturated solution, record what you observed. Did the appearance of the solution change?

4. Record the number of grams of salt you were able to dissolve in the solution at the end of Step 8 before it again became saturated.

CONCLUSIONS
Based on your observations, what can you conclude about the differences between an unsaturated solution and a saturated solution?

Discussion questions

1. What kind of solution did you make in Step 4? How do you know?
2. What kind of solution did you make in Step 6? How do you know?
3. From your results in Step 8, state the number of grams of salt that will dissolve in 100 mL of water at room temperature. How many grams of salt will dissolve in 200 mL? in 300 mL? Draw a bar graph that shows this relationship. Then draw a straight line that connects the top of each bar.
4. Calculate the number of grams of salt that will dissolve in 250 mL of water at room temperature. How many grams of salt would dissolve in 25 mL of water at room temperature? Do these values fall along the line you drew on your graph?
5. The photographs in the margin show two solutions of copper sulphate (bluestone). One solution is saturated and the other solution is unsaturated. Can you tell the solutions apart just by looking at them? What clues will help you to decide which solution is saturated?
6. Would heated water dissolve greater or lesser amounts of salt? What effect would cold water have?

Which solution is saturated and which solution is unsaturated? How can you tell?

Mass concentration

It is possible to describe a solution in quantitative terms. Scientists will often describe a solution in terms of its **mass concentration**. In other words, they calculate how much mass of a solute is dissolved per unit volume of the solution. For example, a solution of salt and water may have a mass concentration of 100 g/L. This means that 1 L of the solution contains 100 g of salt. Knowing the mass concentration of solutions is useful when determining the strength of a particular solution. Here is how mass concentration is calculated.

Sample problem
A student dissolves 40 g of sugar in water to make 250 mL of solution. Calculate the mass concentration of this solution.
Formula

$$\text{Mass Concentration} = \frac{\text{mass of solute}}{\text{volume of solution}}$$

Solution

$$\text{Mass Concentration} = \frac{40 \text{ g}}{250 \text{ mL}}$$

$$= 0.16 \text{ g/mL or } 160 \text{ g/L}$$

Try this!

1. Determine the mass concentration of 200 L of a liquid detergent that contains 50 g of soap solids.
2. Use the data you recorded in Investigation 7 to determine the mass concentration of a saturated solution of salt and tap water at room temperature.
3. A student tries to dissolve 100 g of salt in 100 mL of water. Based on your results in Investigation 7, how many grams of salt do you think would settle to the bottom of the container and remain undissolved? What would be the mass concentration of the solution?

Supersaturated solutions and crystals

When a solution is heated, it will usually dissolve more solute. When this solution cools, it contains more solute than it normally would. These solutions are **supersaturated solutions**. Eventually, however, the excess solute slowly comes out of the solution in the form of crystals. Some of the beautiful crystals you see in gem shops and jewellery stores are formed in this way.

The formation of crystals can happen deep in the Earth, where ground water is heated by volcanic vents and the great pressure of melted rock. As this ground water flows through cracks in the Earth's surface layers, it dissolves various minerals. Several of the solutions that result cool and become supersaturated. This happens when the solutions are forced along cracks closer to the Earth's surface, where they become trapped and cooled. Here, any excess solute crystallizes out of the solutions until they are no longer supersaturated. Crystals formed in this way are often found near hot springs and in underground caves.

Industry uses supersaturated solutions to make crystals, too. The "needles" used in stereo systems to pick up sound from records are examples of manufactured crystals. The tiny microchips that form the basic parts of computers are also made from manufactured crystals.

Would it surprise you to learn that you can make your own crystals from supersaturated solutions? Many people create beautiful crystals as a hobby. They find it challenging to "grow" large, colourful crystals with gleaming, flat surfaces that meet at different angles. You can try to grow your own crystals in Investigation 8. Once you have mastered the technique, you may want to grow other crystals and start a crystal collection.

Stalactites are formed when crystals of carbonate of lime come out of solution.

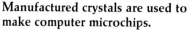

Manufactured crystals are used to make computer microchips.

Caution: Copper sulphate is poisonous. Be careful not to get any in your mouth or near your eyes. As with any poisonous substance, handle the copper sulphate carefully. It is a good idea to wear an apron to avoid stains. Wash your hands thoroughly when you have finished using it.

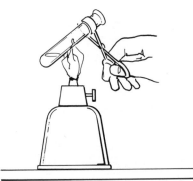

Figure 2–21

Caution: Make sure that the burner is on a level, uncluttered surface. Only light the burner with your teacher's permission. Always wear safety glasses when you heat any substance. Remember to tie back long hair and keep your fingers and clothes away from the flame. Point the test tube away from yourself and other students. Never heat the test tube from the bottom. Hold the test tube on a slight angle with the test-tube clamp, and move the centre of the tube continuously over the flame.

Investigation 8   Growing bluestone crystals

PURPOSE
To observe crystals growing in a supersaturated solution.

MATERIALS
copper sulphate
paper cup
tap water
popsicle stick or a
  glass stirring rod
test tube
test-tube clamp
test-tube rack
alcohol burner
matches
magnifying glass
paper towel
safety glasses

MEASURING TOOLS
balance
5-g mass
50-mL graduated cylinder

HYPOTHESIS
State what you expect will happen when a heated, supersaturated solution of copper sulphate and water cools.

PROCEDURE
1. Use the balance to measure the mass of the paper cup. Then use the balance to measure out 5 g of copper sulphate in the cup as in Step 3 of Investigation 7 (see page 98).
2. Measure 10 mL of water using the graduated cylinder and pour it into the test tube.
3. Put the copper sulphate into the test tube. Stir the solution with the popsicle stick or a glass stirring rod. Place the test tube in the test-tube rack.
4. Put on your safety glasses. Light the alcohol burner with your teacher's permission. Remove the test tube from the rack and secure it in the test-tube clamp. Heat the solution and continue to stir until the copper sulphate is completely dissolved.
5. Place the test tube in the test-tube rack and let the solution cool slowly until it is almost at room temperature. (This is a supersaturated solution).

6. If crystals have not formed, "seed" the solution by dropping a small crystal of the solute into the supersaturated solution, or shake the solution gently. One of these methods will usually cause crystals to form.

7. Examine the crystals as they form using the magnifying glass. Pour off the remaining solution and carefully shake the crystals from the test tube onto a paper towel. Observe the crystals more closely with the magnifying glass.

OBSERVATIONS
1. Record your observations of the solution as it cooled.
2. Record what you observed as the crystals grew.
3. Sketch the crystals you have made. Write a description of the crystals below your drawing.

CONCLUSIONS
What can you conclude about the effect of temperature on a supersaturated solution of copper sulphate and water?

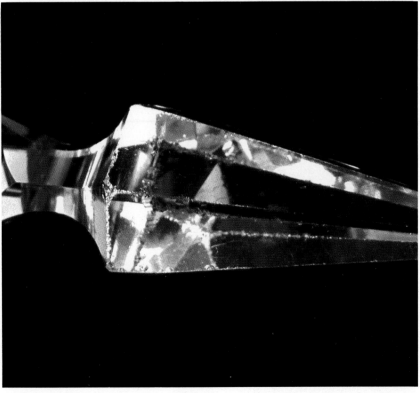

A glass crystal

Did you know?
Many things like salt, sugar, snow, ice, metals, and precious stones are all made of crystals. But glass is not a crystal even when it is cut to look like one. The tiny particles that make up glass are not arranged in an orderly pattern as they are in crystals.

Did you know?
Crystallographers are people who study crystals. To make one large crystal, a crystallographer ties a seed crystal to a string and suspends it in the solution for a week or more.

Discussion questions

1. What type of solution did you make
   a) when some of the solute had dissolved?
   b) when the solution had cooled?
   c) after the crystals had stopped growing?
2. Draw two diagrams to show how the arrangement of particles in a solution probably differs from the arrangement of particles in a crystal. Think of these drawings as scientific models.
3. Why do you think the crystal you added to the solution is called a seed crystal?

Try this!

Present an oral and visual report about crystal growing to your class. Explain your purpose, materials, and procedures. Double or triple the amounts of copper sulphate and water indicated in Steps 1 and 2 in Investigation 8. Use a 500-mL beaker instead of a test tube. Place the beaker containing the supersaturated solution on an overhead projector. Turn on the projector and dim the lights. "Seed" your solution with an extra crystal. Your audience will enjoy watching the crystals grow on the screen.

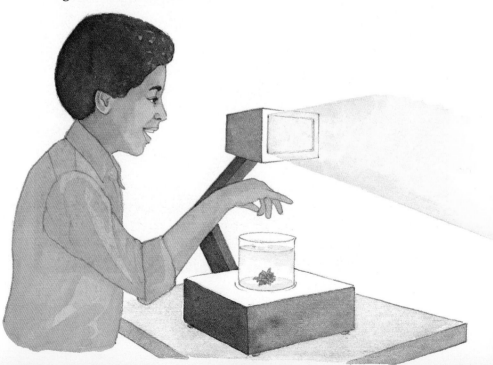

Figure 2–22 Observing crystal growth with an overhead projector

You can grow many interesting crystals using other solutes. Ask your teacher for instructions, or check a chemistry book in your library for information.

Section review questions

1. Describe an unsaturated solution.
2. Suppose you are given a solution in a test tube. How could you use one or two crystals of the solute to determine whether the solution was unsaturated, saturated, or supersaturated?
3. How could you retrieve salt that you had dissolved in a glass of water?
4. Rock candy is the name given to large crystals of sugar. Write down a method you could use to make it.
5. Suppose you dissolved 150 g of sugar in water and made 750 mL of solution. What is the mass concentration of the solution?

2.7 Water: The universal solvent

Every day you use solutions that have water as their solvent. You depend on water to live. Tap water, for instance, contains dissolved minerals that are absorbed by your body to help carry out your life functions and to strengthen your bones. You use solutions to wash your clothes and your body that have water as their solvent. Water is also the solvent for many solutions used in different industrial processes. Papermaking, photography, food preparation, and the production of medicines are just a few examples.

Why is water such an important solvent? First, many substances dissolve in water. In fact, water dissolves more substances than any other solvent. This is why water is often called the universal solvent. Second, water is readily available on Earth and can be stored, packaged, and transported easily to where it is needed. Third, water is safe because it is non-flammable and non-toxic. These are three important reasons why water is such an important solvent.

Water is an important solvent used to develop photographs.

The importance of water to living things

Water-based solutions are also important to other living things. The water in springs, rivers, and lakes dissolves minerals from the rocks, sand, and soil over which it flows. Many of these minerals are essential to the healthy growth of plants. Some of these plants are eaten by small animals that in turn serve as food for larger animals.

The minerals found in natural water influence your life in other ways. Sodium, calcium, and magnesium salts are the most important of these minerals. Water that has a high proportion of these three minerals dissolved in it is said to be "hard." When you wash with hard water, much of the soap combines with the minerals in the water to form a white scum. The scum makes it difficult to get your hair and clothes really clean. For this reason, "soft" water, or water that has a low mineral content, is more effective for doing laundry. On the other hand, you drink hard water because it tastes better and is better for you because of its mineral content. Soft water, like rain water, usually tastes flat. Does your tap water contain minerals? Do you think that distilled water and salt water contain minerals, too? In Investigation 9, you will find out.

Many minerals found in rocks are essential to the healthy growth of plants. Running water helps to dissolve these minerals making them accessible to plants.

Investigation 9   Comparing distilled water, salt water, and tap water

PURPOSE
To investigate whether tap water is pure or whether it contains dissolved minerals.

MATERIALS

masking tape	salt water
marker	3 glass slides
3 paper towels	clothespin
eyedropper	alcohol burner
distilled water	matches
tap water	safety glasses

Caution: Only light the alcohol burner with your teacher's permission. Make sure the burner is on a level, uncluttered surface where it won't be knocked over. Always wear safety glasses when you heat any substance. Tie back long hair and keep your fingers and clothes away from the flame. Heat the slide gently so the glass does not get too hot. Extinguish the flame as soon as you finish using the burner.

PROCEDURE
1. Label each paper towel Distilled Water, Tap Water, and Salt Water, respectively, using the masking tape and marker.
2. Using the eyedropper, place five drops of distilled water on a clean slide.
3. Put on your safety glasses. Light the alcohol burner with your teacher's permission. Use the clothespin to hold the slide. Move the slide back and forth over the flame slowly. Heat the slide until all of the distilled water has evaporated.
4. Place the slide on the paper towel labelled Distilled Water. Allow the slide to cool.
5. Repeat Steps 1–4 for tap water and salt water.

OBSERVATIONS
1. Record what you see left on each slide.
2. Make a sketch of what you see on each slide.

CONCLUSIONS
By comparing your observations and sketches, and what you know about distilled water and salt water, make a conclusion about whether tap water is pure, or whether it contains dissolved minerals.

Discussion questions

1. Make a hypothesis that will explain why tap water contains salt.
2. Why would a lake near a mountain top be more likely to have soft water while a lake at a much lower elevation would be more likely to have hard water?
3. Would it be easier to wash clothes in tap water or in rain water? Explain.

Conserving water resources

Water that is pure enough to drink is said to be **potable**. You depend on potable water for many purposes. Clean lakes and rivers enhance the enjoyment of swimming and boating. Cities and towns obtain their drinking water from these sources. Fish and other forms of aquatic life depend on the water they live in for food, minerals, and oxygen. Green plants living in or near water rely on it for nourishment, too. Waterfowl breed and nest in marshes, while animals, such as moose, eat the yellow water lilies that grow there. Anglers, artists,

What types of pollution do you see in these photographs? What could be done to protect the water from pollution in each case?

naturalists, canoeists, and native peoples are just some of the people who try to protect these resources.

Unfortunately, Canada's once abundant supply of clean water has been abused. Fertilizers, road salt, insecticides, fungicides, untreated municipal sewage, and industrial solvents and solutes have escaped into lakes and rivers. Sometimes this has been accidental, but often the ''dumping'' of these substances into water sources has occurred because it is a convenient way to dispose of them, and water is such an effective solvent.

Pulp and paper mills, which employ many Canadians, are located next to lakes and rivers because of the large quantities of water they need. This water is mixed with various solutes, such as sulphuric acid, during the pulpmaking and paper-making processes. In the past, when the effects of pollution were not completely understood, and pollution laws were less effective, these industries often dumped their used solutions directly into the body of water on which they were located. Nearby cities and towns usually obtained their drinking supply from the same water source. Many people also ate the fish and waterfowl that lived in this water. The full effects of this pollution took years to understand. Now

Hazardous substances that leak from buried drums can seep through the ground and into water supplies.

Water reconditioning at a forest-product mill

it is known that water pollution can kill aquatic plants and animals, make fish and waterfowl unsafe to eat, and threaten city water supplies. Today, these mills must clean up their used solutions by recovering the harmful solutes from them. The water an industry returns to a water source must be as clean or cleaner than the water that was used. This kind of pollution control has only been possible through the co-operation of industry and government.

Over the years, many chemical companies and landfill operators have buried sealed drums containing deadly substances, such as mirex, mercury, dioxin, and PCBs, in land dumps. Today, several of these drums are leaking, and the lethal chemicals are seeping into nearby bodies of water, threatening drinking supplies.

Air pollution also poses a threat to water sources. Pollutants carried into the atmosphere are changed chemically by the sun. Some of these pollutants may damage the atmosphere's important ozone layer, while others dissolve in water vapour and fall back to the Earth as acid rain or snow. This precipitation can seriously damage forests. Eventually, it can also make lakes and rivers acidic. As a result, fish die and waterfowl find it harder to reproduce.

Certain insecticides, fungicides, and fertilizers can cause damage, too. Useful as these chemicals may be in forestry

Sometimes the chemicals that are used to spray fruit trees can be washed into creeks and rivers.

and agriculture, they are easily washed into creeks and rivers following a rainfall. These water sources lead to lakes that supply drinking water.

Fortunately, Canada has a large supply of fresh water. But much of this water is in remote areas and it is still affected by pollution from airborne contaminants. The water you depend on daily is much closer and in far greater danger. Protecting this valuable resource from harmful pollutants is the responsibility of every Canadian. To clean up the damage that has already been done is very expensive and will take many years. However, through research, community awareness, and co-operation between industry and government, water resources can be conserved.

Water pollution can also be caused by airborne contaminants.

Try this!

Visit a lake, stream, pond, or marsh in your area. Observe the animals and plants that live and grow there. Investigate how they depend on water for survival. Look for signs of pollution. List the types of pollution you find, where they occur, their probable causes, and how they could be cleaned up. Take photographs or make sketches, and write a report you could submit to the authorities responsible for water quality in your area.

Did you know?
Canada's boundaries, including its portion of the Great Lakes, contain an estimated 50% of the world's freshwater surfaces. Why might a person from Saudia Arabia or the Sudan, which have little fresh water, consider these resources a sign of wealth?

Section review questions

1. Why is water called the universal solvent?
2. What is hard water? Why is soft water better to wash with?
3. Often liquid wastes are disposed of by pouring them down the drain. What problems can be caused by this practice? What problems are caused by industries and municipalities that dump pollutants directly into lakes or rivers?
4. Sometimes the sources of water pollution are indirect. Name two examples of water pollution that are caused by chemicals that originate far from lakes.
5. What jobs in your area are dependent on clean water? How many jobs would be eliminated if the water in your area was polluted?

Reviving Hamilton harbour

Hamilton harbour is one of the most polluted bodies of water in the world. Located in Hamilton, Ontario, it once teemed with fish, waterfowl, and was a safe recreational area for activities like swimming and boating. But now the water will not support many fish or much wildlife. Researchers have found many cases of deformed turtles and cancerous fish. In recent years, attempts to establish a breeding colony of ducks in the harbour have failed.

For decades, local industries and municipalities have dumped partially processed sewage and industrial wastes into the harbour. As a result, the waters of Hamilton harbour are able to support only sludge worms and bacteria.

Several years ago, Canadian and American scientists proposed dredging the harbour of its polluted muck. However, they soon realized that this process would disturb dangerous, buried chemicals that could be carried to other locations in Lake Ontario. Canadian scientists did further research and developed another process to combat the effect of pollution on fish and waterfowl. They designed a kind of artificial lung that was lowered into the harbour in 1987. Eventually, scientists

hope to pump 50 t of pure oxygen a day into its waters.

Scientists hope that the oxygen will help the decomposition process of sewage and that part of it will go into solution, providing an environment where fish, plants, waterfowl, and other aquatic life can survive.

Although the best way to improve the water quality of Hamilton harbour would be by improving the treatment of sewage and industrial wastes, scientists are optimistic that pumping oxygen into polluted waters can at least help to maintain the aquatic environment and the organisms that live there.

SCIENCE IN SOCIETY

How should we dispose of hazardous wastes?

There are many kinds of wastes. Sewage, nuclear waste, and household garbage are some of the forms you are probably familiar with. But one of the most serious problems facing our environment and our health is the treatment of hazardous wastes.

The largest amounts of hazardous wastes come from manufacturing and chemical companies. These wastes include acids, bases, solvents, and metals. Other hazardous wastes are created by the use of pesticides, the solutions and chemicals used in hairdressing salons and hospitals, and processes like dry cleaning and photographic developing. When we throw out paint thinners, batteries, bleach, and medicines, we are also generating hazardous wastes.

Industries have disposed of hazardous wastes by burying them in the ground or by storing them in holding tanks. Until recently, the monitoring of these sites was inadequate, allowing toxic substances to seep into ground water, eventually contaminating wells, rivers, and lakes. The evacuation of an entire community in 1978 at Love Canal, New York, is an alarming example of what can

happen if the disposal of hazardous wastes is not controlled.

How can we dispose of hazardous wastes safely? Increasingly, governments have put pressure on industries to neutralize or recycle hazardous wastes. One of the most effective treatments for hazardous wastes is incineration. The wastes are burned at extremely high temperatures and are converted to steam, which can be used for energy, and ash, which can be buried safely. But this procedure is very expensive, and many industries continue to store wastes in holding tanks or in the ground. However, special lin-

ers and drainage systems can improve the effectiveness of these kinds of waste treatments, and chemical treatments can detoxify wastes so that they can be buried safely. Careful monitoring of leakage and ground-water pollution can also be practised.

Explore the issue

Divide your class into three groups. Organize a debate about building a hazardous waste-treatment plant in a rural community. The first group should have representatives from government, industry, a waste management firm, and a research group who believe that a treatment plant should be built. The second group should have representatives from the community including farmers, environmentalists, and local citizens who are concerned about the negative impact such a plant would have on their community. Research your group's side of the issue using current magazine and newspaper articles, and present your case to the third group in your class. The third group will decide which debating group offers the most convincing argument.

SCIENCE-RELATED CAREER

Meet Pat Ewen

Pat works as a safety director at Fraser Inc., a paper-producing plant in Thorold, Ontario, where fine paper is made from recycled paper. Over 400 chemicals are involved in the production process, so safety in the workplace is a major consideration.

Q. How did you become involved in the industrial safety field?
A. As a child I always wanted to be a nurse, which I did become. But soon after graduation, I became interested in the occupational health field. So I went to work as a nurse in industry for a chemical company.

Q. Can you describe your job?
A. I play a variety of roles here. I work as a co-ordinator with about 24 superintendents to keep them informed of leg-islation regarding safety and health. I try to see that people are following correct safety procedures. My department investigates all workplace accidents. We take part in the emergency teams, although luckily we've never had a major emergency here. I have another nurse and an assistant working with me. We conduct hygiene and noise surveys.

Q. What about the chemical hazards?
A. Paper production here involves bleaching with chlorine and caustic chemicals, and putting the paper through a series of chemical washers and cleansers. Then all the ingredients are combined to cook—just like a cake recipe—and fillers are added to make the paper firmer. Many chemicals are involved. It's my job to evaluate the components of the chemicals brought into the plant so I can judge what protective equipment will be required by the employees. Sometimes they need eye protection or hand protection. Sometimes disposable coveralls are worn. Employees wear respirators to protect their lungs when chemical powders are poured from one vat into another.

Q. Do you need to know the properties of different chemicals?
A. I have a basic knowledge of chemicals and how they react, but I can also consult our chemist. It's important to know how chemicals enter and affect the body, and how dust gets into the lungs and the damage it can do. It is important to have a science background to work in the safety field because you need to understand the new laws regarding safety. And employees have the right to know what they're dealing with, so I have to be able to explain it.

Q. How do you keep up to date?
A. I attend safety conferences, hygiene seminars, and occupational health seminars. And there is a lot of literature to read about health and safety in the workplace.

Q. Would most people in this field come from a nursing background like you?
A. Not anymore. Community colleges now offer safety technician courses, and some universities conduct courses in occupational health and safety as part of their science programs.

Q. What kind of person makes a good safety director?
A. Someone who's interested in people and is a good listener. You have to really care about people to do this work.

Chapter review

Words to know

Write a brief definition for each of the terms listed below. The location of these terms is indicated by the section number in the brackets.

- concentrated (*Section 2.1*)
- dilute (*Section 2.1*)
- dissolve (*Section 2.1*)
- filter (*Section 2.2*)
- filtrate (*Section 2.2*)
- insoluble (*Section 2.2*)
- mass concentration (*Section 2.6*)
- mechanical mixture (*Section 2.2*)
- mixture (*Section 2.1*)
- potable (*Section 2.7*)
- residue (*Section 2.2*)
- saturated solution (*Section 2.6*)
- soluble (*Section 2.2*)
- solutes (*Section 2.1*)
- solution (*Section 2.1*)
- solvents (*Section 2.1/Section 2.4*)
- supersaturated solution (*Section 2.6*)
- unsaturated solution (*Section 2.6*)

Questions

A. Indicate whether each of the following statements is true or false. Explain why the "false" statements are not true.

1. Tap water is a solution.
2. In the process of heating sap to make maple syrup, the solution becomes more dilute.
3. A concentrated solution of salt and water tastes more salty than a dilute solution of salt and water.
4. When a solution is saturated, you can dissolve only a little more solute in it.
5. In a mechanical mixture, the particles are smaller than the particles in a solution.
6. Air contains about four times as much nitrogen as oxygen.
7. Alloys are solid solutions of two or more elements.
8. When you mix together 50 mL of alcohol and 50 mL of water, you get 100 mL of solution.
9. Dry cleaning does not use liquids to clean clothing.
10. A solute dissolves faster if you break it up into small pieces.

B. Choose the best answer for each of the following.

1. When cold tap water stands for 1 h in a glass in sunlight
   a) bubbles appear on the inside of the glass
   b) it begins to boil
   c) it turns pale green in colour
   d) it turns to a solid
2. When a bubble rises in a glass of a soft drink, it indicates
   a) that the soft drink is getting cold
   b) that dissolved gas is coming out of solution
   c) that the pressure inside the soft drink is increasing
   d) that gas is dissolving in the soft drink
3. When a solute crystal is dropped into a supersaturated solution
   a) it dissolves
   b) it grows larger
   c) it stays the same
   d) the solution begins to boil
4. Water is called the universal solvent because
   a) it can be found everywhere in the universe
   b) everyone uses it
   c) it will dissolve more substances than any other solvent
   d) it can be used instead of any other solvent
5. Hard water
   a) is difficult to swallow
   b) contains many dissolved minerals
   c) is usually found in lakes that are located at high elevations
   d) is easier to wash with than soft water
6. Acid rain or snow
   a) is only a problem for people who like to fish and swim
   b) is not a problem where chimneys are tall enough
   c) can seriously damage forests and water resources
   d) is caused by the careless use of pesticides and fungicides
7. Distilled water
   a) contains no dissolved substances
   b) is hard water
   c) cannot be made from salt water
   d) has a yellowish tinge
8. The differences between a solution and a mechanical mixture are a result of
   a) the temperature of the solvent
   b) the size of the particles
   c) the mass of the solute
   d) the volume of the mixture
9. Antifreeze is an example of
   a) a gas dissolved in a liquid
   b) a liquid dissolved in a solid
   c) a solid dissolved in a liquid
   d) a liquid dissolved in a liquid
10. The dissolving rate of a solid in a liquid solvent usually increases when
    a) the solvent is cool
    b) the solid is in large chunks
    c) the solvent and the solid are not disturbed
    d) small pieces of the solute are stirred in a heated solvent

C. Write full answers to each of the following.
1. Which is the solvent and which is the solute when salt is dissolved in water?
2. State an example of a mechanical mixture.
3. List four differences between a solution and a mechanical mixture. Describe each one.
4. State three reasons why water is our most important solvent.
5. State an example of two other solvents that are frequently used in homes.
6. Explain what would happen to a concentrated solution of sugar and water that is
   a) put into a refrigerator
   b) left on a kitchen counter for several days
7. When would a stream have a higher concentration of oxygen dissolved in it, during a hot summer or during early spring? Explain your answer.
8. Some people believe that one way to solve pollution is to flush poisonous chemicals

down the drain. What would you tell them?

9. Explain two ways in which water can be polluted from distant sources.

Science challenge

1. Susan wants to distill fresh water from sea water. As shown in Figure 2–23, she plans to use a hole dug in the ground, a piece of clear plastic, a cup, and a rock. Explain how her set-up works.

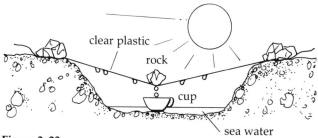

Figure 2–23

2. Do research to find out how a water treatment plant works. Include explanations of these procedures in your report: coarse straining, microstraining, flocculation, settling, sand filtration, chlorination, and fluoridation.

Science project

1. Write a report on water that investigates
   a) the properties that make it a useful and convenient solvent
   b) its uses in the home, in industry, and in the environment
   c) the causes of water pollution and its prevention
   d) the means of purifying water for drinking

2. Some solutes give off heat when they dissolve. This is called an **exothermic** reaction. But many solutes cause heat to be absorbed when they dissolve, resulting in a solution that is noticeably cooler than the water in which the solute was placed. Reactions that cause cooling are called **endothermic** reactions. Design an experiment to test different salts to find the ones that give off heat and the ones that absorb heat when they dissolve. Fill three beakers with 50 mL of water. Then dissolve 10 g of calcium chloride in one beaker, 10 g of sodium chloride (table salt) in another beaker, and 10 g of ammonium chloride in the third beaker. Use a thermometer to record the temperature of the water before and after each solution is made.

3

Force, Work, and Energy

Poised in the starting blocks, muscles tensed and eyes fixed on the finish line 100 m away, these highly trained athletes await the signal to run.

The starting gun blasts and the runners burst from the blocks with tremendous force. The force of their muscles propels them along the track. Nearing the finish line, the athletes strain, pushing themselves to their physical limits as they lunge toward the tape.

The goal of these athletes is to run personal-best times over 100 m. To shave fractions of seconds from their times, they train long hours to develop the muscles that create the force needed to run quickly. When these athletes reach the finish line, they have reached a speed of about 42.85 km/h.

Running is only one example of how a force can be used to create movement. Can you think of other examples where people use their muscles to move themselves or other objects? Are there examples where machines are used to move objects or people? Think of some questions you might ask about these examples that will help you to find out more about force, work, and energy.

This student is exerting a force even though she is unable to move the drawer.

3.1 What is force?

A **force** is any push or pull. Every time you push or pull with your muscles to open a drawer, kick a ball, swim, or do exercises, you are using a force. But a force does not always cause motion. A person who tries to open a drawer that is stuck is exerting force even though he or she may be unable to move the drawer.

There are other kinds of forces besides those exerted by muscles. Some of these forces exist within the nuclei of atoms. Others are exerted by magnets and electricity. In Investigation 1, you will experiment with some of these different forces to see what they can do.

Investigation 1   Different kinds of forces

PURPOSE
To demonstrate different forces and observe their effects.

MATERIALS

3 balloons	board
plastic wrap or sweater	strong nylon
paper	rope
comb	elastic band
2 magnets	spring
brick	Plasticine

PROCEDURE
1. Lift various objects, such as the brick, board, comb, and elastic band, with your hand. Notice which objects feel heaviest and which feel lightest. (The force acting on these objects is called gravity.)
2. Charge two balloons by rubbing them with plastic wrap or against a sweater. Put one balloon on a level surface and bring the other one close to it. Observe what happens. (The force acting on the balloons is called electric force.)
3. Tear a small sheet of paper into pieces about the size of a dime. Then comb your hair several times. Try to pick up the bits of paper with the comb. Repeat this step with other materials.

4. Bring the two magnets close to each other in various ways. Observe what happens. (The force acting on the magnets is called magnetic force.)

5. Try to slide the brick across the board using both of your hands. Place three or four pencils under the brick to act as rollers. Then try to slide the brick again. Observe any difference in the amount of force you must use. (The force you are working against in these examples is called friction.)

6. Divide the class into several teams of three or four students each. Organize tug-of-war matches between the teams. Observe what happens to the rope. What can you say about the size or strength of the winning and losing teams? (The force pulling on the rope is called tension.)

Caution: Make sure the rope you are using is strong enough for this activity. Use a floor mat to protect yourself if you fall.

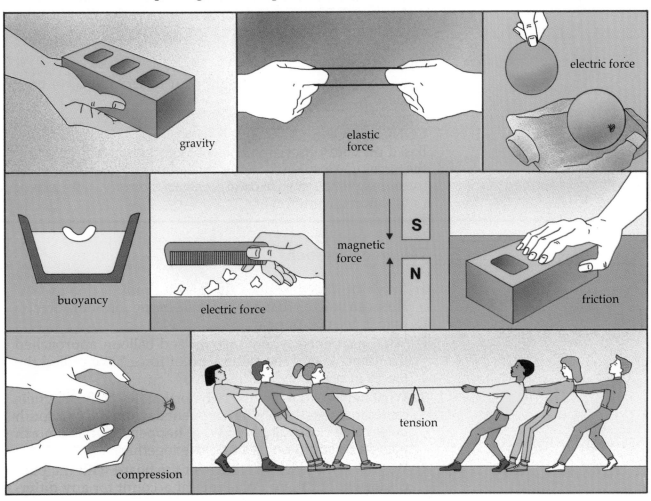

gravity

elastic force

electric force

buoyancy

electric force

magnetic force

S

N

friction

compression

tension

Figure 3–1

Caution: Use elastic bands and springs carefully. Make sure that they do not fly up at you or at someone else. Wear safety glasses when you place them under tension.

7. Partially blow up a balloon and tie off its end. Compress the air inside the balloon into a smaller space by squeezing it between your hands. (This squeezing force is called compression.)

8. Slowly stretch an elastic band or a spring using the fingers of each hand. When it is stretched slightly, carefully let go of one end and observe what happens. (The force that pulls the spring or the elastic band back to its original shape is called elastic force.)

9. Hold a large ball of Plasticine in your hand and raise it into the air. Then support the ball in your hand under water. Is there a difference between how the Plasticine ball feels in the air and how it feels under water? Mould the Plasticine into the shape of a boat and try to float it. What happens? (The upward force acting on the Plasticine in the water is called buoyant force.)

OBSERVATIONS
1. Make written notes detailing your observations for each step.

CONCLUSIONS
Based on your observations, what can you conclude about the forces you examined in this investigation: gravity, electric force, magnetic force, friction, tension, compression, elastic force, and buoyant force?

Discussion questions

1. In which direction does the Earth's pull of gravity act? How can you tell that gravity pulls harder on some objects than it does on others?

2. What happened when one charged balloon approached the other? Could the same kind of force have pulled the pieces of paper toward the comb?

3. What happened when the two north poles of the magnets came close together? What happened when the two south poles came close together? What happened when a north pole and a south pole came close together?

4. Was the brick easier to slide over the board with the pencils or without them? What might account for any differ-

ence in the amount of force that you needed to move the brick?

5. What happened to the rope during the tug-of-war matches? Which teams exerted the most force? Which teams exerted the least force? What might have happened to the rope if the teams had been larger?

6. What happens to the volume of a gas when it is compressed? Can a compressed gas exert force? How do you know?

7. What is the name of the force you were working against when you stretched the elastic band or the spring? Did this force increase or decrease as you stretched the elastic or the spring further? What happened when you let go of one end of the elastic or the spring? Why?

8. Which force pulled the Plasticine ball down when you were holding it in the air? Which force helped to push it up when it was under water?

Let's look more closely at some of the forces you have just explored. The most important of these are the forces known as gravity, electric force, and magnetic force. Another important natural force is nuclear force, which you did not explore in Investigation 1.

Gravity

Sir Isaac Newton (1642–1727) is credited with the discovery of gravity. For some time, Newton had been interested in the moon, wondering why it continued in its almost circular path around the Earth. "Some force must be keeping it there," he reasoned, "or else it would fly off into space." Supposedly, when Newton saw apples fall, he also realized that just as an apple was pulled to Earth, so was the moon.

Later, Newton concluded that all objects in the universe attract each other. The larger the mass an object has, the stronger its force of attraction, or **gravity**, for another object. Also, the closer two masses are to each other, the more they will pull on each other. For example, when two ships are floating a few metres apart, the force of attraction, or gravity, each exerts on the other tries to pull them closer together. The closer they become, the stronger this force is.

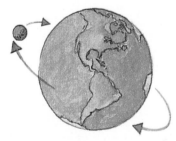

Figure 3–2 The moon and the apple are both pulled toward the Earth by gravity.

Figure 3–3 According to Newton, every object in the universe attracts every other object. The larger their masses and the closer they are together, the greater the combined gravitational force between them.

When scientists plan to send a spacecraft to the moon, they know it will take a very large force to overcome the pull of gravity acting between the spacecraft and the Earth. They also know that as the spacecraft approaches the moon, the gravity of the moon will steadily increase. As the moon's gravity grows stronger, the craft will be pulled toward the surface of the moon at an increasing speed.

The moon's gravity at its surface, however, is only about one-sixth of what you experience on Earth. This is because the moon has less mass than the Earth. Walking on the moon requires only about one-sixth the amount of force that is needed to walk on Earth. So an astronaut can jump about six times higher on the moon than on Earth.

As you can see, the force of gravity varies. Even the force of gravity you experience on the surface of the Earth varies slightly from place to place. It is affected by your distance from the centre of the Earth and by your distance from the equator. Gravity tends to be weaker in high places, such as mountains, which are farther from the Earth's centre. Why do you think gravity is also weaker near the equator?

The pull of gravity acting on an object is also called the **weight** of the object. Because gravity varies from place to place, weight is not constant. For example, the same person could weigh almost 0.5% more at the North Pole than at the equator, but only one-sixth as much on the moon, and nothing at all in outer space. Yet the person's mass at all four locations would be exactly the same. Later in this chapter, you will discover other reasons why it is important to understand this difference between weight and mass.

Astronauts need only about one-sixth the amount of force to walk on the moon as they do to walk on Earth.

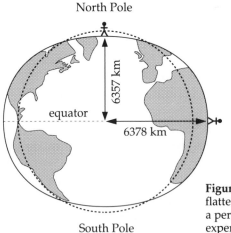

Figure 3–4 The Earth is slightly flatter at the poles. This explains why a person at the North Pole experiences a greater pull of gravity.

Electric force

If you rub an inflated balloon on a sweater, you can "hang" the balloon on a wall. After combing your hair, as you did in Investigation 1, you can pick up bits of paper with the comb. These are demonstrations of electric charge and **electric force**.

Like the force of gravity, electric force decreases with distance. You have to bring your comb quite close to the bits of paper before it will pick them up.

Through experiments, scientists have inferred that there are two types of electric charges — positive and negative. Objects that have the same type of electric charge push away from, or repel, each other. You watched this happen with the two balloons in Investigation 1. Objects that have opposite electric charges attract, or pull toward, each other. This is why the comb and bits of paper attracted one another.

These pushes and pulls are electric forces that are the result of electric charges. But what causes the charges? To answer this question, you must look inside the structure of an atom. Scientists aren't able to see inside atoms, but they have constructed very good models of what atoms might look like. They have also tested these models in many experiments.

Most scientists use a model to show that atoms are made of three major kinds of particles or tiny bits of mass — protons, neutrons, and electrons. According to this model, protons have a positive charge and electrons have a negative charge. Scientists believe that neutrons have no charge, which means that they are neutral. They also believe that the protons and neutrons in each atom form a central core called a nucleus, while the electrons travel rapidly in regions located around the outside of the nucleus. It is the electric force of attraction between the negative electrons and the

A demonstration of electric force

Lightning is caused by an electric charge.

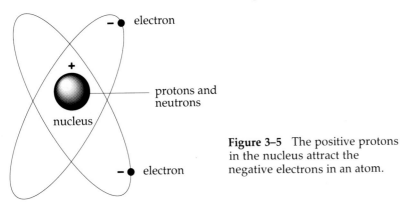

Figure 3–5 The positive protons in the nucleus attract the negative electrons in an atom.

positive protons in the nucleus that helps to keep the parts of the atom together. In a similar way, the force of gravity holds the planets in orbit around the sun. You can picture an atom as being like a tiny solar system. Seen in this way, the sun represents the nucleus of an atom and the planets represent the electrons. Just remember that this is only a simple model. The models scientists use are much more complex.

Magnetic force

When you experimented with the magnets in Investigation 1, you saw the effect of magnetic force. **Magnetic force** is concentrated around the ends, or poles, of magnets. Each magnet has a north pole and a south pole. When the like poles of magnets are held close to one another, such as two north poles or two south poles, they will repel each other. However, if the poles are different, they will attract each other. This is what happens when the north pole of one magnet and the south pole of another magnet are brought close together.

Magnetic force also attracts objects made of iron, nickel, or cobalt. You have probably used magnets to pick up iron filings, nails, tacks, and coins made of nickel. These magnetic elements are attracted by both types of poles. Many industrial processes rely on magnetic force to separate magnetic materials from non-magnetic ones.

The opposite poles of two magnets attract each other.

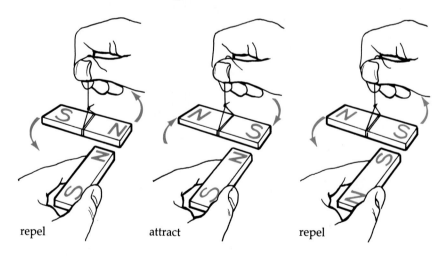

repel   attract   repel

Figure 3–6 Magnets can pull (attract) or push (repel).

Like gravity and electric force, magnetic force decreases with distance. The farther away a magnet is from a magnetic material or another magnet, the weaker the force of attraction or repulsion between them becomes. You have probably noticed that magnetic and electric forces can either attract or repel, but gravity always attracts. Try to remember this important difference between gravity and magnetic and electric forces.

Nuclear force

What force could hold protons and neutrons together in the nucleus of an atom? Why don't the protons repel each other and leave the nucleus? Scientists believe that there is a special force at work in the atom's nucleus, and that it is much stronger than the force of gravity. It could not be electric force, because neutrons have no charge. It could not be magnetic force, because protons and neutrons are not magnetic. Therefore, it is an entirely different kind of force, a force scientists call **nuclear force**.

The nuclear force inside an atom is very powerful, but only over extremely short distances. In certain circumstances, it can be overcome by firing atomic particles like bullets at the nucleus of an atom. If these neutrons are fast enough and aimed very precisely, the nucleus of the atom can be split. Splitting nuclei in this way is called fission, and it is sometimes accompanied by the release of enormous amounts of energy. When fission reactions are carefully controlled, this energy can be harnessed and put to use.

This submarine is powered by nuclear energy—a result of nuclear force.

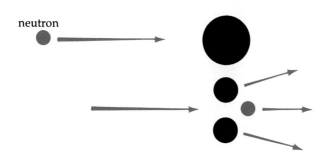

neutron

Figure 3–7 Fission means splitting the nucleus of an atom.

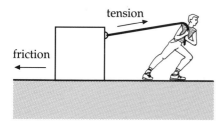
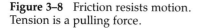

Figure 3–8 Friction resists motion. Tension is a pulling force.

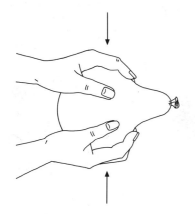

Figure 3–9 Springs can exert an elastic force.

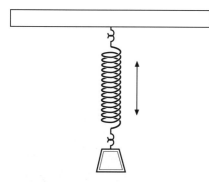

Figure 3–10 Compression is caused by pushing or squeezing.

Other kinds of forces

There are other forces besides gravity, electric force, magnetic force, and nuclear force. Several of these other forces are given special names. Some of the most common are friction, tension, elastic force, compression, buoyancy, and muscular force.

Friction is the force that resists or acts against motion. When you drag a heavy box across a floor, the force of friction works against you. You experienced friction when you tried to slide a brick across a board in Investigation 1. Air friction works against moving objects such as cars, airplanes, and trains. It also works against spacecraft when they re-enter the Earth's atmosphere.

Tension is a stretching force that is caused by pulling against something that resists being pulled. You demonstrated tension in the tug-of-war matches in Investigation 1. You usually speak of the tension in a rope or cable that is used to pull something, or to support something being pulled downward by the force of gravity. If the tension is too great, the rope or cable will snap.

Elastic force is another force that resists a force. Elastic force pulls a stretched or a bent object back to its original size or shape. You can demonstrate elastic force by blowing up a balloon, stretching a rubber band, or by gently bending a plastic ruler. Observe what happens when you let go.

Compression is a pushing or a squeezing force against something that resists pushing or squeezing. You can think of compression as being the opposite of tension; a force exerted against a specific volume or area. Gases, for instance, can be compressed into smaller volumes. This happened when you squeezed the inflated balloon between the palms of your hands in Investigation 1. Your joints encounter compression when you jump and run. Geologists believe that compression deep within the Earth's crust causes rocks to bend and buckle.

Buoyancy is the upward force that causes certain objects to float in certain liquids. When a boat floats on water, the downward force of gravity acting on the mass of the boat is balanced by an upward buoyant force that keeps it afloat. Even an object that sinks in water is affected by buoyant force. As a result of buoyant force, the object seems to be much less affected by gravity when it is submerged. The object feels and acts like it has less weight. This is why the Plasticine ball you submerged in Investigation 1 felt lighter under water than it did when you held it up in the air. Because of buoyancy, divers can lift and move heavier objects more easily under water than they can on land.

Muscular force is the force exerted by the muscles of humans and other animals. You use your muscles all the time. Even when you are asleep, your heart muscle is busy pumping blood while other muscles in your body fill your lungs with air. When you wake up, you use your muscles to get out of bed, to wash, to dress, and to eat breakfast. You used your muscles to perform all of the procedures in Investigation 1. Muscles are attached to bones and are controlled by the brain. When you exercise your muscles regularly, they become larger and stronger. A diet that includes sources of protein, such as lean meat, cheese, and milk, is important for muscle building.

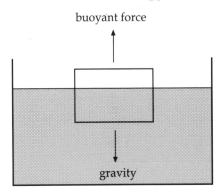

Figure 3–11 When an object floats, the buoyant force is balanced by the force of gravity.

What other activities can you think of where you would use muscular force?

Try this!

Have an arm-wrestling contest with several of your class-mates to see whose arm muscles can exert the greatest force. You should choose contestants who are close to you in height and size. Be sure to appoint another student as a referee. It is the referee's job to enforce the rules and to declare the winner.

Try this!

There are several other forces with special names. Visit your resource centre or library to find out about forces such as shearing force, torque, centrifugal force, and inertia. Prepare an exhibit that shows how one of these forces works. Make a presentation to your class.

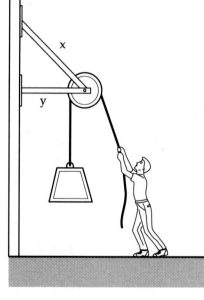

Figure 3–12

Section review questions

1. What force holds the planets in their orbits around the sun?
2. Would you weigh more on Ellesmere Island or in Brazil? Explain your answer.
3. In what two ways are gravitational, electric, and magnetic forces similar? In what way is gravitational force different?
4. State four common examples of friction acting against motion. How does friction help you to walk?
5. In Figure 3–12, Beam X and Beam Y are mounted to a wall, forming a triangular support for a pulley. Which beam is under tension? Which beam is being compressed?
6. State five examples of things that demonstrate elastic force.
7. Can you think of something that floats in air? Which force keeps it up?
8. Which forces are acting on the bicycle in Figure 3–13, helping to speed it up? Which forces are acting against its motion, slowing the bicycle down? In which direction does each of these forces act?

Figure 3–13

3.2 How is force measured?

Forces are at work everywhere around you, influencing everything you do. Almost everything you can think of, such as cars, appliances, machines, and your body, operate and are affected by forces. By understanding and carefully measuring these forces, they can be used wisely and efficiently. Without the ability to measure forces and other quantities, scientists and technologists would never have been able to build computers, cars, or send astronauts into space.

So how is force measured? Force is measured in units called newtons (N), after Sir Isaac Newton, who spent much of his life studying forces. You can think of a **newton** as being the amount of force required for you to hold up an average-sized apple in your hand. The instrument usually used to measure forces, such as tension, elasticity, and gravity, is the newton spring scale or force meter. It has a spring with a pointer attached to it, and a scale calibrated in newtons. The greater the force, the more the spring and the pointer are pulled along the scale. Would you like to see how it works? In Investigation 2, you can use what you know about elastic force in springs to make your own force meter. Then you will calibrate it yourself, and use it to measure forces.

Figure 3–14 It takes approximately one newton of force to support an apple.

Investigation 2   Measuring forces

PURPOSE
To make and test a simple force meter.

MATERIALS
sheet of overhead
   transparency film
two-hole button,
   approximately 1.5 cm in
   diameter
Scotch tape
scissors
pencil
needle-nose pliers with
   cutters

MEASURING TOOL
ruler

light-duty spring,
   approximately 75–100 mm
   long, or an elastic band
roll of bare copper wire (No.
   12 gauge)
plastic shopping bag
masking tape
marker
10 or more identical objects,
   such as golf balls,
   flashlight batteries, or
   bolts
safety glasses

PROCEDURE

PART A   ASSEMBLY

1. Roll the transparency film into a tube large enough for the button to fit inside easily. Tape the film in this position with five or six pieces of Scotch tape.

2. Use the pliers to cut off a piece of the pencil approximately 4 cm long.

3. Hook one end of the spring, or tie the elastic band, around the middle of the pencil. Secure the spring in place by bending it with the pliers.

4. Cut 30 cm of bare copper wire off the roll. Make a 180° loop about 3 cm back from one end of the wire, and slip the loop over the unattached end of the spring (or through the elastic band.)

5. Feed the long end of the wire through one of the holes in the button. Slide the button up the wire. Feed the short end of the wire through the second hole, then use the pliers to twist the wires together so the button is secured. (The button will be the pointer for your force meter.)

6. Slip the entire assembly into the tube. Tape the pencil securely to the top of the tube with the plastic tape. (The long end of the wire should stick out from the bottom of the tube.)

7. Bend the bottom end of the wire to form a hook.

8. Cut another piece of copper wire about 8 cm long and use it to make a handle. Attach the wire to the pencil as shown in Figure 3–15.

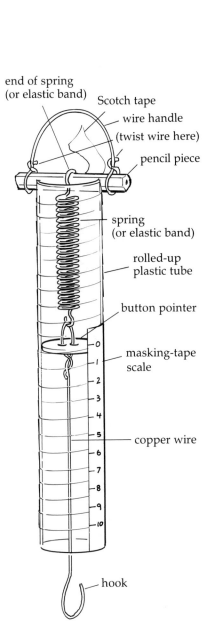

end of spring
(or elastic band)

Scotch tape

wire handle
(twist wire here)

pencil piece

spring
(or elastic band)

rolled-up
plastic tube

button pointer

masking-tape
scale

0
1
2
3
4
5
6
7
8
9
10

copper wire

hook

Figure 3–15

PART B   CALIBRATION AND TESTING

1. Tape a strip of masking tape along the tube. You can use the marker and the tape to mark off a scale and calibrate your force meter.

2. Hold the force meter by its handle. Hang an empty plastic bag on the meter's hook. Make a mark opposite the button pointer. Label this mark "0" (zero).

3. Place identical objects, such as golf balls, flashlight batteries, or bolts, into the bag one at a time.

4. After each object is placed in the bag, make a mark opposite the button pointer. (The number of objects in the bag will be the label for the mark. Each mark indicates the downward force of gravity exerted by the objects you have chosen as your measurement standard.) Continue to mark the scale until you have used all of the objects. Depending on the objects you have used, your meter is now calibrated to measure force in "golf balls," "flashlight batteries," or "bolts."

5. Remove the objects you used to calibrate your force meter. Use the meter to pull and lift several different objects. For example, you might try pulling a shoe across a table or lifting a pocket calculator with the meter. Before you begin, estimate the amount of force you think is required to move each object. Record the actual amount of force indicated by the button pointer and compare the difference.

Caution: Be careful when using springs and elastic bands. Wear safety glasses when you place them under tension as they can snap or fly up at you.

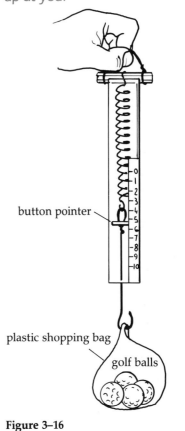

button pointer

plastic shopping bag

golf balls

Figure 3–16

OBSERVATIONS

1. Record your estimated and measured forces for each test in a chart like the one below.

Test	Kind of Force	Estimated Force	Measured Force	Difference
1. Lifting a Book	gravity	? golf balls	? golf balls	? golf balls
2.				
.				
.				
.				

CONCLUSIONS
What can you conclude about your ability to estimate forces?

Discussion questions

1. Suppose everyone was able to calibrate his or her force meter in standard units of force such as newtons. What would be some of the advantages of using standard units?
2. What are some of the limitations of your force meter?
3. How could you change your force meter so it could be used to measure pushes as well as pulls? Draw a diagram to show how you would do it.
4. In what way do you think that a force meter is an example of the application of science? Do you think your force meter can be used to measure all forces?

Try this!

You can calibrate your force meter to read in newtons. First, remove the calibrated masking tape and replace it with a new piece. Then hook your force meter to a commercial force meter calibrated in newtons. Pull the meters gently apart until the reading on the commercial scale reads 1 N. Hold the meter in this position while a partner carefully marks the masking tape beside the button pointer and labels it ''1 N.''

Caution: Be careful when you are pulling the meters apart. Make sure they are not aimed at anyone. Wear safety glases when you calibrate your meter in newtons.

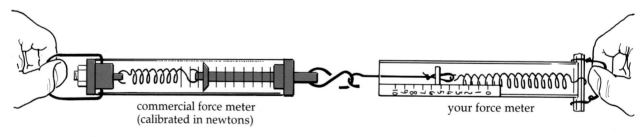

commercial force meter
(calibrated in newtons)

your force meter

Figure 3–17

Now pull the meters apart until the commercial scale reads 2 N. Again have your partner mark the tape. Continue in this way until your force meter is fully calibrated in newtons.

Now let's see what it's like to use standard units to estimate and measure force. If you like, you can use your newly calibrated force meter in the next investigation or a commercial one calibrated in newtons.

Investigation 3 Estimating and measuring forces

PURPOSE
To estimate and measure forces using a force meter calibrated in newtons.

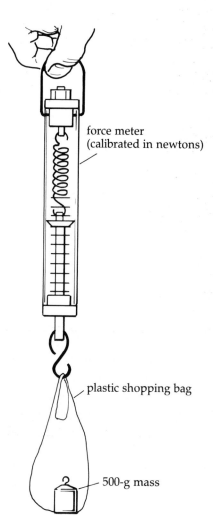

force meter
(calibrated in newtons)

plastic shopping bag

500-g mass

Figure 3–18

MATERIALS
elastic band
plastic shopping bag
chair
safety glasses

MEASURING TOOLS
force meter calibrated from 0–10 N
6 objects, such as books, ranging in mass from 100–1000 g (1 kg)

PROCEDURE
1. Pull on the force meter with your hands. Notice how much pull it takes to get readings of 0.5 N, 1 N, 1.5 N, 2 N, and so on.
2. Put on your safety glasses. Stretch an elastic band to a length of 30 cm. Estimate how much force it took. Hook the elastic band onto the force meter and stretch the band to 30 cm again. Take a reading from the scale and compare it with your estimate. Then release the band slowly and watch the pointer as you do.
3. Put one of the six objects in the plastic bag. Estimate the force of gravity acting on the object. Measure it using the force meter. (The force of gravity acting on the empty bag is so small that you can ignore it.)
4. Repeat Step 3 with each of the other five objects.
5. Estimate the force required to drag a chair across the floor and then measure it using your force meter.

Caution: Remember to wear your safety glasses and to hold the elastic band securely while stretching it so it will not fly away if it snaps. When stretching the elastic band on the force meter, make sure it is not aimed at anyone.

OBSERVATIONS

1. List your observations in a chart like the one below.

Test	Estimated Force (N)	Measured Force (N)	Difference (N)
1. Stretched Elastic Band			
2. Object A			
3. Object B			
4. Object C			
5. Object D			
6. Object E			
7. Object F			
8. Dragging a Chair			

Discussion questions

1. A man of average size experiences a gravitational force of about 800 N. What do you think the force of gravity acting on your body is?
2. If an elevator can overcome a gravitational force of 10 kN, approximately how many people can it carry at one time? Assume that one-half of the passengers are men and the other half are women. (1 kN = 1000 N)
3. Which types of forces did you encounter in this investigation? State two other examples of each type of force.

Section review questions

1. What unit is used to measure force? Who is it named after and why?

2. Approximately how much force is required to lift two golf balls? How much force is needed to lift ten golf balls?
3. Engineers are people who design machines, buildings, roads, appliances, and many other things. Why do you think it would be important for an engineer to be able to measure different forces?
4. Could a force meter be used to measure tension in a rope? Use a sketch to show how this could be done.

3.3 Mass and the force of gravity

You have already seen that the force of gravity acting on an object may change when that object is moved to a different location. The force of gravity pulling downward on an object, or a mass, is called weight. Weight, however, is not constant. It is not a reliable indicator of the amount of matter in an object. This means that a spring scale, like the force meter or your bathroom scale, will give different measurements for the weight of the same object depending on whether the object is on the moon, on Earth, or even at different locations on Earth.

However, there is another instrument that can be used to determine the mass of an object, regardless of where the object is. This instrument is an equal-arm balance. It measures only an object's mass, not the pull of gravity on an object.

To use an equal-arm balance, you place an object on one side of the balance. Then you place standard masses on the other side until the two sides are balanced. Adding up these standard units gives you the mass of the object.

Mass is constant for any object and does not vary from place to place. Consider a 5-kg block of steel. Whether on Earth, on the moon, or on Jupiter, its mass will always be 5 kg. However, the force of gravity acting on this block of steel changes from 50 N on Earth, to 8 N on the moon, and to 130 N on Jupiter.

On the surface of the Earth, the force of gravity is fairly constant. But scientists and technologists often need to know how much force is acting on objects in order to build safe elevators and rockets with enough thrust.

What other objects might you measure with an equal-arm balance?

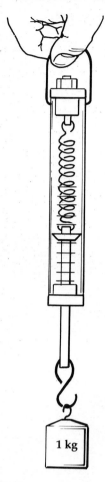

Figure 3–19

Investigation 4 Investigating the force of gravity

PURPOSE
To find the force of gravity acting on a 1-kg mass.

MATERIALS
plastic shopping bag
tap water

MEASURING TOOLS
force meter calibrated from
     0-20 N
1-kg mass
500-mL graduated cylinder
     or 1-L container

PROCEDURE
1. Suspend a 1-kg mass from the hook of the force meter. Measure the force of gravity in newtons acting on the mass.
2. 1 L of tap water has a mass of 1 kg. Using the measurement you obtained in Step 1, predict what the force of gravity acting on 0.5 L of water will be. Then pour 0.5 L of water into the plastic bag. Determine the force of gravity acting on the water. (The force of gravity acting on the empty bag is so small that you can ignore it.)
3. Repeat Step 2 using 1.5 L of water. Then repeat the step using 2 L of water.

OBSERVATIONS
1. Record your observations in a chart like the one below.

Mass	Predicted Force of Gravity (N)	Measured Force of Gravity (N)
1.0 kg		
0.5 kg		
1.5 kg		
2.0 kg		

2. Draw a graph that indicates how the force of gravity acting on an object changes as the mass of the object increases

(see Figure 3–20). Use the measurements you made in this investigation.

CONCLUSIONS
Do you think the force of gravity acting on the Earth is predictable for different masses? What conclusions can you make?

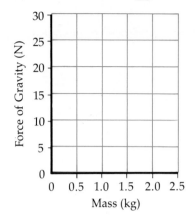

Figure 3–20

Discussion questions

1. Based on the relationship you graphed in Observation 2, how many newtons of force would you expect to measure acting on a 2500-g mass?
2. What would you predict the force of gravity acting on 1 kg of sugar to be?
3. Determine your mass in kilograms using the scales in your school. Then calculate the force of gravity acting on your body.
4. What would your mass be on the moon? What would the force of gravity be acting on you there?

Section review questions

1. State two examples that would cause the force of gravity acting on an object to change.
2. Explain why the mass of an object is the same everywhere in the universe.
3. What would you predict the force of gravity to be acting on a chunk of ice that has a mass of 1.0 kg? What would you predict the force of gravity to be on a 15-kg watermelon? What would the force of gravity be on 10 L of water?
4. How much force would it take to hold up a 50-kg student? What would your answer be if the student was on Jupiter?

Gravity in space

While orbiting the Earth, astronauts are able to float inside and outside their space vehicles. Men and women who have experienced this "weightless" sensation have found it unusual and enjoyable. Weightlessness is sometimes explained as the absence of the force of gravity in space. However, while the effect on astronauts is similar to the lack of gravity, gravity does affect the space vehicle and its occupants. In fact, gravity is the only force that acts on the orbiting space vehicle, but the astronauts do not feel its effect. How is this possible?

The answer lies in the scientific laws of physics. When you throw a baseball or shoot a basketball, it follows a curved path through the air and eventually returns to the ground. While the ball is moving through the air, the force of gravity exerts a downward force on it. This downward force causes the ball to move along a curved path, which is called the object's trajectory. The greater the force or the height of the object, the longer the curved path it follows.

If the force exerted on an object, such as a space vehicle, is strong enough to move the object fast enough, the trajectory of the object can actually match the curve of the Earth's surface. When this happens,

the spacecraft enters a stable orbit around the Earth. If gravity were not acting on the spacecraft, it would not move in a curved path. Instead it would travel in a straight line away from the Earth.

Astronauts do not feel the effects of the force of gravity because they are constantly falling toward the curved surface of the Earth. For every metre astronauts fall toward the Earth's surface, the surface of the Earth curves away from them by one metre. In the absence of any other forces, astronauts experience "weightlessness."

The laws of physics associated with the force of gravity and the movement of objects

are central to scientists' basic understanding of the universe, and also to our ability to travel in space. These laws have been understood for some time. However, it was only in 1957 that scientists and engineers were able to harness forces that were powerful enough to accelerate a capsule to sufficient velocity to enter an orbit around the Earth. This capsule was called *Sputnik* and was launched by the Soviet Union.

Today, many countries have developed the technology needed to launch people and satellites into orbit around the Earth. These countries include Brazil, China, France, the Soviet Union, and the United States.

3.4 Work and energy

If you talk to some people, it seems all they ever do is work. They use the word in many different ways. They do homework, housework, and shop work, but to scientists the word work has a special meaning. For them, **work** means that a force has been exerted, and that motion in the direction of the force has resulted.

The scientific meaning of work isn't as difficult to understand as it might seem. Suppose a tow truck tries to push a car that is stuck for nearly an hour. No matter what the operator does, the tow truck is unable to move the car. In spite of all the force the tow truck has exerted, it still hasn't done any work, in the scientific sense, because the car hasn't moved. But if another tow truck comes along and pulls the car free a few minutes later, it will have done the work the first truck could not do.

Figure 3–21

Another way to think of work is as a force applied through a distance. This idea is reflected in the way scientists calculate the amount of work (*W*) done. To do this, they multiply the force (*F*) involved, in newtons, by the distance (*d*), in metres. The formula is $W = F \times d$.

Example
How much work is done when a box weighing 20 N is raised by 1.5 m?

Solution

$$\text{Work} = \text{force} \times \text{distance}$$
$$\text{or } W = F \times d$$
$$= 20 \text{ N} \times 1.5 \text{ m}$$
$$= 30 \text{ N·m}$$

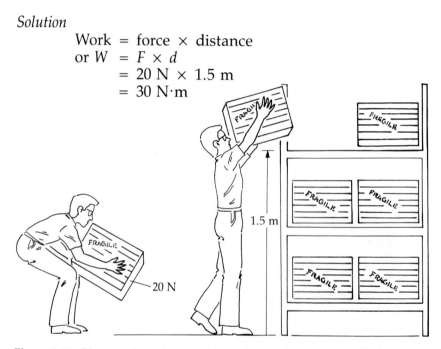

Figure 3–22 How much work must this worker perform to place this box on the shelf?

You may not recognize the measurement unit in the answer. It is called a newton metre (N·m). It means that a force of one newton has been applied (pushed or pulled) one metre in the direction of the force. The raised dot is a multiplication symbol that is used in the SI system. One newton metre is equal to another SI unit called a joule (J). The joule is named after James Prescott Joule (1818–1889), an English scientist who performed many experiments in the field of work and energy. So the work done in this example can be written as 30 J.

In Investigation 5, you will look at some examples of work being done and how it can be measured.

Investigation 5 · Exploring work

PURPOSE
To identify and measure work being done.

MATERIALS
4 books
rope
string
chair

MEASURING TOOLS
force meter calibrated from
    0–20 N
metric scales
metre stick

PROCEDURE

1. Tie one end of the rope to a chair and the other end to the force meter.

2. Use the metre stick to measure a clear path 5.0 m away from the chair. Then measure the force that is needed to drag the chair over this distance. Repeat this step at least two more times. Average the results of your measurements to check their reliability.

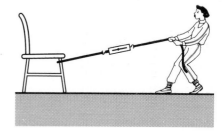

Figure 3–23

3. Calculate the amount of work you have done on the chair in joules, based on the average value you calculated in Step 2. (Include your calculations in the following chart.)

4. Measure the force of gravity acting on the four books by suspending them with the string from the force meter. Raise the books until they are 2.0 m from the floor. How much work did you do on the books? Repeat this step at least two more times. Average your results.

5. Measure your mass on the metric scales. Estimate the force of gravity acting on you in newtons. Repeat this step and average your results as you did in Steps 2 and 4. Did you do any work while you stood still on the scales?

6. Measure the vertical height of a flight of stairs. You can do this by carefully measuring the height of one step and multiplying by the number of steps. (Or you can hang a length of string vertically from the top of the stairs to the bottom and then measure the string.)

7. Climb the stairs and calculate how much work you did based on the average of your measurements of force and distance.

OBSERVATIONS
1. Record your observations and calculations in a chart like the one below.

Type of Work	Average Force	Average Distance	$W = F \times d$
Dragging a Chair			
Lifting Books			
Standing on Scales			
Climbing Stairs			

Discussion questions

1. How much work would you do on two chairs if you pulled them three times as far as you did in Step 2?
2. How much work would you do on only half the number of books you used in Step 4 if you raised them five times as high?
3. How much work did you do in Step 5? Why?
4. How much work would you have done on your body if you had climbed a rope the same vertical distance as you did climbing the stairs in Step 7?
5. How much work would you have done on the four books in Step 7 if you had carried them up the stairs?

Try this!

Think about each of the situations described below. State which forces are acting in each case. State whether any work is being done in each case.
1. An air bubble rises to the surface of an aquarium.

2. A boy reads a newspaper that is resting on his lap.
3. A girl pops a paper bag behind her brother's head.
4. Fireworks rise high into the sky.
5. A nuclear submarine patrols Canadian Arctic waters.
6. The cable on a crane is used to lift a heavy concrete slab into place as part of a new building.

Energy

"Ah, look," says your uncle who just woke up. "I don't feel very energetic today. Let's go skiing tomorrow."

"No way!" says your cousin. "We're full of energy. We want to go skiing and skating, too!"

"Yeh!" you chime in, "let's have some breakfast and hit the slopes and the ice rink!"

Like the word work, the word energy is sometimes used in different ways. But as scientists define it, **energy** is the ability to do work. According to this definition, you could not run, walk, exercise, ski, skate, or do any work without energy. You obtain this energy from the food you eat. Most cars and trucks derive their energy from gasoline. Electric generators are driven by the energy of falling water, burning coal, or nuclear reactions. But the most important source of

Without energy, you would be unable to ski, walk, or run.

The energy of falling water from Niagara Falls drives generators that produce electricity.

energy is the sun. It warms the Earth, causes plants to grow, and drives the wind.

The water flowing over Niagara Falls has enough energy to do the work of turning enormous electric generators. The energy of falling water was once used to turn water wheels that ground wheat and other grains into flour.

Since energy is the ability to do work, work and energy are expressed in the same SI unit — the joule (J). The kilojoule (1 kJ = 1000 J) and the megajoule (1 MJ = 1 000 000 J) are larger units derived from the joule. These units are used to describe large quantities of energy.

Example
How much energy would a ski-tow generator use to pull a skier to the top of a hill that is 200 m high? The skier is acted upon by 900 N of gravitational force.

Solution

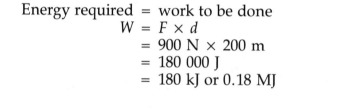

$$\text{Energy required} = \text{work to be done}$$
$$W = F \times d$$
$$= 900 \text{ N} \times 200 \text{ m}$$
$$= 180\ 000 \text{ J}$$
$$= 180 \text{ kJ or } 0.18 \text{ MJ}$$

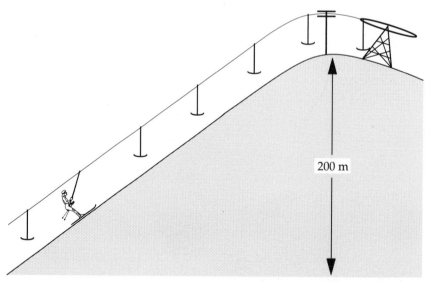

200 m

Figure 3–24

Try this!

Energy comes in many different forms. You can't see these forms, but you can see the effects they cause. Look around your community and try to find examples of the energy forms listed in the chart below. Then copy and complete the chart in your notebook. When you have finished your chart, compare it with a friend's or a classmate's. What effects or uses did you miss?

Which type of energy powers this turbine?

Form of Energy	Effects or Uses of Energy
Light Energy	• helps plants to grow; allows people to see . . .
Heat Energy	
Sound Energy	
Magnetic Energy	
Electric Energy	
Nuclear Energy	
Wind Energy	
Chemical Energy	
Elastic Energy	
Gravitational Energy	
Mechanical Energy	

Section review questions

1. A crane pulls on a heavy load for 20 min but does not move it. Has any work been done? Explain your answer.

2. How much work is done when an apple with a gravitational force of 1.0 N acting on it is raised by 3.2 m?

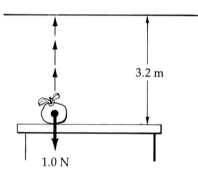

Figure 3–25

3. To stop a car, an average braking force of 800 N is applied over a distance of 30 m. How much work is done?

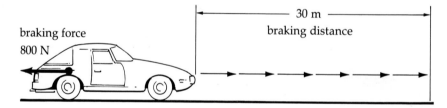

Figure 3–26

4. To force the north poles of two magnets together, a girl uses an average force of 0.6 N over a distance of 5.0 cm. How much work does she do?

5. To go from the first floor to the second floor of a building, a boy climbs a ladder, while his brother, who has the same mass, climbs the stairs. Who does more work?

6. How much energy would it take to lift four books that have a gravitational force of 14 N acting on them from ground level to a height of 1.5 m?

SCIENCE IN OUR LIVES

The importance of energy

Our need for energy is enormous. Manufacturing industries create products with it, our homes are heated by it, and cars, buses, trucks, trains, and airplanes operate by using it. In fact, we use millions and millions of megajoules of energy each day. Every machine that you can think of needs energy to run.

Much of this energy comes from fossil fuels. These non-renewable fuels include coal, oil, and natural gas. Unfortunately, some of these energy sources, such as oil, are running low. Scientists warn that fossil-fuel deposits are becoming harder and more expensive to find, and that world supplies of oil will be greatly reduced early in the next century.

Many of the things we take for granted, such as driving a car, heating our homes, or even mowing the grass with a gas lawn mower would be affected by a fossil-fuel shortage. Manufacturing processes that rely on the energy provided by fossil fuels would also be affected.

There are alternatives, however. More energy-efficient machines, appliances, and vehicles could be developed. The non-renewable energy sources we now have can be

Fossil fuels provide cars and trucks with energy.

conserved. Renewable sources of energy, such as the sun, wind, and tides can be harnessed. We may need to rely on nuclear power plants for more of our electric energy, although critics and environ-mentalists worry about the dangers of accidents and the problems of radioactive waste. Many challenges face your generation. One of the most important challenges will be the wise use of energy.

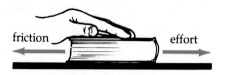

Figure 3–27

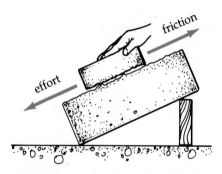

Figure 3–28 Friction acts against motion. It is caused by rough surfaces and molecular attraction.

3.5 Friction

Push this book across a flat desk. Notice how it resists being pushed? The force that resists the pushing is called **friction**. Friction always acts against the movement of one object or surface rubbing against another object or surface. Only in a vacuum can motion take place without friction because in a vacuum there is no matter to rub against.

Sometimes friction is caused by the bumps and hollows on surfaces that come in contact with each other. The surfaces may look and feel smooth, but a microscope would reveal that they have holes, bumps, and dust particles. Friction can also be caused by attraction between the molecules that come in contact at the surfaces. This type of friction can occur between surfaces in any of the three states of matter—solid, liquid, and gas.

There are three types of friction: starting friction, sliding friction, and rolling friction. Starting friction is the amount of force it takes to start an object sliding across a surface. Sliding friction is the amount of force it takes to keep an object sliding at a constant speed once it has started to slide. Rolling friction is the amount of force it takes to slide an object over rollers such as small balls or cylinders. Which of these three types of friction do you think is the greatest? Which do you think is the least? You will find out in Investigation 6.

Investigation 6   Investigating friction

PURPOSE
To investigate starting friction, sliding friction, and rolling friction.

MATERIALS
2 boards, approximately
  50 cm long (one rough
  and one smooth)
brick
50-cm length of string
4 round pencils or short
  pieces of dowelling

MEASURING TOOL
force meter calibrated from
  0–20 N

HYPOTHESIS

State which of the three types of friction will be the greatest and which will be the least. State the differences you would expect to find between sliding an object over a rough surface and sliding it over a smooth surface.

PROCEDURE

1. Place the rough board on a flat surface. Place the brick, large surface down, on top of the rough board. Tie the string around the brick (see Figure 3–29).
2. To measure starting friction, hook the force meter to the string and gently pull on the brick until it just starts to move. Read the force meter just as the brick starts to move. Record your measurement.
3. Repeat Step 2 two more times. Average your results and record them.
4. To measure sliding friction, pull the brick across the board until it moves at a constant speed (see Figure 3–29). Read the force meter at the same time and record your measurement.
5. Repeat Step 4 two more times. Average your results and record them in your chart.
6. To measure rolling friction, place the pencils (or pieces of dowelling) under the brick. Pull the brick over the pencils and read the force meter as you pull. Record your measurement.
7. Repeat Step 6 two more times. Average your results and record them.
8. Repeat Steps 1–7 using the smooth board.

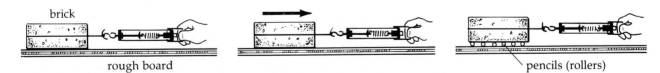

brick

rough board

pencils (rollers)

Measuring starting friction:
Pull until the brick just starts to slide. Read the force meter at that moment.

Measuring sliding friction:
Pull until the brick slides at a constant speed. Read the force meter as the brick is sliding.

Measuring rolling friction:
Read the force meter while the brick is sliding over a series of rollers.

Figure 3–29

OBSERVATIONS
1. Record your measurements in a chart like the one below.

Type of Friction	Measurement on Rough Board				Measurement on Smooth Board			
	Test 1 (N)	Test 2 (N)	Test 3 (N)	Avg. (N)	Test 1 (N)	Test 2 (N)	Test 3 (N)	Avg. (N)
Starting Friction								
Sliding Friction								
Rolling Friction								

CONCLUSIONS
Based on your measurements and observations, which of the three types of friction is the greatest and which is the least? What can you conclude about the effect of different surfaces on starting friction, sliding friction, and rolling friction?

Discussion questions

1. List four variables that you controlled in this investigation.
2. Suppose an airplane is forced to land at an airport without its landing gear. What should the captain and ground crew expect? Explain your answer.
3. A car is stuck in the snow. Suppose your older sister was trying to drive the car. Should she apply the gas gradually to avoid sliding, or should she give the car lots of gas causing the wheels to spin? Explain your answer using your knowledge about starting and sliding friction.

There are four factors, or variables, that determine how much friction will occur between surfaces that rub together. Each factor is listed below.

1. **The amount of friction is affected by the nature of the surfaces that rub together**. Are the surfaces soft or hard? Are they sticky? Are they rough or smooth? Are they wet or dry? For example, the tire of a car has about 30% less ''grab'' on wet concrete than it does on dry concrete. This is why you will often see road signs that read, ''Caution: slippery when wet.''

2. **The amount of friction increases when the force pushing the surfaces together increases**. Heavy cars have less trouble pulling out of snow than light cars. The greater mass of heavy cars means that there is more gravitational force pushing the tires down against the road. This increases the friction, giving the car more traction.

3. **Sliding friction is less than starting friction**. More force is required to start a surface sliding over another than to keep it sliding. Try pushing this book across your desk again and you'll see that it takes more force to start the book sliding than it does to keep it sliding.

4. **Rolling friction is less than sliding friction**. Wheels and rollers reduce the frictional effect of bumps and hollows. You observed how much more easily a brick moved across a surface when you put pencils under it in Investigation 6.

You have seen that friction is very important for transportation. Cars and trucks would be unable to move forward or to stop without it. But without friction, you would be unable to run or to walk because your feet would slip on every surface.

Without friction, why would these marathon runners be unable to compete?

Reducing friction

You have seen that friction is important to many of the things you use or do every day. But knowing how to reduce friction is important, too, because friction increases the amount of work required to do any job, since it is an additional force that has to be worked against.

Much of the extra energy friction creates turns into heat, and this heat can often be damaging. When a car is allowed to run too low on oil, for example, heat caused by metal rubbing against metal can make the engine seize up. Friction also increases the wear on moving things, such as tires, shoes,

Did you know?
Birds and airplanes need streamlined wings and bodies in order to fly. The more streamlined they are, the faster and farther they can fly on the same amount of energy. Birds change the position of their wings in flight to increase or decrease air friction.

The wear on these running shoes is the result of friction.

and machinery parts. An active tennis player may go through a pair of shoes every month. Car owners who skimp on maintenance soon learn that it is much cheaper to replace grease or oil than to buy new bearings or engine parts.

There are several ways to reduce friction. Here are four of them.

1. Solid surfaces can be made smoother by sanding and polishing. Smoother surfaces have fewer holes and bumps, and do not hold dust particles as well.

2. Solid surfaces can be lubricated with oil, grease, wax, or graphite. Lubricants form a slippery film over solid surfaces that keeps them slightly apart and causes dust particles to float away.

3. Rollers, ball bearings, or wheels can be used to create rolling friction instead of sliding friction, reducing the amount of force required to move an object.

4. Shapes can be streamlined to reduce friction between solids and air or water. Streamlined shapes offer less resistance to movement through these mediums. What shapes do airplanes and boats have that makes it easier for them to move through air or water?

As you have seen, friction can be reduced in a number of ways. But sometimes it is important to increase friction by making surfaces rougher, removing lubricants, eliminating rolling friction, and using shapes that are not streamlined. Putting sand on an icy road is an example where friction has been increased to give vehicles more traction in bad weather.

Friction increases the wear on moving things such as tennis shoes.

Why do you think some athletes wear close-fitting clothing?

Why would a streamlined shape be important to this bird?

Section review questions

1. What causes friction?
2. Define the terms starting friction, sliding friction, and rolling friction. Of the three types, which is the greatest and which is the least?
3. State three examples where friction is helpful.
4. State four ways to reduce friction. How can reducing friction be helpful?
5. How can you use friction to help you stop when you are wearing roller skates?

3.6 Machines

You have already discovered that force, work, and energy have specific scientific meanings. The same is true of the word machine. Some people think that machines are huge and noisy, and are used mostly in construction or industry. But scientists define **machines** as devices that make work easier. Machines can be as simple as a bottle opener or a nail, or as complex as a space shuttle or a computer printer.

There are various ways machines can make work easier. They can increase the effort, or force, that is applied to a given task, or increase the speed at which a task is performed. Machines can even transfer or change the direction of a force to make that force useful for doing certain kinds of work.

Think of a bicycle. To ride forward, you must use your leg muscles to exert downward force on the pedals. The pedals are attached to a gear. Gears are machines that are used to transmit force. They are also used to increase or decrease force. A single-speed bicycle has two gears linked by a chain. The gear attached to the pedals is linked by a chain to drive the gear attached to the rear wheel. Your downward push on the pedals turns the rear drive wheel, which gives the bicycle a forward thrust.

Many bicycles offer cyclists a choice of gears. To climb hills, a cyclist "gears down," or selects a lower gear. A lower gear increases the force acting on the drive wheel and makes pedalling easier. Less ground is covered with each rotation

Computers are complex machines that make work easier.

This cyclist is applying effort to move his bicycle forward.

of the pedals, however, so the cyclist's speed is slower. To go faster on level ground, or when going down a hill, the cyclist switches to a higher gear. Pedalling then becomes more difficult because less force acts on the drive wheel. This is offset, however, by the fact that more distance is covered with each rotation of the pedals. The cyclist's speed increases.

The force applied by the cyclist is called the **effort**. The total of the forces the machine must work against is called the **resistance**. The resistance to the motion of a bicycle is a combination of air resistance, gravity, and the friction of moving parts rubbing against one another.

It may surprise you to learn that although machines can make a job easier, they do not reduce the amount of work that must be done to accomplish it. When you gear down your bicycle to go up a hill, you gain in force but lose in the amount of distance travelled with each rotation of the pedals. This means that you exert less effort for each rotation, but you have to pedal faster to cover the same amount of ground as before. You do the same amount of work you did before, but it is spread out to make it easier. Just the opposite happens when you "gear up" on level ground. You lose in force but gain in distance.

Figure 3–31 Cyclists use a low gear when climbing hills and a high gear when descending.

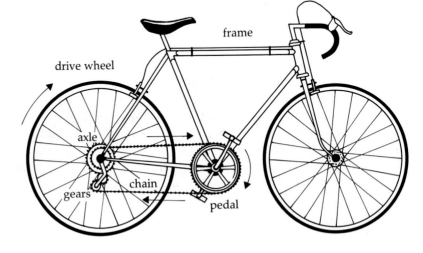

Figure 3–30

Do you remember the various ways machines can make work easier? They can transfer force from one place to another, change the direction of a force, increase the amount of force applied to a task, or increase the speed at which work is done. As you have learned, multiple-speed bicycles make work easier in three of these four ways. Can you state what they are?

More complex machines, such as a bicycle, are actually a combination of simpler machines. Seeing the ways simple machines operate makes it easier to understand how complex machines function.

Try this!

Look at a variety of hand tools to discover how they are used. Examine a screwdriver, hand drill, pliers, saw, chisel, claw hammer, and nutcracker. Notice where force is applied to each tool. Where is the force transferred when you use the tool? Make a sketch of each tool and use arrows to indicate the forces of effort and resistance that act on it. Put on safety glasses and hammer a nail part way into a board. Try to remove the nail using your fingers. Then use the claw on the hammer to pull it out. What can you say about how a machine can increase force?

Six simple machines

All complex machines are made up of various combinations of two or more simple machines. No matter how complex a machine looks, there are just six types of simple machines that can be used to make a complex one. These simple machines are the inclined plane, the lever, the pulley, the wedge, the wheel-and-axle, and the screw. Each has certain advantages and disadvantages in helping to perform various tasks.

The inclined plane
A ramp is an example of an inclined plane. This type of machine is as useful today as it was to the Egyptians who built the pyramids. You see inclined planes being used in staircases, ladders, loading docks, vehicle ramps, and high-

Caution: Always wear safety glasses when you hammer or extract a nail. Make sure that you are at least two metres away from other people. To avoid injury, hold the shank of the nail between the thumb and forefinger of one hand and use your other hand to tap the head of the nail with the hammer. Remove your fingers from the nail once it is "started."

Where is force being applied to this tool?

Did you know?

All six simple machines were in use before the third century B.C. Archaeologists have discovered that the lever, the wedge, and the inclined plane were all known to early peoples more than 100 000 years ago.

Pulleys are being used to help lift this net.

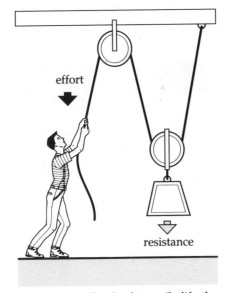

Figure 3–34 This load is easily lifted using pulleys.

way grades. Just how helpful an inclined plane is depends on how steep it is. It takes much more effort to raise an object up a steep plane than up a gradual one, but it also requires less time. A gradual plane takes longer to ascend, but requires less effort.

Figure 3–32 These workers are using an inclined plane to load the truck.

The lever

The lever is probably the most common type of simple machine. It is used in many kinds of tools. Pliers, hammers, nutcrackers, scissors, crowbars, seesaws, and rowboat oars are all examples of levers. The place where a lever pivots is called its **fulcrum**. The greater the distance from the fulcrum to the effort, the more force you can exert on the resistance.

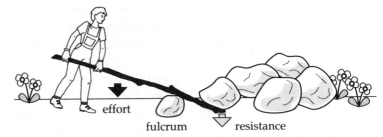

Figure 3–33 This person is using a log as a lever to move the rock.

The pulley

Pulleys can be used in various combinations to raise heavy loads with relatively little effort. The person in Figure 3–34 has to exert only about half the force that would be required to lift the same load without the help of pulleys.

The wedge

A wedge consists of two inclined planes back to back. Axe blades, chisels, needles, nails, knives, and air hammers are all examples of wedges. Wedges are used to force things apart. Sometimes this action separates an object into two pieces. Splitting a log is an example. Wedges are not very

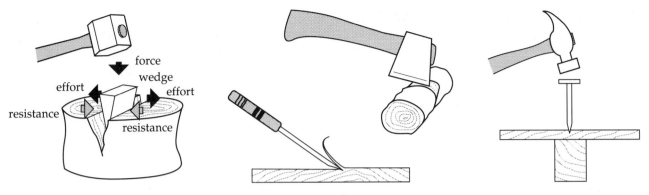

efficient, however, because they have large surface contact areas. Much of the energy used to drive a wedge changes to heat as a result of friction.

Figure 3–35 Wedges are used in many different tools.

The wheel-and-axle

This type of machine consists of two wheels, one large and one small, which are mounted on the same axle or central shaft. A little effort on the big wheel can be used to make a much larger force on the small wheel. The capstan is a good example of this type of machine. Until early in this century, capstans were used on sailing ships to haul in nets and to raise anchors. Sailors pushed on long arms mounted in a big wheel causing it and the smaller wheel to turn at the same time. The force is so strong that a rope wound onto the smaller wheel raised the heavy anchor. Other examples of wheel-and-axle machines are steering wheels, water wheels, potters' wheels, and Ferris wheels.

Sometimes the use of a wheel-and-axle machine is hard to recognize. Can you find it in a screwdriver, a water faucet, and a door key? If you were to think of the wheel-and-axle as a rotating lever, where would the fulcrum, the effort, and the resistance be in each of the previous examples?

A potter's wheel is an example of a wheel-and-axle machine.

Figure 3–36 A capstan is a wheel-and-axle machine that was used to pull up an anchor.

Did you know?

The screw was the last of the six simple machines to be invented. Archimedes, an early Greek scientist and mathematician, used the screw to raise water in the third century B.C. Spun by foot or turned by hand, the screw was widely used for irrigation.

Figure 3–37   Different types of screws

The screw

The screw is really just an inclined plane that revolves around a cylinder. Screws form parts of many machines. They are used in two principal ways: to fasten objects together and to lift heavy loads. Examples are the vice, or the clamp, and the jackscrew, which is sometimes used to lift houses. Bolts, nuts, and pipe threads are other examples of screws.

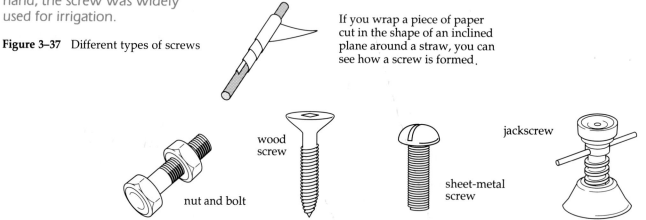

If you wrap a piece of paper cut in the shape of an inclined plane around a straw, you can see how a screw is formed.

nut and bolt

wood screw

sheet-metal screw

jackscrew

Table 3.1   The invention of simple and complex machines

Date	Machine	Inventor(s)
100 000 B.C. or earlier	lever, wedge, inclined plane	unknown
3000 B.C.	wheel-and-axle	unknown
3000 B.C.	sail	unknown
8th century B.C.	pulley	unknown
3rd century B.C.	water screw, block-and-tackle	Archimedes (Greek)
3rd century B.C.	pump	Ctesibius (Greek)
2nd century B.C.	lathe	unknown
1st century B.C.	vertical waterwheel	unknown
1185	vertical windmill	unknown
1335	mechanical clock	unknown
1656	pendulum clock	Christiaan Huygens (Dutch)
1712	steam engine	Thomas Newcomen (English)
1776	submarine	David Bushnell (American)
1783	gas balloon	Joseph Montgolfier (French)
1786	steamboat	John Fitch (American)
1798	papermaking machine	Nicolas-Louis Robert (French)
1822	electric motor	Michael Faraday (English)
1834	screw propellor for ships	John Patch (Canadian)
1835	steam shovel	William S. Otis (American)

Table 3.1   The invention of simple and complex machines

Date	Machine	Inventor(s)
1837	telegraph	Samuel Morse (American)
1839	bicycle	Kirkpatrick MacMillan (Scottish)
1850	grain binder	John E. Heath (American)
1851	washing machine	James T. King (American)
1853	elevator	Elisha G. Otis (American)
1853	automatic fog horn	Robert Foulis (Canadian)
1860	internal combustion engine	Etienne Lenoir (French)
1872	electric typewriter	Thomas Edison (American)
1869	vacuum cleaner	Ives McGaffey (American)
1869	rotary snowplough for locomotives and the snowblower principle	J.W. Elliott (Canadian)
1876	telephone	Alexander Graham Bell (Canadian)
1877	phonograph	Thomas Edison (American)
1883	electric street car and trolley pole	John J. Wright (Canadian)
1885	automobile	Carl Benz (German)
1888	motion picture camera	E.J. Marey (French)
1891	motion picture projector	Thomas Edison (American)
1892	acetylene gas torch	Thomas Willson (Canadian)
1892	diesel engine	Rudolph Diesel (German)
1900	altimeter and depth sounder	Reginald Fessenden (Canadian)
1903	airplane	Orville and Wilbur Wright (American)
1906	AM radio	Reginald Fessenden (Canadian)
1907	electric vacuum cleaner	James M. Spangler (American)
1913	refrigerator	A.H. Goss (American)
1913	talking motion pictures	Thomas Edison (American)
1927	aircraft variable pitch propellor	Robert Turnbull (Canadian)
1923	television	V.K. Zworykin (American)
1926	liquid-fuel rocket	R.H. Goddard (American)
1930	jet engine	Frank Whittle (English)
1933	FM radio	Edwin H. Armstrong (American)
1938	electron microscope	James Hillier and Albert Prebus (Canadian)
1939	helicopter	Igor Sikorsky (American)
1940	paint roller	Norman Breakey (Canadian)
1942	nuclear reactor	Enrico Fermi (Italo-American)
1946	electronic computer	J.P. Ecker and J.W. Mauchly (American)
1954	solar battery	Pearson and others (American)
1959	snowmobile	Armand Bombardier (Canadian)
1969	Sub-igloo diving station	Joseph B. MacInnis (Canadian)
1981	Canadarm	Spar Aerospace Ltd. (Canadian)
1987	microwave airplane	Group of scientists from (Canadian) University of Toronto and Federal Government

Input, output, and efficiency

To really understand the advantages and disadvantages of a machine, you must know how to measure its efficiency. The **efficiency** of a machine is a measure of the total amount of work that was done to make the machine function (its work input) in comparison with how much useful work it accomplishes (its work output). This is usually expressed as a percentage.

$$\text{Efficiency} = \frac{\text{work output}}{\text{work input}} \times 100\%$$

As you may already have guessed, some work has to be done against the force of friction whenever a machine is used, because every machine has surfaces that offer resistance or that rub against other surfaces. The greater the force of friction, the less efficient the machine will be, and the greater the amount of energy that will be needed to operate it. Some of the energy is wasted in the form of heat. Therefore, the work output of a machine is always less than its work input, because there is always some loss of energy due to friction. This means that the efficiency of a machine is always less than 100%. The following example will help you to understand this idea.

Example
The force of gravity acting on a cart is 310 N. However, a force of only 130 N is required to pull the cart up a 10-m inclined plane to a height of 4 m. Calculate the work input and the work output. Determine the efficiency of the machine from these calculations.

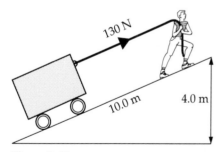

Figure 3–38

Solution
The work input is the work done to pull the cart 10 m up the inclined plane.

$$\text{Work input} = \text{force} \times \text{distance}$$
$$= 130 \text{ N} \times 10 \text{ m}$$
$$= 1300 \text{ N·m or } 1300 \text{ J}$$

The work output is the work that must be done to raise the cart by 4 m against the force of gravity.

$$\begin{aligned}
\text{Work output} &= \text{force} \times \text{distance} \\
&= 310\ \text{N} \times 4\ \text{m} \\
&= 1240\ \text{N·m or 1240 J}
\end{aligned}$$

Now that you know the work input and the work output, you can calculate the efficiency using the formula.

$$\text{Efficiency} = \frac{\text{work output}}{\text{work input}} \times 100\%$$

$$= \frac{1240\ \text{J}}{1300\ \text{J}} \times 100$$

$$= 95.4\%$$

As you can see, an inclined plane can be an efficient way to raise a heavy load. Do you think that more or less force would be needed if the slope of the plane were increased? You will find out in Investigation 7.

Investigation 7   The advantage of using a ramp

PURPOSE
To investigate the relationship between the amount of force needed to ascend an inclined plane and the slope of the plane.

MATERIALS
roller skate
string about 50 cm long
6 identical books
a board, approximately
   2 cm × 20 cm × 1 m

MEASURING TOOL
force meter calibrated from
   0–20 N

HYPOTHESIS
State what will happen to the amount of force needed to ascend an inclined plane as its slope is increased.

PROCEDURE
1. Measure the force of gravity acting on the skate by hanging it from the force meter.
2. Stack two books at the end of a long table. Make an inclined plane by placing one end of the board on top of the books. Rest the other end of the board on the table.

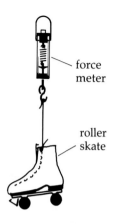

Figure 3–39

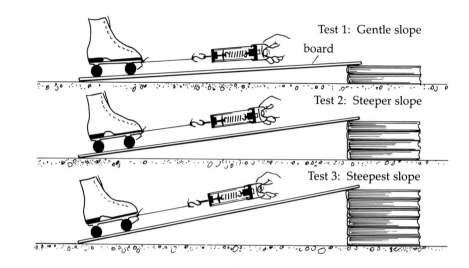

3. Using the force meter, measure the force required to pull the roller skate slowly up the ramp. Repeat your measurements two more times and average your results.

4. Increase the slope of the plane by adding two more books to your stack. Again measure the force required to pull the roller skate up the ramp. Repeat this step two more times and average your results.

5. Place the final two books on the stack. Repeat Step 4.

OBSERVATIONS

1. Record your observations in a chart like the one below.

Measurement of Force	Test 1 (N)	Test 2 (N)	Test 3 (N)	Avg. (N)
Gravity				
Gentle Slope				
Steeper Slope				
Steepest Slope				

CONCLUSIONS
What can you conclude about the amount of force needed to ascend an inclined plane as its slope is increased?

Discussion questions

1. Review the procedure and identify the variables you controlled in the investigation.
2. How many times easier was it to pull the skate up the gently sloping ramp than to lift it straight up?
3. Suppose that the six books make a ramp 1.0 m long and 25 cm high.
   a) Calculate the work input required to pull the skate all the way up the ramp.
   b) Calculate the work output.
   c) Calculate the ramp's efficiency. Use the following formula.

$$\text{Efficiency} = \frac{\text{work output}}{\text{work input}} \times 100\%$$

4. Why is the efficiency of a machine always less than 100%?
5. Can the efficiency of an inclined plane be changed? Explain your answer.
6. How would your results differ if you placed a rock on the roller skate?

The role of scientific research

The research conducted by scientists has created a wide body of knowledge about the nature of forces and simple machines. Engineers and other technologists use this knowledge to invent more complex machines for specific purposes, such as building office complexes, improving air travel, and pumping oil through pipelines.

The application of scientific knowledge has produced the many useful home appliances you use every day. Further scientific research may result in the invention of machines that will help us in new ways, or that will replace older technologies that use precious energy resources inefficiently. For example, scientific research and understanding have helped

How do you think the knowledge gained from scientific research has changed the way we communicate?

This pilotless airplane, which is powered by the energy of microwaves, is the result of scientific research.

scientists and technologists to develop new devices to help the physically disabled. Can you name one or two recent examples of these devices? Can you think of new machines that are helping us in other ways?

Fortunately, scientific researchers and technicians have been able to use their knowledge about force, work, friction, and energy to design better and better machines. Throughout the centuries, machines have become more and more efficient, enabling humans to do work faster, more easily, and with less effort. Continuing research means that new devices are invented that make work more productive and provide more time for leisure. The dishwashers, automatic coffee makers, power tools, sewing machines, food processors, and microwave ovens found in many homes are the results of scientific research and development.

One recent Canadian invention is a pilotless airplane that can fly almost indefinitely. It flies by using the energy of microwaves beamed to it from a transmitter on the ground. Such a technological achievement could have wide applications. In the future, a fleet of these airplanes could fly 20 km above cities to relay television and radio signals, as well as police emergency calls. Cameras on board could send back information about traffic. In remote areas, the airplanes could be used to detect forest fires, conduct surveys, or relay information about crop growth.

In West Germany, research scientists are experimenting to find ways to run machines using renewable energy. In one research project, these scientists have mounted solar panels on the roof of a van. Energy from the sun is absorbed by the solar panels and changed into electric energy. This energy runs the van and the different appliances inside the van.

The development of machines that use renewable energy resources, such as this solar-powered vehicle, could have important applications in the future.

Try this!

Examine newspapers and magazines every day for a week and clip out references to new machines. Paste each one on a separate sheet of paper. Underneath each clipping, write a short description of how the machine will make work easier and more productive. Will it provide more leisure time or any other benefit? What other machine(s) might each new machine replace? What effect might this have on the economy, politics, social services, and education?

Section review questions

1. In what ways do machines make work easier?
2. Draw diagrams that show how each of the six simple machines operate.
3. Identify a machine, not discussed in this section, that combines two or more simple machines. Make a sketch of how it operates.
4. In what way is the wheel-and-axle like the lever? In what ways are the screw and the wedge like the inclined plane?
5. What is meant by work input and work output?
6. Why do all machines have an efficiency of less than 100%?
7. State some advantages of various machines.
8. What four things must scientific researchers be able to measure in order to make machines more efficient?

J. Armand Bombardier

In 1987, a panel of engineers rated the snowmobile as one of Canada's ten best engineering achievements. The CN Tower did not even make the list.

The snowmobile was invented by J. Armand Bombardier, who was born in Valcourt, Quebec, in 1908. He had a flair for inventing. At 15 he made his first snowmobile by mounting an old car engine on a farm sleigh. Then he attached a large propellor to the engine. Five years later, he started work on a smaller snowmobile, but it took until 1959 before he could market the first Ski-Doo. That year, Bombardier sold 225 of them at $1000 each. Today, thousands of snowmobiles are sold each year in many countries around the world.

Within a few years of their introduction, snowmobiles revolutionized life in remote areas of Canada. Snowmobiles helped many people needing medical attention to obtain help in time. Farmers used them to rescue stranded cattle. Native peoples in the Arctic used them to hunt, trap, visit relatives, and transport goods. Hydro workers, foresters, and prospectors all praised the snowmobile as a tool they had waited for to do their job more effectively in the winter. Tour-

Bombardier's first Ski-Doo

ist-based industries found that they could extend their operating seasons with the snowmobile, by selling it as a machine for fun and recreation.

Bombardier was happy that his invention had done so much for so many people. But he was saddened that his invention had also led to serious accidents and environmental damage. Critics thought snowmobiles were noisy, gasoline wasters, and a threat to wildlife. Farmers and landowners saw them as destructive to croplands, orchards, and shrubs. Unthinking snow-

mobile operators sometimes badly injured or killed themselves by running into barbed wire, racing into oncoming road traffic, or plunging through soft ice into open water in the dead of night.

No technological advance comes without its effects — good *and* bad — on society. But the inventors of new technologies are not to blame. It is up to us to decide how, when, and where new inventions should be used, and that they should be used wisely.

SCIENCE IN SOCIETY

Is our dependence on machines a problem?

Machines do many things for us. They make products such as clothing, shoes, bicycles, toys, and even hot dogs more plentiful because they increase the production of these goods. Farm equipment and food-processing machines make more food available to us. Cars, trucks, buses, airplanes, and boats transport goods quickly and enable us to travel from place to place.

Society depends on machines. Can you imagine what your life would be like without telephones, computers, washing machines, televisions, light bulbs, vacuum cleaners, or sewing machines? Without them, you would have to spend many hours each day doing tasks such as weaving, sewing, and washing your own clothes by hand. You would have very little time to pursue hobbies or participate in the sports you like to play. Machines make work easier and give you more leisure time to do the things you enjoy doing.

However, many pollution problems have been linked to the use of machines. The machines used in metal-smelting plants, for example, contribute to increased amounts of

The use of robotics to manufacture cars

air pollution. Many industries produce waste water that flows into rivers and lakes causing water pollution. Industrial machines use large

quantities of non-renewable energy. In some cases, they have reduced the number of jobs available for workers.

Understanding the impact of machines on society, on resources, and on the environment will help us to develop more energy-efficient machines for the future, plan retraining programs for workers whose jobs may be threatened by new technology, and use machines wisely to improve the quality of our lives without damaging the environment.

Explore the issue

Divide into groups of four and choose one machine to investigate for each group. Two group members should research the positive aspects of the machine you have chosen, and the other two should research its negative aspects. Use your library and current newspapers and magazines for your research. Prepare a report on your group's machine and present it to the rest of your class for discussion about the machine's advantages and disadvantages to society.

Meet Ian Baker

Ian works as a general contractor in the building trade. He is hired by people who want to build additions or cottages, or who want to renovate their houses. He supervises a group of subcontractors on every project.

Q. Did you always want to go into the contracting business?
A. I always wanted to run my own business, to do it my own way. My father is an engineer, and I was around sites with him when I was a kid, so it's a bit in my blood, I guess.

Q. What background did you have in business?
A. I quit school in grade 10 and started to work as an office boy, then at a textile company, then as a salesman. Finally, I went into the brokerage business when I was only

21. I woke up and realized I had nowhere else to go, so I went back to school. I took high-school courses, and I was able to get into Waterloo University where I took political science and economics.

Q. How have you managed to learn the technical aspects of your trade?
A. I learn by hiring a fully licenced person and working with that person constantly until I know everything he or she knows.

Q. Is there much mechanical knowledge required in your work?
A. Almost everything in this job involves something mechanical. You always have to think of the most labour-efficient ways of doing things. Right now I'm building a boathouse in Muskoka. In order to get the timbers down the hill to the site, it was more efficient to have them brought to a government dock nearby and hauled over by boat. This was faster than carrying them one by one down the hill.

Q. How have machines changed your kind of work over the years?
A. There has been immense change. For instance, before chain saws were used, an eight-by-eight-inch (20-cm × 20-cm) timber would have to be hewn by hand with

an adze. It would take all day. Now one person can make that timber in under an hour.

Q. Do the tools and machines keep improving?
A. Sure. The basic principles are the same, but using the chain saw example, the saws now have automatic oiling and they're made to be anti-vibration so the operator doesn't get tired.

Q. Do you have to keep buying new equipment all the time?
A. Yes. I'm always buying new power tools. The latest tool I bought was a portable cross-cut mitre saw, which is probably the most startling invention for my business. There has never been a portable saw like this before, and it makes it far easier to cut angles in wood trim. This saw will save me the cost of one carpenter per day for the length of the job.

Q. What do you like best about your job?
A. I like the freedom of being my own boss. Although you are directed by a number of forces—your customer and material suppliers—you still run the show. I like being up-to-date about materials and methods, and being able to experiment with new ideas. It's fun to be creative and to invent new ways to do things.

Chapter review

Words to know

Write a brief definition for each of the terms listed below. The location of these terms is indicated by the section number in the brackets.

- electric force (*Section 3.1*)
- energy (*Section 3.4*)
- force (*Section 3.1*)
- friction (*Section 3.1*)
- gravity (*Section 3.1*)
- joule (*Section 3.4*)
- magnetic force (*Section 3.1*)
- newton (*Section 3.2*)
- nuclear force (*Section 3.1/Section 3.5*)
- weight (*Section 3.1/Section 3.3*)
- work (*Section 3.4*)

Questions

A. Indicate whether each of the following statements is true or false. Explain why the "false" statements are not true.

1. There is no force of gravity away from the Earth.
2. Charged balloons will stick to walls because of magnetic force.
3. A tow truck does not do work on a car that is stuck unless the car moves.
4. Work requires energy.
5. Force is measured in newtons using an equal-arm balance.
6. The mass of an object changes depending on the planet where the object is located.
7. When a force of 3 N is moved through 5 m, the work done is 15 J.
8. Friction is a force you could live without.
9. Lifting objects using a ramp takes more force and less energy than lifting them straight up.
10. All machines cause pollution and unemployment.

B. Choose the best answer for each of the following.

1. A force
   a) acting on a moving object may change the direction of the object
   b) acting on a moving object may increase the speed of the object
   c) acting on a moving object may slow the object down
   d) may do any of the above

2. Magnetic forces
   a) attract
   b) attract and repel
   c) repel
   d) are stronger under water

3. The force of gravity between two masses
   a) is stronger if the masses are farther apart

b) is stronger if the masses are closer together
c) is always the same at any distance
d) sometimes attracts and sometimes repels

4. A machine can make work easier by
   a) increasing the effort applied to a task
   b) making the distance to the work less
   c) making the work less
   d) making the force of resistance less

5. A joule is the amount of work done when
   a) a force of 1 N moves up
   b) a force of 1 N moves down
   c) a force of 1 N moves up and down
   d) a force of 1 N moves through a distance of 1 m

6. The force of gravity acting on a 20-kg object is
   a) 200 N   c) 30 N
   b) 2 N   d) 10 N

7. To raise a 3-kg object to a height of 5 m requires an amount of energy equal to
   a) 15 J   c) 150 J
   b) 1.7 J   d) 8 J

8. Scientists should try to invent machines that use
   a) less oil and more natural gas
   b) renewable types of energy
   c) non-renewable types of energy
   d) more energy

9. An example of a renewable type of energy is
   a) energy from coal
   b) energy from the sun
   c) energy from oil
   d) energy from natural gas

10. The lower the efficiency of a machine
    a) the higher the amount of wasted energy
    b) the better the machine
    c) the higher the work output
    d) the less fuel it will use

C. Write full answers to each of the following.
1. Define force. State three examples of pulling forces and three examples of pushing forces.

2. Which force stops a satellite orbiting the Earth from flying off into space? Use a diagram to illustrate your answer.

3. State two reasons why an object weighs less at the equator than it does at the poles.

4. Which force holds electrons around the nucleus of an atom?

5. In what way are gravity, electric force, and magnetic force similar? How do they differ?

6. State one example of each of the following forces.
   a) elasticity   c) compression
   b) tension   d) buoyancy

7. Describe one easy way to remember how strong a force of 1 N is.

8. If an object is subjected to 12 N of gravity on Earth, which force would it be subjected to on the moon? If an object has a mass of 24 kg on the moon, what would its mass be on Earth?

9. How much work is done when a person exerts a force of 50 N to push a box 5.5 m across the floor of a room? What is the name of the force the person is working against?

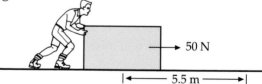

50 N

|← 5.5 m →|

Figure 3–40

10. Why is no machine 100% efficient? What is the efficiency of a machine that requires 60 J of input for an output of 40 J?

11. Draw each of the six simple machines performing a task. List an advantage and a disadvantage for each machine.

12. State two examples where more friction would be advantageous and two examples where less friction would be preferable. How could you achieve these results for each of your examples?

13. Why should you support the development and use of energy-efficient machines that are powered by energy from renewable sources?

Science challenge

1. A chocolate bar can provide 1000 kJ of energy. How high up a mountain could a boy climb with the energy from one chocolate bar, assuming that a gravitational force of 500 N was acting on him?

2. Read the following statement. Discuss it with your friends and family, then prepare a report that explains why you agree or disagree with it.
   ''Our employment patterns, environmental policies, and leisure-time activities are not really influenced by the development of new machines.''

3. Research the life and accomplishments of Sir Isaac Newton. Write a report explaining what he achieved and why it is still important today.

4. Research the cause of ocean tides. Use diagrams to explain why they occur.

Science project

1. Investigate the relationship between the amount of stretch of an elastic band or a spring from which various masses are hung, and the force exerted by gravity on these masses. Display your results in the form of a graph. List the variables you had to control. You can extend your investigation to compare how wood and plastic rulers bend when they are clamped to a table and have various loads placed on their free ends. (Wear safety glasses for both of these investigations.)

2. Build one or more complex machines that incorporate several of the six simple machines. Be prepared to demonstrate each machine and to discuss its input, output, and efficiency. You should also be able to state where and how you dealt with problems caused by friction.

Soil and Plant Ecology

John and Erica's grandfather once owned a farm in Vineland, which is east of Hamilton, Ontario. When John and Erica were driving with their grandfather from Toronto to Niagara Falls, Mr. Braun pointed out the new factories and warehouses that had been constructed on what was once farmland.

"I remember when that land was all orchards and vineyards," said Mr. Braun.

"Every time we drive to Niagara Falls," said Erica, "we see new subdivisions or factories."

"I guess people need more places to live and work," said John. "I wonder, though, if we should be developing this rich farmland. Are there alternatives?"

"We will be more dependent on imported fruits and vegetables if we can't grow our own," said Mr. Braun.

Agricultural land in Canada is an important resource. The rich soil of the Niagara Peninsula, for example, is ideally suited to the growth of fruits such as peaches, pears, cherries, and grapes. But what makes this soil so valuable, and why should we be concerned about protecting it? In this chapter, you will discover some of the unique qualities of soil and its importance to plant life. **175**

We are dependent on plants for many things.

4.1 What is soil?

Without soil, many thousands of species of land plants would not survive. We use plants in the production of many manufactured goods such as building supplies and medicines. The leaves, stems, roots, seeds, and fruits of plants provide us with much of our food. Animals that eat plants supply us with meat, milk, eggs, and leather goods.

You can see that protecting soil is very important to the quality of our lives. But what exactly is soil? Are all soils the same? Do soils contain living and non-living things? The best way to find out about how soil is composed is to examine it carefully. Investigation 1 will give you an opportunity to take a closer look at soil.

Investigation 1   Examining soil

PURPOSE
To investigate the components of soil.

MATERIALS
4 tall jars with lids
garden trowel
masking tape
marker
large spoon
4 sheets of white paper
magnifying glass
4 toothpicks or popsicle sticks

HYPOTHESIS
State the things you might find in soil.

PROCEDURE
1. Find four different places where you can collect soil near your school. Try to include a variety of places such as a playground, a flower bed, a wooded area, or a sand pit.
2. At each location, collect a soil sample using the garden trowel. Fill each of the jars half-full with the soil sample and replace its lid. Use the masking tape and the marker

to label the jars. Write the location where the soil samples were collected on the labels. Give each location a number.

3. When you return to class, place a spoonful of each soil sample on a separate sheet of white paper.

4. Carefully examine each sample using the magnifying glass. Sort through the soil samples with a toothpick or a popsicle stick. Notice the overall colour of each sample.

5. Compare the size of the soil particles in each sample. Look for evidence of plants and small animals that are either alive, dead, or decaying.

6. Feel the textures of the soils by pinching some between your fingers. Are they rough or smooth? Wet or dry?

7. Compare the odour of each sample. Is it odourless or does it smell musty?

8. Fill the jars with water and replace the lids. Shake the jars and let them stand overnight. The next day, examine each jar carefully. Notice whether the soil in each jar has settled in layers, and whether some materials are floating on the surface of the water.

Caution: Be sure to wash your hands after completing this investigation.

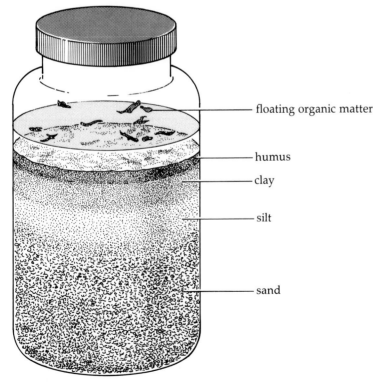

- floating organic matter
- humus
- clay
- silt
- sand

Figure 4–1

OBSERVATIONS

1. Record your observations in a chart like the one below.

Observations	Source of Soil Sample			
	Location 1	Location 2	Location 3	Location 4
Colour				
Particle Size (fine, medium, or coarse)				
Evidence of Plants and Animals				
Texture of Soil (rough, smooth)				
Odour of Soil (musty, odourless)				
Moisture (wet, dry)				
Effects of Settling				
Presence of Floating Particles				
Additional Observations				

CONCLUSIONS

Based on your observations, what conclusions can you make about the composition of soil?

Discussion questions

1. Summarize the differences of the soil samples you collected.
2. What evidence of plants and animals were you able to find?

3. Describe the kinds of non-living things you found in each sample.
4. Did any of the samples show signs of settling in layers? What kinds of particles settled closest to the bottoms of the jars? What kinds of things did you see floating?
5. If you saw bubbles rising as you poured water into the jars, what do you think this tells you about soil?
6. What evidence did you find that soil may contain water?

The composition of soil

By now, you probably have guessed that **soil** is made up of several kinds of materials or components. One of these components—the mineral component—consists of particles that come from weathered rock. Chief among these particles is **sand**. Sand ranges in size from 0.05–2.00 mm in diameter.

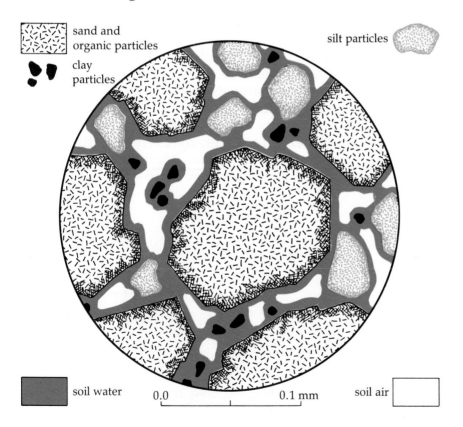

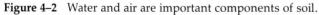

Figure 4–2 Water and air are important components of soil.

Along with larger rock particles, sand was the soil component that settled first to the bottom of your jars. Finer mineral particles called **silt** then settled on top of the sand. Silt ranges in size from 0.05–0.002 mm in diameter, too small to see without a magnifying glass or a microscope.

Even finer mineral particles called **clay** settled on top of the silt. Clay particles can only be seen with a microscope. They supply plants with many of the nutrients they need for healthy growth and reproduction.

Another soil component is organic matter. Organic matter comes from decaying plants and animals. When this matter is completely decayed, it is called **humus**. Some humus may have floated to the tops of your jars. Humus is usually a rich brown or black colour. Humus helps to keep soil moist and provides plants with several of the other nutrients they need to grow. Soil rich in humus is often called ''fertile soil.''

Two other major components of soil are water and air. Water and air fill the spaces between particles of sand, humus, silt, and clay. These spaces are known as pores. Soil water is important because it dissolves the nutrients that are necessary for plant growth. It is also required for photosynthesis and respiration, and to prevent wilting. Soil air is important because it is composed partly of oxygen, which is needed for root respiration.

Most land plants require a good balance between soil water and soil air. Soil that is very wet, for example, after heavy rain, has too much soil water and not enough soil air. On the other hand, long, dry periods may cause soil to have too

This field of corn requires the moisture and nutrients it receives from the soil to grow well.

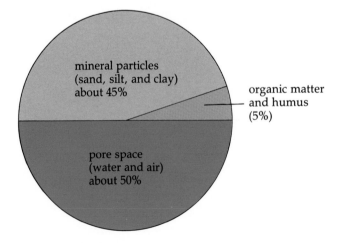

mineral particles
(sand, silt, and clay)
about 45%

organic matter
and humus
(5%)

pore space
(water and air)
about 50%

Figure 4–3   The composition of soil

much air compared with the amount of water it contains. Plants that do not have the adaptations to survive such conditions could die.

Soil is made of four components: mineral particles, organic matter, water, and air. If a particular soil does not have a balance of these components, then farmers and gardeners must improve it before it will be suitable for growing plants and crops.

Try this!

You can demonstrate how the relationship between water and air affects growing plants. Grow two bean plants in separate pots filled with the same soil. Place them side by side in a sunny window. Each day, water one plant until some of the water runs out into a dish under the pot. Water the other plant only often enough to keep the soil slightly moist. Do not allow any water to remain standing in its dish. Water the two plants in this way for several weeks. Observe any differences in the tops and roots of the two plants. What can you conclude?

Soil textures

In Investigation 1, you determined how each of the soil samples felt. **Soil texture** refers to the fineness or coarseness of a soil. Soil texture is determined by the proportions of sand, silt, and clay particles that are present in soils. For example, a soil consisting mainly of sand will feel coarse and gritty. A sandy soil contains little clay and silt. It will not be very fertile because it cannot hold much water, and it provides few of the nutrients that most plants need.

Unlike sandy soils, clay soils feel slippery and sticky. They are composed mainly of clay combined with small amounts of silt and sand. Clay soils are very fertile. However, they may hold too much water after heavy rainfalls. After drying in the sun, clay soils can turn very hard and may crack.

Silty soils are between sand and clay soils. They feel smooth, not sticky or coarse. They contain mostly silt com-

Sandy soil provides nutrients for only certain types of plants.

bined with small amounts of sand and clay. Silty soils are moderately fertile and have a high water-holding capacity.

Most soils are not made up of sand, clay, or silt alone. Usually, they are a combination of all three types. Figure 4–4 shows the many different soil types that are possible. Each type is named according to the percentages of sand, silt, and clay it contains. Try reading the "soil triangle." What percentages of sand, silt, and clay might a "silty-clay" soil contain? What would you call a soil that contained 65% sand, 10% silt, and 25% clay?

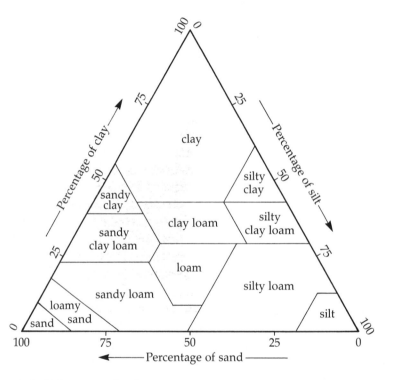

Figure 4–4   Soil texture triangle

Did you know?
Most potting soils are specially formulated loams. Large amounts of humus are often added to potting soils to enhance their fertility.

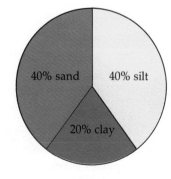

Figure 4–5   A well-balanced soil

Near the bottom of the triangle, you will notice the term loam. **Loam** is a mixture of sand, silt, and clay that shows the characteristics of each of these mineral particles equally. Most flowers and vegetables grow well in loam because it is fertile, holds water well, and has good drainage. A well-balanced loam is about 40% sand, 40% silt, and 20% clay by mass. Because the characteristics of clay are more pronounced than those of silt or sand, less clay is needed to produce a good loam.

Try this!

Investigate soil texture at several sites near your home. At each site, place a spoonful of soil into the palm of your hand and mix it with water until it is wet but not runny. Rub the soil out into a thin layer on your palm. Clay soil will feel smooth and slippery, and it will have a shine. Silty soil will also feel smooth and slippery, but it will have no shine. Sandy soil will feel gritty and look dull. You can perform another soil-texture test by forming the wet soil into a ball. Sandy soil falls apart. Clay soil holds its shape. Silty soil will feel much like clay, but it will not hold together. How would you expect loam to feel?

Remember to wash your hands after this activity.

Soil layers

Have you ever walked along a river bank and noticed different layers of soil near the top of the bank? Perhaps you also noticed similar layers while watching a construction crew dig into the ground. The first layer of soil is called the **topsoil**. It is often not more than 20 cm in depth. Initially, topsoil is darker in colour than the next major layer below it. Topsoil is the most fertile layer of soil, partly because it contains humus. Humus is formed from animal droppings, decayed plants, bacteria, protists, fungi, and the bodies of soil animals such as insects and worms. Many soil animals and micro-organisms both live and die in topsoil. Small animals, such as worms, mice, and moles, improve the soil by digging tunnels that allow air and water to reach the roots of plants. Plants, except water plants, obtain most of their nutrients from topsoil. Most soil animals live in this layer as well. Because topsoil lies next to the surface of the Earth, it is the layer of soil that is most frequently carried away by wind and moving water.

Below the topsoil is another major layer. It is called **subsoil**. Subsoil is usually much lighter in colour than topsoil because it contains less humus. Subsoil is more tightly packed than topsoil because it is compressed by the soil above it, and because there are fewer plant roots and animals living in it. Both topsoil and subsoil layers are usually wider near the mouths of rivers. The reason for this is that the rivers flood

Did you know?

Geologists estimate that it takes almost 200 years for 1 cm of topsoil to form in southern Canada. Farther north, geologists estimate that topsoil takes much longer to form. Why do you think topsoil would take longer to form in the North?

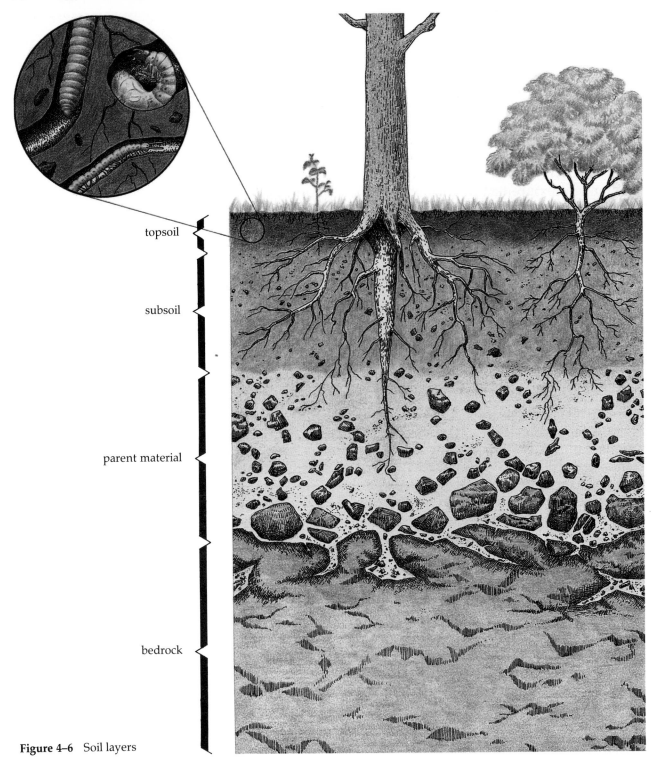

topsoil

subsoil

parent material

bedrock

Figure 4–6 Soil layers

the land surrounding these areas each spring and leave deposits of soil.

Below the subsoil is another major layer called **parent material**. This layer usually contains large deposits of sand, gravel, pebbles, boulders, and rock that make it hard to dig into. Parent material is the major source from which subsoil and topsoil are formed. Below the parent material is bedrock, which is solid rock. Bedrock is the material from which the parent material may have developed. In many parts of Canada, bedrock can be seen above the ground.

A blasting cut for a tunnel through bedrock

Section review questions

1. Suppose someone said to you, "Soil is just useless dirt." What would you say in response?
2. What is soil made of?
3. Why is humus an important part of good soils?
4. Why is it important for good soils to have a large percentage of pore space?
5. Describe how you could make loam. Why would loam be a better soil to grow plants in than sand, silt, or clay alone?
6. What is parent material? Which soil layers usually lie above this material? Which are found below it?

Why do you think the movement of glaciers is a weathering agent?

4.2 The origin of sand, silt, and clay

Sand, silt, and clay make up one of the most important components of soil—the mineral component. Scientists believe that these particles were formed from rocks that were broken down over many thousands of years into smaller and smaller pieces. This process is called **weathering**. The agents of weathering are wind, moving water, freezing and thawing, growth of plant roots, movement of glaciers, and the action of chemicals. You can see how some of these weathering agents work in Investigation 2.

Investigation 2   The effects of weathering

PURPOSE
To investigate how various weathering agents can create mineral particles from rock.

MATERIALS
10–15 small porous rocks   hammer
   (limestone)   safety glasses
wooden board   sand
large sheet of white paper   5 lima beans
plastic ice cream or yogurt   plastic drinking cup
   container and lid   potting soil
plastic shopping bag   plaster of Paris
tap water

PROCEDURE
1. Rub two pieces of rock together over the white paper. What do you see falling on the paper?
2. Put 10 small rocks into the plastic container and half fill it with water. Secure the lid and shake the container back and forth 50 times. Open the container and look for small particles of rock on the bottom. Put the lid back on and shake the container another 50 times. Are there more particles?
3. Seal a few pieces of the porous rock in a plastic bag half-full of water. Put the bag in a freezer overnight and examine it for rock fragments next day.

Caution: Flying chips from the rock can permanently damage your eyesight or that of someone else if you are not careful. Make sure that other people are at least two metres away from you while you break up the rock. Be sure to wear your safety glasses. As an added precaution, cover the rock with a cloth as you break it up with the hammer.

4. Put on the safety glasses and break up one of the rocks carefully using the hammer. (Place a wooden board under the rock to protect the surface you are working on.) Examine a piece of the broken rock and note how sharp its edges are.

5. Clean and dry the plastic container from Step 2. Put the broken piece of rock from Step 4 into the container with two handfuls of dry sand. Place the lid on the container and shake the container back and forth 50 or more times. Open the lid and check the edges of the broken rock again. Do you see signs of weathering? Shake the container 50 more times. Check the rock again. Imagine how this rock would look after thousands of years of exposure to blowing sand.

6. Soak five lima beans in water overnight. Fill a clear plastic cup about three-quarters full with potting soil. Plant the bean seeds about 2 cm deep. Water the soil lightly. Mix some plaster of Paris with water and pour a layer about 1 cm deep over the soil. Leave the cup on a shelf and check it each day. What eventually happens to the plaster of Paris?

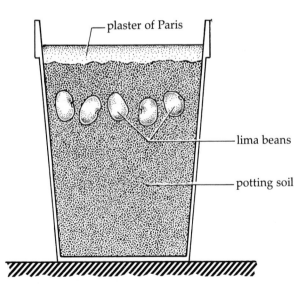

Figure 4–7

OBSERVATIONS

1. Make written notes about your observations at the end of each step.

2. Make sketches of your observations where appropriate.

CONCLUSIONS

What can you conclude about the effects of weathering agents on soil formation?

Discussion questions

1. Why would a fast moving river not be likely to "silt up"? Where would you expect to find the silt?
2. You find a jack pine whose roots are growing down into the cracks of exposed bedrock. What is likely to happen to these cracks as the jack pine continues to grow?
3. State one reason why you might expect to find sandy beaches along the shores of oceans and large lakes.
4. Glacial deposits from the last ice age contain smooth-edged boulders, stones, and gravel as well as sand. What weathering agents probably created these materials?
5. What situations or happenings in nature could cause the kinds of weathering you observed in this investigation?

Section review questions

1. How do scientists believe sand, silt, and clay particles in soil are formed?
2. What is weathering?
3. State four agents of weathering and explain how these agents cause soil to form from rock.
4. Which weathering agent would not be present in tropical areas?
5. Which agent would not contribute to weathering in a desert region?

SCIENCE IN OUR LIVES

Creating humus from organic waste

The sand, silt, and clay that form the foundation of most soils are the result of the weathering of rocks. Without the addition of organic matter, however, these soils would be too infertile to support most species of land plants. Fortunately, most soils contain anywhere from one to six percent of organic matter by volume (much less by mass). This organic matter comes from decaying plant and animal matter. It helps the soil to hold moisture, and, at the same time, allows more air to enter soil pores. Organic matter also acts as an important storehouse of essential plant nutrients.

Before these nutrients can become available to growing plants, organic matter must be decomposed into very fine particles called humus. This action is accomplished by micro-organisms living in the soil. Wise gardeners take advantage of this action by composting their kitchen leftovers, grass clippings, dead plant matter, and other organic wastes to create more humus. Making humus is an excellent way to change organic wastes into a useful, soil-enriching product. Humus

The heat generated in a compost pile kills weed seeds and harmful organisms. Why do you think this is important?

helps to replace much of the organic matter lost to the soil with each harvest.

Composting is usually carried out in a special bin or pit. There are many different designs available for compost piles, but all of them work on the same principle. A layer of organic wastes, about 20 cm thick, is laid down first. Egg shells and leftover vegetables are examples of suitable materials that can be used. A layer of soil about 5 cm thick is then added, followed by another layer of organic waste, another

layer of soil, and so on.

A compost pile is kept moist for a few months and turned occasionally while the decomposition process takes place. Micro-organisms in soil, such as bacteria and fungi, digest the wastes and heat the compost to about 65°C. The heat kills weed seeds and harmful organisms. It also speeds up the creation of humus. The decomposed compost is then spread on gardens and flower beds as a fertilizer rich in nutrients.

4.3 Requirements for plant growth

Plants need more than just sunshine, water, and air. They need a balanced diet of essential nutrients. These nutrients consist of 16 different chemical elements that plants need to grow, to reproduce, and to stay healthy. Of these 16 elements, there are nine that plants need in relatively large quantities. Six of the nine are usually available to plants through the medium of soil. These six elements are nitrogen, phosphorus, potassium, calcium, magnesium, and sulphur.

These leaves are exhibiting nitrogen deficiency.

Potassium helps to keep plants, such as this corn, strong and resistant to disease.

- **Nitrogen** gives plants their dark green colour. Plants grown in soils that cannot supply sufficient amounts of nitrogen exhibit yellowing leaves and extremely stunted growth. Humus, micro-organisms, and well-rotted manure all help to supply nitrogen to plants.

- **Phosphorus** promotes rapid growth in plants and is also important for root, bud, and seed development. Fresh organic matter and certain minerals are good sources of phosphorus. Plants that cannot get enough phosphorus grow and mature slowly. Young leaves may be greyish-green, while older leaves may have reddish and purplish areas.

- **Potassium** builds strength, disease resistance, and improves the quality of plant seeds. Fresh organic matter and several minerals make potassium available to plants. Plants deficient in potassium are stunted. The edges of older leaves typically turn brown and die.

- **Calcium** is needed for the development of healthy cell walls and leaf growth. Calcium is derived from soil minerals. Plants that do not obtain enough calcium may be unable to grow new leaves, stems, and roots.

- **Magnesium** enables plants to make chlorophyll and to carry out other important functions. Magnesium is found in soil minerals. Plants that cannot obtain enough magnesium have difficulty manufacturing food. The leaves of these plants are often yellow with green veins.

- **Sulphur** is important in the composition of plant proteins and hormones. Plants need sulphur to grow new cells. Soil minerals and organic matter are all sources of sulphur.

Plants deficient in sulphur often have yellow veins in their leaves.

The other elements that plants must have in large quantities are hydrogen, carbon, and oxygen. Plants process these three elements into food during photosynthesis. Hydrogen is obtained from the water in soil, while carbon (from carbon dioxide) and oxygen are derived from the air.

The elements plants need in much smaller quantities are often known as the micro-nutrients. There are seven micro-nutrients: boron, copper, iron, manganese, molybdenum, zinc, and chlorine. Most of these elements come from the mineral component of soil.

The leaves on the right are exhibiting boron deficiency.

The role of fertilizers

An ideal soil will supply growing plants with the correct quantities of the nutrients they need. One of the ways farmers try to improve soils lacking in nutrients is to add **fertilizer** to them. Farmers use two types of fertilizer—organic fertilizers and synthetic fertilizers. Organic fertilizers are derived from natural sources. Manure, bonemeal, and compost are examples of organic fertilizers. Manure from goats, sheep, and horses is high in nitrogen. But manure should be aged for at least three months before it is used, because it may be too strong otherwise. Bonemeal contains about 20% phosphorus. It is very slow acting and safe to use. Well-rotted compost is a good source of nitrogen, phosphorous, and sulphur.

Did you know?
Statistics Canada reports that the use of fertilizers on Canadian farms increased by one-third from 1981 to 1986.

Why do you think using too much fertilizer might be harmful to the soil?

Synthetic fertilizers are made from chemicals. They are combined in different ways to supply nutrients in the correct proportions for various crops. Each bag of synthetic fertilizer bears numbers such as 10–20–15. These numbers indicate the fertilizer's percentage of nitrogen, phosphorus, and potassium compounds. Other nutrients that may be present are often listed separately.

Caution: Make sure you check with your teacher and school caretaker before trying this activity.

Try this!

Test the effect of a selected fertilizer on plant growth. Select a grassy area in your schoolyard. Use a hammer, wooden stakes, and string to lay out four 1-m × 1-m squares on the site. Label the squares 1–4. Read the directions on the fertilizer bag. Do not apply fertilizer to Square 1. It will be your control. Use a cup to evenly spread half the recommended

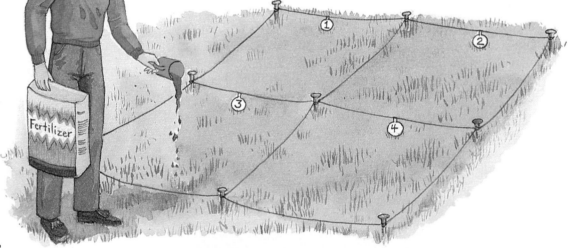

Figure 4–8

Caution: Be sure to wash your hands thoroughly after handling fertilizers. They can irritate your skin, and many fertilizers contain chemicals to control weeds.

amount of fertilizer on Square 2. Spread the recommended amount of fertilizer on Square 3 and twice the recommended amount on Square 4. Water the squares thoroughly. Continue to water the squares regularly to keep the ground moist. Record any changes to the way the grass grows in each of the four squares. Why do you think these changes took place?

Soil types and plant growth

There are many varieties of commercial fertilizers, and each contains a different mixture of nutrients. Commercial fertilizers vary in composition because of the different soil types farmers and gardeners must deal with. Some soils are poor in nutrients, and some soils cannot make nutrients available to plants. Other soils may be rich in several nutrients but deficient in others. The type of soil that plants grow in is just one of the factors that can affect plant growth. You will discover how important soil type is to plant growth in Investigation 3.

Investigation 3   The effect of soil type on plant growth

PURPOSE
To investigate the effects of different soil types on the growth of plants.

Successful gardeners know the correct amount of fertilizer to add to the soil.

MATERIALS
5 plastic flowerpots
  of equal size
clay pot fragments
sandy soil
silty soil
clay soil
organic soil
  (peat moss or leaf mould)
loam
masking tape
marker
package of green bean seeds
  (bush)
paper towels
aluminum tray
tap water
watering can

MEASURING TOOL
ruler

HYPOTHESIS
State in which of the soils you would expect the green bean seeds to grow best and why.

PROCEDURE

1. Place a few clay pot fragments over the holes in the bottom of each plastic flowerpot.

Figure 4–9 What do you think is one of the purposes of the clay pot fragments? What about the drainage holes?

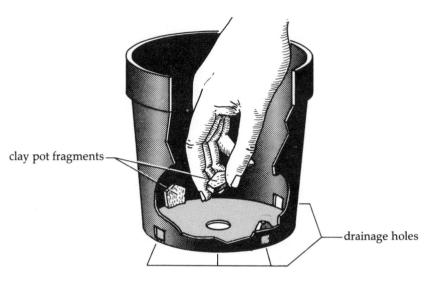

clay pot fragments

drainage holes

2. Fill each pot to within 2 cm of its top with a different soil type.
3. Use the masking tape and marker to label each pot according to its soil type.
4. Wrap 20 green bean seeds in wet paper towels. Keep them moist until they begin to sprout.
5. Moisten the soil in each pot and plant four seeds 1 cm deep in each one.
6. Place the five flowerpots on an aluminum tray in a sunny, warm place. Keep the soil in each pot moist by watering it regularly.

OBSERVATIONS

1. Observe the growth of the green bean plants in each pot over two to three weeks.
2. Measure the heights of the plants and count the number of leaves. Record your observations in a chart like the one on page 195.

Soil Type	Observations After 1 Week		Observations After 2 Weeks		Observations After 3 Weeks	
	Height	Number of Leaves	Height	Number of Leaves	Height	Number of Leaves
Sandy						
Silty						
Clay						
Organic						
Loam						

3. Record any size and colour differences in the leaves of the plants in your notebook.

CONCLUSIONS

Based on your observations, what conclusions can you make about the type of soil that best supports the growth of green bean plants?

Discussion questions

1. Why was it important to control the variables in this investigation? How might your results have been influenced if you had not used controls?
2. Why do you think it was necessary to observe the growth of the green bean plants over a two-to-three week period?
3. What results might you have observed if you had planted the green beans in a soil composed of one-quarter peat moss, one-quarter sand, one-quarter clay, and one-quarter silt? Why?
4. Suppose you wanted to develop and package potting soil. How could you use the results of your investigation to develop an effective product?

How do greenhouses help to make plants grow?

The importance of water and sunlight

Without enough water and sunlight, the plants that you depend on for food would not grow. Plants absorb dissolved nutrients from soil water. They also use this water to manufacture food in the process called photosynthesis. Plants use the food they make to give them energy. This process is called respiration. Photosynthesis cannot take place without the energy green plants absorb from sunlight. You will discover how important water and sunlight are to green plants in Investigation 4.

Investigation 4   Water, sunlight, and plant growth

PURPOSE
To investigate how well plants grow when given different amounts of water and exposed to different amounts of sunlight.

MATERIALS
package of radish seeds
8 small, plastic pots
   of equal size
potting soil
masking tape
marker
4 foam cups
tap water
2 aluminum trays

MEASURING TOOL
10-mL graduated cylinder

HYPOTHESES
State how the growth of radish seedlings will be affected by different amounts of water. State how the growth of radish seedlings will be affected by exposure to different amounts of sunlight.

PROCEDURE

PART A
1. Soak the radish seeds in water for 2 h. Fill the pots with potting soil to within 2 cm of their tops.
2. Plant five radish seeds in each pot and cover them with just enough soil to hide them.

3. Select four of the pots. Use the masking tape and the marker to label them 1 mL, 2 mL, 3 mL, and 4 mL, respectively.
4. Place the plants in an aluminum tray near a window where they will each receive the same amount of sunlight. Every day, use the graduated cylinder to give each pot the exact amount of water stated on its label.

PART B
1. Label the other four pots 2 h, 4 h, 6 h, and 8 h, respectively.
2. Place the pots in an aluminum tray on a window ledge. Water each pot with 4 mL of water and cover it with a foam cup.

Figure 4–10

Figure 4–11

3. Each morning at the same time, remove all four cups and rewater each pot with 4 mL of water.
4. After 2 h, replace the cup over the pot labelled 2 h. Replace the other cups according to the times marked on each pot.

OBSERVATIONS
1. Observe the plants in each test group for two weeks.
2. Make sketches or take photographs to show how the plants in both groups appeared initially, after one week, and at the end of two weeks.

CONCLUSIONS
What can you conclude about how different amounts of

water affect plant growth? What can you conclude about the effect of varying amounts of sunlight on plant growth?

Discussion questions

1. Why do you think it was necessary to use five seeds in each pot and four pots in each group?
2. "Different species of plants have different water requirements." Explain this statement.
3. List one or more plants that grow best where the ground is very damp. What kinds of plants grow best where the soil is very dry? Why?
4. List several plants you believe grow best in the shade. How could you design an experiment to test your hypothesis?

Plant growth and soil pH

When water passes through soil, chemicals and gases in the soil dissolve in the water. Depending on what these chemicals and gases are, these solutions can make the soil **acidic**, **basic**, or **neutral**. (Basic soils are usually referred to as **alkaline** soils.)

Acids are sour-tasting, corrosive substances. Bases can also be corrosive. They have a bitter taste and a slippery feel. When the amount of acid in a soil is matched by an equal amount of base, the soil is said to be neutral.

Most of the plants grown for food grow best in soils that are slightly acidic, slightly alkaline, or neutral. If the soil is too acidic or too alkaline, valuable nutrients needed by plants may be bound up in chemicals that are difficult to dissolve. In fact, knowing how acidic or alkaline a soil is can be used as a good indication of the nutrients a soil will supply, and which nutrients the soil is likely to be lacking.

To test whether soil is acidic or alkaline, a farmer or a gardener can measure the pH of the soil. The pH scale runs from 0 to 14. (See Figure 4–12.) A pH of 0 is highly acidic. A pH of 14 is highly alkaline. A pH of 7 — between 0 and 14 — is neutral. Each whole number on the pH scale differs from the next whole number by a multiplication factor of ten. For

Why is it important for farmers to test the pH levels of the soil?

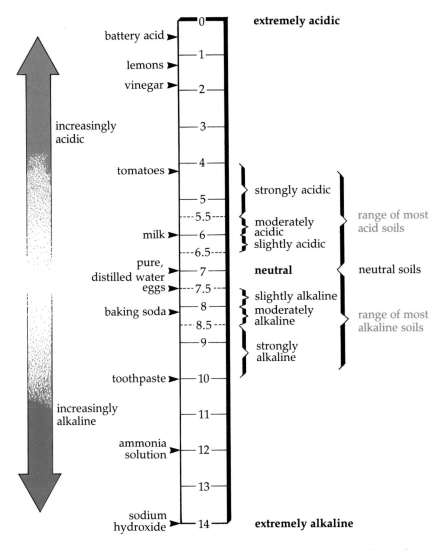

Figure 4–12 The pH of the most productive soils is usually between 6.0 and 7.5.

example, soil with a pH of 8 is ten times more alkaline than a soil with a pH of 7. Can you say how much more acidic a soil with a pH of 5.5 is than one with a pH of 7?

Soil pH can be measured with pH paper. This treated paper will change colour when it is placed in contact with moist soil. The colour of the paper is then compared to a set of colours on a pH scale. Soils that are too acidic can be corrected by adding ground limestone to them. Limestone adds calcium, which you have seen is a major plant nutrient. Soils that are too alkaline can be corrected by adding powdered sulphur.

Caution: Be sure to obtain permission before you remove soil samples.

Try this!

Test different soils to find out which ones are acidic and which ones are alkaline. Purchase some pH papers and a pH scale from a garden centre. Then collect samples of different types of soil after it has rained. Take your samples from locations such as a field, a garden, a wooded area, or the shore of a lake. Place a piece of pH paper firmly in contact with each sample. When the paper turns colour, match it to one of the colours on the pH scale. Which soils do you think would be good to grow plants in? Which would need correction? Why?

Section review questions

1. What are the nine main elements that plants need? Which elements are found in soils?
2. Describe the difference between organic and synthetic fertilizers and state examples of each type of fertilizer.
3. What do the numbers ''10–7–5'' on a bag of fertilizer tell the purchaser? Why are these labels important?
4. Explain some of the effects that soil type has on plant growth?
5. How could a farmer find out if soil is acidic or alkaline? Why are these tests important?
6. Why is sufficient sunlight a requirement for plant growth?

Using fertilizers carefully

In the last century, the best fertilizers people used to help grow their crops were usually organic ones such as manures, bonemeal, and crop residues. These fertilizers were, and still are, good fertilizers, but they do not supply all the nutrients that plants may need. Organic fertilizers are also bulky, hard to store and apply, and often have very strong odours.

In this century, scientists have produced more complete fertilizers synthetically. These fertilizers have overcome many of the disadvantages of organic fertilizers. They can be mixed to correct the deficiencies of individual soils or made super-strength to encourage bumper crops. Synthetic fertilizers do not, however, provide the soil with organic matter and humus.

Farmers and gardeners were quick to use synthetic fertilizers. Their crop yields increased dramatically. When it came time to plant again, they used more fertilizer or switched to better ones.

It was some time before some of the hazards of using these synthetic fertilizers became apparent. Those farmers who had stopped using natural fertilizers found that the organic content of their soils was decreasing. The organic component of a soil is a major factor in its ability to absorb water. Without sufficient water, plants cannot absorb nutrients regardless of their source, nor can they carry out photosynthesis or respiration.

There is a greater possibility of improperly applying or using too much synthetic fertilizer. As a result, soil-nutrient levels can rise and become toxic to plants. Heavy rains wash nutrients that are not used by plants into streams, ponds, and lakes. There they cause an increased growth of aquatic plants such as algae. When these plants die and decay, they use up life-giving oxygen that is dissolved in the water. This oxygen-robbing process, called eutrophication, makes it difficult for fish, snails, frogs, and many other water-dwelling creatures to survive. The water becomes stagnant and unsafe to swim in or to use as a drinking-water source.

Fortunately, many farmers now understand that fertilizers must be used carefully, at the right time and in the right proportions. Many farmers have also returned to the use of organic fertilizers to fulfill at least part of their needs. The result is a healthier environment and better, more reliable crops.

An example of soil layering

4.4 Other characteristics of soils

You already know some of the major characteristics of soils. For example, soil texture can vary depending on the size of mineral particles. Soils are laid down in layers, have different colours, and even different odours. Soils contain varying amounts of air and water, as well as humus, organic matter, and mineral particles. Soils can also be acidic, alkaline, or neutral.

Now you will learn about three other important characteristics of soils. First, soils have different capacities for holding water. Second, they also have different percolation rates, or abilities to allow water to pass through them. Third, soils have different abilities to attract water into their pore spaces, a process known as capillary rise. Each of these three soil characteristics is important to soil fertility, and it is therefore of great interest to agriculturalists. Let's take a closer look at each characteristic.

Water-holding capacity

You probably know that the **water-holding capacity** of a soil is very important. A soil that cannot hold water well will allow rain to quickly drain away after a shower. Little water will be left in the soil's pore spaces to dissolve nutrients that plants can use. Plants also need water for photosynthesis and respiration, and to keep their leaves and stems erect. Plants that cannot absorb enough water for their needs soon wilt. Unless they get more water, they usually die.

Fortunately, there is an easy way to improve a soil's water-holding capacity. As every experienced gardener knows, you simply add organic matter, usually in the form of peat moss or manure. Organic matter holds water much like a sponge. In time, organic matter decays into humus and releases more nutrients for plant growth.

Try this!

Set up a demonstration to show how effective peat moss is

at increasing the water-holding capacity of soil. Begin by rolling up two clear overhead transparency sheets along their
lengths to form tubes. Tape each tube together to make a
waterproof seal. Cover one end of each tube with some light
cloth held in place by an elastic band. Then fill one tube about
three-quarters full with sandy soil. Fill the other tube to the
same height with an equal mixture of sand and moist peat
moss. Punch holes through opposite sides of the top of each

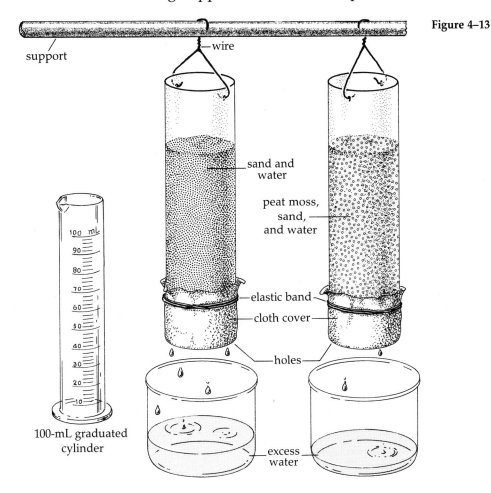

Figure 4–13

support

wire

sand and
water

peat moss,
sand,
and water

elastic band

cloth cover

holes

excess
water

100-mL graduated
cylinder

tube with a large pin. Make hooks out of pieces of wire to
suspend the tubes over empty containers. Use a graduated
cylinder to slowly pour 75 mL of water into the top of each
tube. Wait for 15 min until the water has stopped draining
into the containers. Then use the graduated cylinder to measure the water collected in each container. Record your results
in a chart like the one on page 204.

	Sandy Soil (mL)	Sandy Soil and Peat Moss (mL)
Water Poured into Tube	75 mL	75 mL
Subtract Water Collected in Container	_?_ mL	_?_ mL
Equals Water Held in Soil	_?_ mL	_?_ mL

Did the soil mixture with peat moss hold more water than sandy soil alone? Which soil would be better for growing plants?

Percolation rate

The **percolation rate** of a soil is the rate at which water will pass through the soil as it is pulled by the force of gravity. Rain is of little use to land plants if it is unable to penetrate the soil. If a soil has a low percolation rate, for example, most of the water from a heavy rain will simply flood its surface and run away. A soil with a moderate percolation rate will soak up the water and gradually allow it to percolate down to the deepest plant roots. However, in a soil with a high percolation rate, water will move down through the soil quickly. Most plants will then not be able to absorb enough water before it moves too deep for roots to reach. Can you see why farmers and gardeners prefer soils with moderate percolation rates?

Try this!

Carry out an investigation to see if percolation rates are related to soil types. Clean the two tubes you made for the *Try this!* activity on pages 202–204 and replace their cloth filters. Make a third tube and cover one of its ends with a cloth filter. Fill each tube three-quarters full with a different soil. Use sandy soil in the first tube, clay soil in the second tube, and potting soil (a loam rich in humus) in the third tube. Suspend the three tubes over the containers. Use a graduated cylinder to pour 75 mL of water into each one. Collect the water that percolates out of the tubes in an aluminum tray placed underneath them. Wait 15 min, then discard the water and remove the tray. Place a plastic cup beneath each tube. Pour 30 mL of water into the top of each tube. Measure the time it takes for the water to stop percolating through each soil type into the cups. Compare the percolation times of the three soil types. Which type of soil shows the fastest percolation time and which the slowest? Why do you think it would be necessary to water crops more frequently if they were planted in sand instead of in loam and humus? What could happen to crops growing in clay if it rained frequently?

Figure 4–14

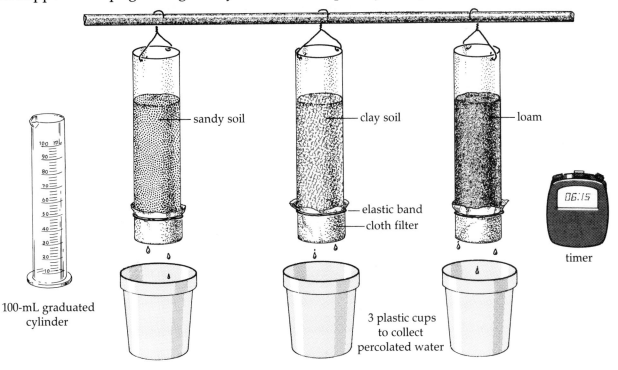

sandy soil

clay soil

loam

elastic band
cloth filter

timer

100-mL graduated
cylinder

3 plastic cups
to collect
percolated water

Capillary rise

Capillary rise is the ability of a soil to pull water into its small pore spaces, and to hold it there against the force of gravity. You can probably find an example of capillary rise right in

Some of the water in this dish will rise in the soil to the plant's roots.

your home. When a potted plant sits in a dish of water, some of the water will enter the hole in the bottom of the pot and rise in the soil, reaching the roots of the plant. The same thing happens in gardens and in farmers' fields. Water must rise in the soil to levels where plant roots can make use of it.

Try this!

Compare how capillary rise works in coarse, medium, and fine soils. Clean and fill the three tubes from the *Try this!* activity on pages 204–205 with sandy, clay, and loam soils, respectively. Then place three equal-sized bowls on a table close to a wall. Break several pencils into short lengths that can be laid flat in the bottom of each bowl. Use two pencil lengths per bowl. Balance each tube on the pencil lengths in each bowl by leaning the top of the tube against the wall. Pour an equal amount of water into each bowl. Observe what

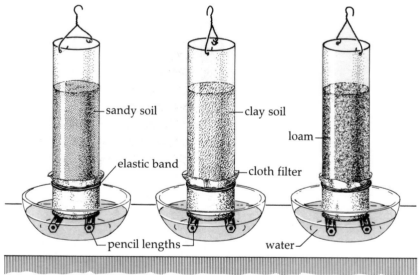

Figure 4–15

happens to the water. Continue to add more water to keep 2 cm or more in the bowls. After 30 min, measure the height to which the water has risen in each tube. Repeat your measurements over the next few days and record your results. Be sure to keep some extra water in the bowls. In which soil did the water rise the highest? In which soil did it rise the least? Why do you think this happened?

Water content

You already know how important water is to the soil plants grow in. The three soil characteristics you have just examined are a few of the factors that affect the overall **water content** of soils. Even soils that feel quite dry have some water content.

Try this!

Clean and dry three empty soup cans of the same size. Be sure to remove their labels. Use a waterproof marker to label cans A, B, and C, respectively. Determine the mass of each can with a balance and record it in your notebook. Collect three different soil samples from locations close to your school or home. Fill each can half-full with one of the samples. Determine the combined mass of each sample and its container. Subtract the mass of each can to calculate the mass of each soil sample. Record these calculations in your notebook. Heat the samples on top of a hot plate set at "medium" or in a 170°C oven for 2 h. Let the samples cool for 15 min, then determine the combined mass of each can and sample again. Subtract the mass of each can to determine the mass of the soil samples alone. What differences do you observe? Was the "dry" sample really dry? Which sample had the highest water content? Explain your answers.

You are now familiar with several of the characteristics of soils and how to determine what these characteristics are. How well do you think you can put these new skills and knowledge to use to discover the characteristics of some unknown soil samples? Will you be able to judge the suitability of each soil for gardening and farming? You will find out in Investigation 5.

Caution: Be sure to obtain permission before you remove soil samples.

Caution: Use oven mitts or tongs to remove your samples from the hot plate or the oven. Be sure each sample has cooled before you attempt to redetermine its mass. Be sure to turn off the hot plate or the oven when you have finished the activity.

Investigation 5 Determining the characteristics of unknown soil samples

PURPOSE
To test your skills in assessing the characteristics of unknown soil samples.

MATERIALS
4 soil samples
white paper
tap water
magnifying glass or
  microscope
spoon
plastic cups
clear transparency sheets
Scotch tape
cloth
elastic bands
wire
scoop
soup cans
bowls
pencils
scissors

MEASURING TOOLS
pH paper and pH scale
graduated cylinder
balance

Caution: *Be sure to wash your hands after testing the soil sample.*

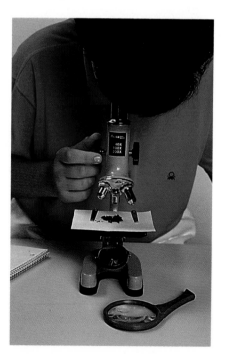

PROCEDURE

1. Ask your teacher to divide the class into four groups.
2. Your teacher will supply each group with an unknown soil sample. Place the sample on a sheet of white paper.
3. Determine the texture of the soil in the sample. Is it like sand (gritty), silt (smooth), clay (slippery), or loam (a combination)? To find out, place a small amount of the sample in your hand, mix it with some water, and rub it between your fingers. Discuss your findings with the others in your group.
4. Use the magnifying glass or the microscope to examine the size of the soil particles in each sample. Based on what you see, infer whether the amount of pore space in each sample is low, medium, or high.
5. Describe the colour of the soil in each sample as either dark, moderately dark, light-coloured, and so on.
6. Place four spoonfuls of the sample in a plastic cup half-full of water. Place the palm of one hand over the top of the cup and shake it. After 15 min, check for any floating organic material. In your experience, do you think this amount of organic content is high, medium, or low?
7. Use pH paper and a pH scale to determine whether the sample is acidic, alkaline, or neutral.

8. Select items from the materials list to design and conduct an investigation to test the water-holding capacity of the soil sample. (See the *Try this!* activity on pages 202–204.) Decide whether the water-holding capacity of your sample is low, medium, or high in each case.

9. Design and conduct an experiment to test the percolation rate of the soil sample. (See the *Try this!* activity on pages 204–205.) Decide whether the soil's percolation rate is low, medium, or high in each case.

10. Test the ability of the soil sample to attract water through capillary rise. Design and conduct your own investigation. (See the *Try this!* activity on page 206.) Decide whether the capillary rise of your sample is low, medium, or high.

11. Determine the water content of your sample. (See the *Try this!* activity on page 207.)

OBSERVATIONS

1. Record the observations of your group in a chart like the one below.

Soil Characteristic	Group # _____ Soil Sample
Texture	
Pore Space	
Colour	
Organic Content	
pH Level	
Water-holding Capacity	
Percolation Rate	
Capillary Rise	
Water Content	

2. Make a chart on the chalkboard to compare the findings of all four groups.

CONCLUSIONS
Based on your observations, what can you conclude would be the best soil for plant growth?

Discussion questions

1. Explain why pore spaces in soil are so important?
2. Describe the colour and texture of a good garden soil.
3. Which variables did you have to control to test the water-holding capacity of your soil? Which variables did you have to control to test the percolation rate of your soil?
4. If you had a garden with the poorest of the soils your class tested, what could you do to improve the quality of the soil?
5. Which unknown soil would you want in the fields of a farm you were planning to buy? Why?

Section review questions

1. What is meant by the water-holding capacity of a soil? Why is it important to plant growth?
2. What is meant by percolation rate and capillary rise? Why are these soil characteristics important to plant growth?
3. List five other soil characteristics that are important to plant growth. Explain why each characteristic is important.
4. What type of soil would have a good water-holding capacity, a high percolation rate, and would exhibit good capillary rise?
5. What kind of percolation rate would you expect a heavy clay soil to have?

SCIENCE IN OUR LIVES

Soil characteristics, climates, and crops

Why are grains like wheat and barley grown primarily in the prairie provinces? Why aren't the great forests of northern Ontario and Québec cleared for farms? Why is Prince Edward Island renowned for its potatoes. And why does the Niagara region of Ontario produce so much fruit?

The answers to these questions are related to the soil characteristics of each region. Farmers know that certain plants grow better in some soils than they do in others. They also know that climate plays an important role in deciding which crops will grow best in their region.

Small grains like wheat and barley are adapted to neutral to alkaline clay soils. These crops grow best where the summers are short, hot, and fairly dry. As a result, they are well suited to the prairies where many other plants do not grow well. Similarly, the vast spruce and fir forests of northern Ontario and Québec are adapted to acidic, organic soils with great water-holding capacities. Cranberries also grow well in these regions. Farm crops would not tolerate the soils northern forest plants grow in. They would also be unable to endure the cool summers and frigid winters of these areas. Potatoes, although tolerant of a wide variety of soil and climate conditions, thrive in the loamy, well-drained soils of Prince Edward Island. The moderate tempera-

tures and long daylight hours during the summer in Prince Edward Island also contribute to their growth. The Niagara region of Ontario, like similar regions in the Annapolis and Okanagan valleys of Nova Scotia and British Columbia, respectively, has fairly long summers and soils rich in minerals. These two factors suit the Niagara region to the cultivation of tender fruits such as peaches and grapes.

As you can see, successful farming is not a hit-and-miss operation. It requires careful consideration of the characteristics of the soil of a region and the climate conditions that exist in that region.

Why do you think these crops wouldn't grow in the same region?

Slugs live in the soil.

Plants supply organic material to the soil when they decompose.

The leaves of this plant have been damaged by larvae.

4.5 Soil communities

Fertile soil is the home of many living organisms such as plants, algae, fungi, bacteria, and small animals. Some of the animals found in soil are large enough to see. But others are so small they can only be seen with a magnifying glass or a microscope. The larger animals include small mammals such as mice, groundhogs, moles, rabbits, and chipmunks that burrow in the ground. Smaller animals include ants, beetles, millipedes, centipedes, spiders, mites, slugs, snails, and earthworms. Very small organisms that require a microscope to observe them are nematodes, protozoa, and rotifers.

Soil, with all its living and non-living parts, is a balanced ecosystem containing producers, consumers, and decomposers. The producers are plants because they supply organic matter to the soil when they decompose. Consumers include organisms such as insects, worms, and spiders that prey on other animals and protists. Other consumers, such as nematodes, are organisms that consume plant roots. The wastes of these organisms are broken down into smaller particles by decomposers such as bacteria, other protists, and fungi. Decomposers also break down the bodies of organisms when they die.

The number and variety of living organisms in a soil depends on how much organic matter and humus the soil contains, on the amount and size of the soil pores, and on the soil pH.

Soil organisms improve soils in many ways. Tunnels made by worms and burrowing animals open up soils so that air and water can pass more freely through them. Other animals help to mix the organic matter with the mineral matter of soils. Decaying organisms and their wastes contribute to the amount of humus in soils, making the soils more fertile. Certain bacteria and plant roots add nitrogen.

Sometimes, however, too many of certain kinds of soil organisms can harm crops. For example, slugs, larvae, beetles, and rodents may chew on and damage vegetables before they are harvested. Plant diseases can be caused by organisms such as insects, bacteria, and fungi. To fight them, farmers and gardeners often spray their plants with pesticides or fungicides. In so doing, they may not realize that

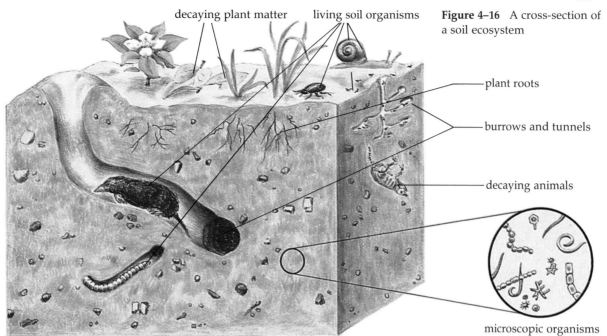

decaying plant matter   living soil organisms

Figure 4–16 A cross-section of a soil ecosystem

plant roots

burrows and tunnels

decaying animals

microscopic organisms

they may kill a broader range of organisms than they mean to. This can seriously upset the balance of the soil community. In order to maintain this balance, these chemical compounds must be used sparingly and only when needed.

In Investigation 6, you will examine the soil communities of two different soils. Do you think different soils will affect the kind and quantity of living things you find?

Did you know?
The amount of land subjected to pesticide spraying increased 50% between 1981 and 1985.

Investigation 6   Observing soil communities

PURPOSE
To discover how different soils affect the makeup of soil communities.

MATERIALS
spade or shovel
2 large, plastic bags
large sheet of white paper
    (about 1 m × 1 m)
popsicle sticks
5 or 6 small jars
plastic sandwich bags

MEASURING TOOL
ruler

HYPOTHESIS
State whether you would expect to find greater numbers and varieties of living organisms in soil taken from a garden or from soil taken from a ravine.

PROCEDURE

PART A

1. With a partner, obtain a sample of topsoil from a garden, about 30 cm on a side and 8 cm deep. Place it carefully in one of the large, plastic bags.
2. Empty the sample onto the large sheet of paper. Note as many of the soil's characteristics as you can, then break it apart.
3. Use the popsicle sticks to look for organisms of all kinds. Place them in separate jars or in plastic sandwich bags. Look for organisms such as worms, ants, snails, spiders, millipedes, larvae, and different kinds of plants. You may also find eggs of certain insects. Count the number of each type of organism that you find.

Be sure to obtain permission before you remove soil samples.

Figure 4–17

4. When you have completed Part A, return your soil sample to its original location.

PART B
1. With your partner, obtain a soil sample from a ravine. Place it in the other large, plastic bag.
2. Repeat Steps 2–4 in Part A.

OBSERVATIONS
1. Record your observations of Part A in a chart like the one below.

Characteristics of Garden Soil		Type and Number of Organisms
Texture		• weeds, 5
Pore Space		• black ants, 14
Colour		
Organic Content		
pH	• acidic	
Water-holding Capacity	• high	
Percolation Rate	• fast	
Capillary Rise		
Water Content		

2. Record your observations of Part B in a chart like the one below.

Characteristics of Garden Soil	Type and Number of Organisms
Texture	• dandelions, 3
Pore Space	• earthworms, 8
Colour	

Organic Content		
pH		
Water-holding Capacity		
Percolation Rate		
Capillary Rise	• small	
Water Content	• medium	

CONCLUSIONS
Which soil type supported more types of living organisms? Why?

Discussion questions

1. How do the characteristics of a soil appear to affect the amount of life it can support?
2. Does the amount of animal life in a soil appear to have any relationship to the amount of plant life in that soil? What can you infer about this relationship?
3. What might happen to the plant life in garden soil if all the animal life in the soil disappeared? How would the soil's characteristics change in time?

The earthworm: An important soil organism

The earthworm is a living soil fertilizer. It processes soil, living micro-organisms, and decaying organic matter. The earthworm processes what it can of this material, then excretes the rest in lumps of smooth, enriched soil. The soil that passes through an earthworm is much richer than the original soil swallowed by the worm. In fact, this soil has been found to contain five times more nitrogen, eleven times more potash, seven times more phosphorus, three times more magnesium, and 40% more humus. Can you think of other reasons why earthworms make soils more fertile? Fer-

Earthworms enrich the soil.

tile soils are capable of supporting more crops. Earthworms are very important members of soil communities.

Try this!

Have you ever thought of building a worm farm? To build one, find an old plastic dishpan about 50 cm long, 30 cm wide, and 15 cm deep. With a nail and hammer make 40–50 holes in the bottom of the pan to let out excess water and to help aerate the soil. Cover the bottom of the pan with a layer of small stones, then with a layer of dry grass clippings about 3 cm thick. Now you are ready to collect the soil and the worms. Take your pan and a spade to a shaded spot where there is dark, moist soil containing lots of humus. This could be in a garden or on the edge of a woods. Fill the pan to within 3 cm of its top with soil and worms. Based on what you have learned in this chapter, design several experiments to test the

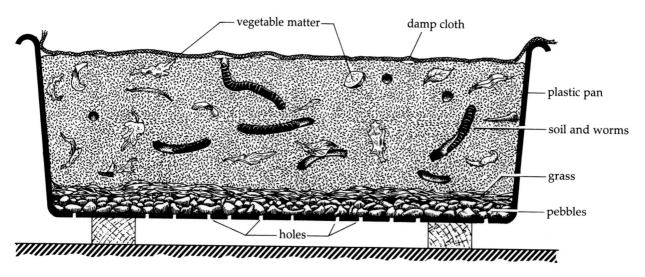

Figure 4–18

quality of the soil. In the top layer of soil, mix in some leaves, potato peelings, or other discarded vegetable parts. Cover your worm farm with a damp cloth and store it in the shade

Be sure to obtain permission before you remove any soil. Remember to return the soil to its original location.

on two pieces of wood so that air can get under it. To feed your worms, sprinkle a little cornmeal and potting soil on top of the farm about once a week. Remember to keep the soil damp but not too wet. After three weeks, note any differences you see in the soil. Repeat your soil tests to determine if the quality of the soil has changed. Suggest reasons for your results.

Section review questions

1. List several examples of the types of organisms that live in soil.
2. What does it mean when a soil community is said to be a balanced ecosystem?
3. Explain how too many of certain kinds of organisms can harm crops.
4. Where would you probably find a soil that exhibits much plant and animal life?
5. A certain soil is very alkaline, has a very high percolation rate, a low water-holding capacity, and a coarse, gritty texture with large pores. Explain why you would or would not be likely to find many plants, animals, and other organisms living in this soil.
6. How is an earthworm like a living soil fertilizer?

4.6 Soil conservation

Soil, water, air, and sunlight are the physical things green plant life requires. All life depends on them indirectly. We have harnessed these resources through farms to supply ourselves with a constant, varied, and steady source of food.

Maintaining plentiful supplies of food depends on our willingness to conserve and protect the soil. Soil management, therefore, is an important responsibility for farmers. The major objectives of soil management are to increase the organic content of soil, to maintain soil fertility, and to protect soil from being carried away by wind and water, a process known as soil **erosion**. These objectives can be achieved by properly tilling the soil, by choosing the right crops and planting them at the right time, and by controlling soil moisture through drainage and irrigation.

Field irrigation

Contour ploughing

Tilling means to plough or break up the soil. To properly till sloping land, farmers plough around hills, rather than up and down them. This method of ploughing is called **contour ploughing** because it follows the contours of the land. Contour ploughing makes it difficult for water to run straight down the slopes and form gullies by washing away valuable topsoil. Where the land is steeply sloped, it can sometimes be formed into a series of terraces. More land can then be planted, while the terraces catch and hold water to help prevent erosion.

Did you know?
Along with the Okanagan Valley in British Columbia, the Niagara Peninsula supplies most of Canada's peaches, grapes, cherries, and other tender fruits. From 1981 to 1986, the Niagara Peninsula lost 6% of farmland that was available in 1981 to development.

An experienced farmer also knows when to till and how often. Too much tilling breaks down the soil into very fine pieces. In this state, the soil can be blown or washed away easily. Soil that is broken down too much can also be easily compacted, thereby losing valuable pore space. A properly tilled soil has small, uneven chunks and contains a large amount of dead plant matter. Proper tilling increases both the amount of pore space in a soil and its percolation rate. It also helps to reduce soil erosion and to increase the soil's organic content.

The type of crop grown, and how it is sown and cared for, is also important to good soil management. For example, it is poor farming practice to plant row crops, such as corn and soybeans, on the same fields continuously. These crops have few roots to hold the soil together, and the dead plant matter they produce is more difficult to break down than that of other crops. A better practice is to alternate these crops with forage plants such as hay for horses and cattle. Forage plants offer better protection against erosion, and they break down more quickly to release nutrients into the soil. The practice of alternating crops every few years is known as **crop rotation**.

Another way farmers try to prevent soil erosion is by planting rows of trees between their fields. These trees act as windbreaks. As a result, the wind is less likely to blow topsoil across large open areas.

Drainage and irrigation methods are used to carry away excess water or to provide water to dry lands. Both methods help to maintain soil fertility and to reduce the risks of erosion from wind and too much rain.

Terraced rice paddies

Investigation 7   Reducing erosion

PURPOSE
To investigate whether plant growth is effective in reducing
erosion.

MATERIALS   MEASURING TOOL
2 long pans or lengths of   metre stick
   plastic eavestrough
garden soil
grass sod
paring knife
6 books of equal size
2 baking dishes
tap water
watering can
plastic drop sheet
2 large sheets of construction
   paper

HYPOTHESIS
State how you believe plant growth helps to reduce erosion.

PROCEDURE

PART A
1. Place a layer of garden soil 4 cm deep in each of the two
   long pans or lengths of plastic eavestrough.
2. Completely cover the soil in one pan with some grass sod
   cut to fit it.

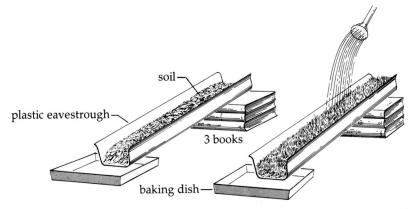

Figure 4–19

3. Support one end of each pan on three books. Place a baking dish under the lower end of each pan.
4. Fill the watering can and pour its contents rapidly down the length of one pan. (This procedure simulates stream erosion.) Repeat the procedure in the second pan. Note what happened to the soil in each pan.

PART B

1. Lay a plastic drop sheet on the floor to test whether plant growth reduces splash erosion. (Splash erosion is caused by raindrops dislodging soil particles as the rain strikes the soil's surface.)

Figure 4–20

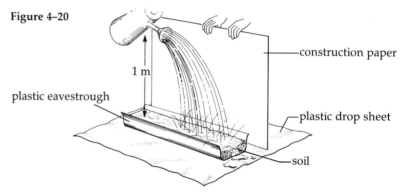

construction paper

1 m

plastic eavestrough

plastic drop sheet

soil

2. Place the pan containing the bare soil along the centre of the plastic sheet. Ask a partner to support a large sheet of construction paper so it hangs beside the pan as shown in Figure 4–20.
3. Fill the watering can and sprinkle water from a height of 1 m onto the soil in the tray. Observe what happens to the construction paper.
4. Ask your partner to support the second sheet of construction paper while you replace the pan holding the bare soil with the pan containing the sod.
5. Sprinkle water on the sod-covered soil. Observe the construction paper and compare the amount of splash erosion produced with the amount you observed in Step 3.

OBSERVATIONS

1. Record your observations for Part A, Step 4 in your notebook.
2. Record your observations for Part B, Steps 3–5 in your notebook.

CONCLUSIONS
What can you conclude about the effect of plant growth on
erosion?

Discussion questions

1. Why should farmers be concerned about soil erosion?
2. When would farmers be most likely to experience the
   worst threats from erosion?
3. Describe how you could test whether plant growth is
   effective against wind erosion.
4. Think of an example where the techniques of soil conservation learned about in this investigation could be applied
   in a real situation.

Try this!

Find out how conservation authorities in your region are
involved in preventing and controlling erosion and flooding.
Investigate the use of dams and flood-control gates on creeks
and rivers. Examine maps of your area and identify major
watersheds, farms, parks, and other developments along
creeks and rivers. How could these areas be adversely
affected by erosion and flooding? What steps are being taken
to prevent erosion and flooding from occurring? Write a
report about how important the work of conservation authorities is.

A flood-control gate

Section review questions

1. What are three major objectives of a good soil management program?
2. What are three ways of achieving proper soil
   management?
3. What is meant by a) soil erosion, b) contour ploughing, c)
   terracing, and d) tilling of soil?
4. Are there ways, other than by erosion, that soil can be
   damaged? Explain your answer.

Donald Lobb

Donald Lobb operates a farm near Clinton, Ontario. Some time ago, he and his neighbours began shifting their farming operations into high-return row crops such as corn. Before long, they began to see evidence of soil erosion and soil degradation. The entire area was affected. On his own farm, Donald Lobb saw grooves cut by running water and washouts. During a period of 12 years between 1970 and 1982, about 25 cm of topsoil was transported to the bottom of a sloping field in a watershed on his farm.

The economic significance of this kind of erosion was brought home by the decline in crop yields from the tops of small hills and slopes where most of the erosion was occurring. Unfortunately, much of the valuable topsoil on Lobb's land was going into municipal drainage ditches. The yield losses were not caused by a lack of phosphorus and potash, as shown by soil tests, but by the loss of humus and organic matter from the eroded locations.

Lobb decided that he needed to practice a more vigorous soil conservation program. He rearranged his fields across slopes wherever he could, and he created natural water drain-

Donald Lobb learned how to control this kind of soil erosion.

age paths of grass and legumes. He also developed a modified terrace system, and he planted windbreaks on the edges of the terraces and fields to intercept the winds. He reforested land unsuited to farming and began a four-year crop rotation program. Now he grows corn for two years on the same plot of land, followed by one year of soybeans, and one year of cereal grains (winter wheat or barley). The residues of these plants help to return organic matter to the soil. In addition, Lobb has reduced the amount of tilling he does.

Years after he began to make these changes, Lobb is encour-

aged by the results he sees. Many of his erosion problems are under control. The amount of organic matter in previously eroded locations is slowly returning to normal. Despite these improvements, Lobb continues to strive to find even better methods to conserve his soil.

SCIENCE IN SOCIETY

Should we use agricultural land for urban development?

Soil is an important resource in all countries. The need to produce food for human consumption is universal. In Canada, agriculture is big business. However, in many regions there is competition for valuable agricultural land. New industries need locations to build factories and warehouses. They also need roads to link them to other businesses. People who work in these factories and warehouses need homes and services such as gas stations, hospitals, and shopping facilities.

In many Canadian communities, urban and industrial development is spreading over some of the land with the best soil for agriculture. For example, land use in Peel County in Ontario has shifted dramatically from agriculture to urban development in past decades. The following case study represents a hypothetical situation in a community experiencing urban growth.

An industrial developer wants to purchase a large tract of farmland from four farmers. The farmers, who have struggled to make ends meet because of rising production costs and low prices for their products, have agreed to sell

the land. They see that the land, because it is on the fringe of a rapidly growing community, is more valuable than the crops they can grow from the rich soil.

The developer must obtain approval from the municipal government to build the roads and the warehouses. City officials want this development because it will increase the municipality's tax revenues and will attract new citizens to their community. Other landowners in the area are also supportive because the development will increase the value of their property. Their land will probably be bought by other developers who will build homes, apartments, gas stations, and shopping centres.

The land to be developed has rich soil and has produced crops of a high yield for over 100 years.

Explore the issue

Lobbying is used by groups who want to influence the decisions of government bodies. Divide your class into three groups. Group 1 will represent the developer and the farmers who want to sell their land. Group 2 will represent a lobby group from the agricultural sector who want to reduce the amount of land being absorbed by the growth of the community. Group 3 will represent the municipal officials who will have to determine the weight of each argument and make a decision. Groups 1 and 2 will organize their position and nominate a spokesperson. Group 3 will formulate a list of questions to pursue. Groups 1 and 2 will present a brief summary of their position through their spokesperson. Group 3 will ask questions of these groups. Group 3 will also consider the merits of the two points of view and prepare to make a decision. Groups 1 and 2 will prepare their final argument and present it to Group 3. Group 3 will make a decision.

Meet Roger Brant

Roger is a farmer who lives on the Mohawks of the Bay of Quinte reserve near Belleville, Ontario, where he farms 284 ha of land. One of three full-time farmers on the reserve, Roger raises about 80 head of dairy and beef cattle, and grows cash crops as well. He is also the secretary treasurer of the Indian Agricultural Program of Ontario, which helps other native people to become farmers.

Q. Did you study at an agricultural college?
A. No. I studied to become an electrician at Loyalist College in Belleville, Ontario.

Q. What was the most difficult part about starting to farm?
A. It's very difficult for native people to get financing, and this is one reason why I became involved with the Indian Agricultural Program of Ontario. I finally managed on my own to get money, but I'm hoping this program will help my boys and other native people who want to go into agriculture.

Q. Was there much to learn about agriculture?
A. I learned everything the hard way because I hadn't been to agricultural college. My land is very low and the soil is heavy clay. For years, I was working it whenever I had time. I finally found out that you have to work land only when it's ready.

Q. What problems did you have with the soil?
A. Because I was working the soil when I should have left it alone, it was being pressed when it was damp, and this causes compaction. I could see my crop production going down even though I was fertilizing and spraying weeds.

Q. What did you do to solve the problem?
A. I started going to seminars put on by the Ontario Ministry of Agriculture and Food. I learned about drainage and discovered some of the things I was doing wrong. I had been putting my best crops on the same fields, and this was adding to compaction and soil breakdown.

Q. Were you able to improve the soil?
A. Yes. I did some tiling for drainage. These are 10-cm perforated plastic tiles that are put in the ground every 13.5 m across a field. The tiles drain to an outlet in a lower area. They were expensive to install, but worth it because once the moisture was removed, I didn't get compaction and the soil improved about 100%.

Q. What other improvements did you make?
A. I started crop rotation, which also made a big difference. The crops grew much better under this system than they did when I planted them in the same field.

Q. Do you think young people should go to agricultural college before becoming farmers?
A. Oh, yes. I would have been much further ahead if I had taken time off and gone to study for a few years. It's a big field now. But it's not just farming. There are so many other aspects and so much to know.

Q. What do you hope for the future for other native people?
A. We have a land base that is little used on our reserves, and I hope through the Indian Agricultural Program we can promote more agriculture on native lands.

Chapter review

Words to know

Write a brief definition for each of the terms listed below. The location of these terms is indicated by the section number in the brackets.

- capillary rise (*Section 4.4*)
- clay (*Section 4.1*)
- erosion (*Section 4.6*)
- fertilizer (*Section 4.3*)
- humus (*Section 4.1*)
- loam (*Section 4.1*)
- percolation rate (*Section 4.4*)
- sand (*Section 4.1*)
- silt (*Section 4.1*)
- soil (*Section 4.1*)
- soil texture (*Section 4.1*)
- subsoil (*Section 4.1*)
- topsoil (*Section 4.1*)
- water content (*Section 4.4*)
- water-holding capacity (*Section 4.4*)

Questions

A. Indicate whether each of the following statements is true or false. Explain why the ''false'' statements are not true.

1. Soil is composed of mineral particles, organic matter, water, and air.
2. Soil is only used by growing plants.
3. Subsoil is very fertile.
4. Weathering is nature's way of making soil from rock.
5. Plants need only sunshine, moisture, and air to grow.
6. The more fertilizer you give to a plant, the better it will grow.
7. All garbage can be composted in a compost pile.
8. Most of the plants that are grown for food prefer slightly acidic or neutral soils.
9. Forage crops like hay are used in crop rotation.
10. Capillary rise occurs when a soil rises above ground level.

B. Choose the best answer for each of the following.

1. You can improve the water-holding capacity of soil by
   a) watering it more often
   b) adding more sand to it
   c) packing it down
   d) adding humus

2. If the percolation rate of soil is too high, it will
   a) start to drip
   b) leave little water available to plants
   c) leave too much water available to plants
   d) turn the soil alkaline
3. One way to improve the water-holding capacity of a soil is to
   a) add fertilizer
   b) add organic matter
   c) till it repeatedly
   d) plant corn in it for several years
4. A soil community is
   a) all the plants living in soil
   b) disturbed by too much noise
   c) a place where everyone gathers to talk about soil
   d) all the living organisms present in soil
5. Erosion can be reduced by
   a) increased ploughing
   b) planting trees for windbreaks
   c) planting soy beans and other row crops
   d) ploughing down slopes
6. Too much tilling is harmful because
   a) it encourages erosion
   b) it kills earthworms
   c) it breaks up rocks
   d) it is hard on seedlings
7. The pH of a soil can be affected by
   a) adding earthworms to it
   b) breaking or loosening it
   c) adding limestone to it
   d) testing its nutrient levels
8. The numbers on a bag of synthetic fertilizer indicate the percentage of
   a) nitrogen, phosphorus, and potassium compounds
   b) loam, phosphorus, and sulphur compounds
   c) nitrogen, potting soil, and phosphorus compounds
   d) nitrogen, magnesium, and phosphorus compounds

9. If you always keep the soil of a plant very wet, it will
   a) cause the plant to grow much faster
   b) have little room for air in the pores
   c) mean the plant will need more sunlight
   d) encourage more worms to grow
10. If you own a farm with good soil
   a) you will never have to add fertilizer
   b) you can till it as much and whenever you want
   c) you can grow any crop you want
   d) you must still follow a good soil-management program

C. Write full answers to each of the following.
1. Describe five characteristics of fertile soil.
2. List four ways topsoil differs from subsoil. Describe how topsoil and subsoil affect the growth of plants.
3. Suppose you want to develop a good, productive vegetable garden, but find that your soil is all sand. What could you do to make it into a fertile loam?
4. Describe how large and small animals contribute to the formation of soil.
5. Describe several of the methods farmers can use to conserve their soil.
6. Draw and label a diagram to show how soil is composed.
7. Explain how you would compare the water-holding capacity of two soil samples. How is the soil's ability to hold water related to its fertility?
8. What tilling methods can farmers use to protect against erosion?
9. Explain how to make compost. How can this product be used to improve the quality of soil?

Science challenge

1. "Environments are balanced systems best left alone. Tampering with one component, or living thing, in an environment often harms other components, or living things, in that environment." Explain the meaning of these statements as they relate to soil. Support your explanations with examples.

2. Hydroponics is a method of growing plants without soil. The plants grow in a liquid solution containing nutrients normally found in topsoil. Research more about hydroponics. Use your library and contact the Ministry of Agriculture to find out how greenhouse operators use hydroponics today. What crops are they growing, and where are these crops marketed? How many people are employed by hydroponic farming? What promises does this farming technique hold for the future?

Science project

1. Design an experiment to test which organic matter is best for starting seedlings of various vegetables—peat moss, humus, compost, or leaf mould.

2. Devise an automatic watering system for plants that will keep them moist, but not too wet or too dry.

3. Experiment with different methods to find out how to make a sample of subsoil more fertile.

4. Build a model of a properly managed farm. Use a piece of chipboard approximately 30 cm × 60 cm as a base. Assign a different set of soil characteristics to each field, and state how it would be managed in notes accompanying your model. Be sure to show how each field would be contour ploughed, and how crop rotations would be used.

Heat and Temperature

"What a blizzard!" said Sara, stomping into the ski chalet. "The forecast called for low temperatures, but no one predicted this."

While Raoul and Charlene lit wood in the fireplace, everyone rubbed their hands together and blew on their fingers. "You know," said Darren, shivering, "we could be here all night."

"Then let's jam some rags around the doors and windows," suggested Stephanie, "or we'll lose all our heat through the gaps."

"Here, let me help you," said Jerri, grabbing the poker. "Ow! Why is this thing so hot?"

"And why does my face feel so hot while my back feels frozen?" asked Brad.

"I've got a better question," said Raoul. "Why is Jerri blowing on her fingers?"

"You're right, Raoul. That *does* seem strange. A few minutes ago we were blowing on our fingers to warm them. Now I'm blowing on them to cool them off. Makes you wonder what heat is."

You will find out in this chapter.

In what ways do you think these children are keeping or producing heat to stay warm?

5.1 What is heat?

Canadians spend a lot of effort and large amounts of money on heat. Because of our climate, we have become experts at finding ways to produce heat. In winter, we try to keep heat inside our clothing and homes. In summer, we try to lose it. We cool our car engines all year long to prevent overheating. Understanding the scientific nature of heat could save us both money and trouble.

Heat has always been important, but its nature mystified scholars for a long time. Around 400 B.C., Aristotle, a Greek philosopher and scientist, thought that heat was a combination of fire and air. Even though there was no scientific evidence for this idea, it lasted for two thousand years.

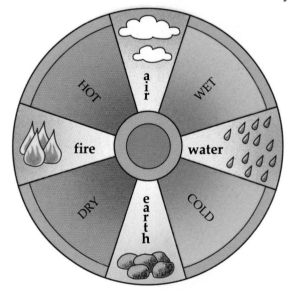

Figure 5–1 Aristotle thought fire was a substance like earth, water, and air. He said that hot, wet, dry, and cold were produced by combining these four ''substances.''

The first heat experiments began in the 1600s. At that time, scientists noticed that heat seemed to flow from hot objects to cold ones. The Caloric Theory was developed from their observations. It stated that heat was an invisible fluid called caloric. Scientists of that time thought caloric caused heat conduction in a fire poker. When a poker was held in a fire, they thought caloric flowed through it into the handle. When the poker was removed, they thought caloric flowed out again.

 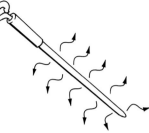

Heating: caloric flows in   Cooling: caloric flows out

Figure 5–2 The early Caloric Theory of heat assumed that heat was like an invisible fluid.

In science, theories are used to explain what has been observed and to make predictions. A valid theory can be used to explain observations of natural occurrences. But the Caloric Theory could not explain why hands become warm when they are rubbed together. And careful measurements showed that heating a poker did not change its mass. Some scientists said this was because the caloric fluid had no mass. Others began to doubt that heat was a kind of matter.

In those days, scientists did not realize that heat is a form of energy. By 1800, however, many researchers used a scientific approach to investigate heat. Eventually, the Caloric Theory had to be discarded because it could not explain their findings. Instead, the results seemed to show that heat was related to motion.

Safety check

Here are a few safety rules to keep in mind while doing the investigations in this chapter.
1. Heating devices, such as alcohol burners, are to be used only on flat, horizontal surfaces.
2. During open-flame experiments, a multi-purpose fire extinguisher and a fire blanket should be available.
3. Safety glasses must be worn when heating any substance. Loose hair and clothing must be tied back.
4. Alcohol must be kept in approved containers and stored outside the classroom in a safe storage area.
5. Take precautions to avoid burns when hot containers and liquids are being handled.

6. Be careful when handling glass beakers, flasks, and test tubes. If you do break something, use a dustpan and a whisk to sweep up the broken pieces. Do not use your hands.

Investigation 1   Investigating heat and motion

Caution: Be careful not to scald yourself when you pour hot water from the kettle into the beaker.

PROBLEM
Will hot water or cold water show more evidence of motion?

MATERIALS
2 beakers   eyedropper
electric kettle   food colouring
tap water

HYPOTHESIS
State the difference(s) you expect to observe when drops of food colouring are added to hot water and to cold water.

PROCEDURE
1. Fill one beaker half-full with hot water from the kettle. Pour an equal amount of cold water into the second beaker.
2. Holding the eyedropper about 1 cm above each liquid, add two drops of food colouring to each beaker.

OBSERVATIONS
1. Observe the beakers for 5 min. Record what you see in each beaker.

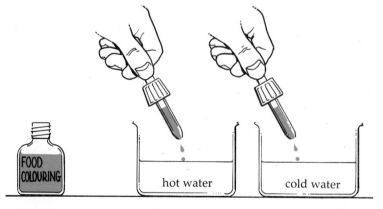

Figure 5–3

2. Record any differences you see between the fluids in the beakers.

CONCLUSIONS

What can you conclude about heat and motion based on your observations?

Discussion questions

1. What past experiences helped you to make an accurate prediction about the outcome of this investigation?
2. Describe how hot water must differ from cold water to account for your observations.
3. Can you make a generalization about heat and motion based on your conclusions?
4. Does your generalization suggest how heat is conducted through a poker? Explain your answer.
5. Does your generalization suggest why your hands warm up when you rub them together? Explain your answer.

Heat and molecular motion

After 1800, scientists carried out many heat experiments with solids, liquids, and gases. Their findings helped to develop the modern **Kinetic Molecular Theory**.

1. All substances are made of tiny particles called molecules.
2. The molecules are in constant motion. The energy they possess because of this motion is called **kinetic energy**.
3. Heating a substance speeds up the molecules. This increases their kinetic energy.

According to the Kinetic Molecular Theory, heat is a form of energy produced by molecular motion. This theory can help you to understand the effects of **heat energy**. For example, the Kinetic Molecular Theory can explain what happens when a poker is placed in a fire.

At room temperature, the molecules of a solid iron poker vibrate only slightly. When the poker is inserted into a fire, the molecules nearest to the flames begin to vibrate more rapidly. That is, their kinetic energy increases. As the molecules bump into each other, they pass kinetic energy from

Figure 5–4 The Kinetic Molecular Theory states that heat energy is produced by molecular motion.

one molecule to the next until all the molecules are vibrating more rapidly. This explains how heat energy is conducted along the poker.

The Kinetic Molecular Theory can also explain why rubbing your hands together warms them up. Rubbing forces molecules in your skin to move faster. This increases their kinetic energy. The extra molecular motion adds heat energy to your hands.

Try this!

Imagine if you could go back 200 years in a time machine. To scientists of that time, you would be an expert on heat and energy. Imagine the questions they might ask you. Write down three you think they would probably ask. Try to answer these questions in a way that could relate to their experiences and that they could understand. (Researching what it was like to live 200 years ago might help you to develop questions scientists of that time might ask.)

Section review questions

1. Write a definition for heat according to
   a) Aristotle's ideas
   b) the Caloric Theory
   c) the Kinetic Molecular Theory
2. Which of the above definitions is still accepted today? Explain why the others are not accepted now.
3. Use the Kinetic Molecular Theory to explain what you think will happen to a red-hot poker when it is thrust into water.
4. What do you think will happen to the molecular motion in the water as a result of the hot poker being thrust into it?

Count Rumford

Count Rumford (1753–1814) was an unusual thinker for his time. As an engineer, he applied pure science to solve practical problems such as designing the first double boiler. As a scientist, he also looked for clues to the nature of things in everyday situations.

Rumford was born Benjamin Thompson in Massachusetts while it was still under British rule. After the American Revolution, he fled to England and helped to found an important scientific society there. Rumford was made a count by the ruler of Bavaria, where he went to help reorganize the army.

Rumford became skeptical of the Caloric Theory while supervising the production of weapons. Again and again, he observed great heat building up as the bore of a brass cannon was drilled out. Red-hot chips of metal flew into the air, and the drill bit generated steam when doused with water.

Rumford was not satisfied with the explanation that caloric fluid was coming to the surface of the brass from within. He saw a strong connection between movement and heat. In his words, "It appears to me to be extremely difficult, if not quite impossi-

ble, to form any distinct idea of anything capable of being excited and communicated, in the manner that Heat was excited and communicated in

these experiments, except it be Motion."

Rumford's belief that heat is related to motion was shown to be correct.

5.2 Sources of heat

Heat cannot be created or destroyed. It can only be produced by converting some other form of energy. This section will examine five sources of heat: chemical energy, mechanical energy, electric energy, radiant energy, and nuclear energy. All of these heat sources can be used to heat a substance by increasing the speed of the molecules.

Chemical energy

When a piece of coal burns, the carbon in it combines with oxygen in the air. This chemical reaction produces carbon dioxide gas. At the same time, it converts the chemical energy stored in the carbon to heat energy.

Many other fuels may be burned to provide heat for homes and industry. Some examples are oil, natural gas, wood, and dried vegetation or animal matter. Fuels are chosen according to their chemical-energy content, cost, and convenience. Regardless of the kind of fuel that is used, burning a fuel always requires an oxygen supply and some form of starting energy such as heat from a match.

Chemical energy is also the source of heat for your body. Heat is produced when oxygen combines with sugar molecules from your food. If you overeat, the excess chemical energy from the sugar will be stored in fat molecules.

All of the above examples produce wanted heat. But chemical energy may be the source of unwanted heat. For example, some of the chemical energy stored in a flashlight cell is converted to heat. This wastes the energy meant to produce light.

Why is a burning match an example of heat energy?

Try this!

Many buildings burn down every year as a result of spontaneous combustion. This means that fires start burning by themselves, without being purposely lit. In barns, spontaneous combustion usually starts just after fresh hay is stored. To find out how this can happen, obtain a garbage bag full of fresh grass clippings. Spread half of the clippings out on newspaper, and seal the rest in the bag with a twist tie. On the next day, carefully plunge your hand into both samples. How could your observations explain how spontaneous combustion occurs in barns? What advice would you give a farmer about how to store a tonne of fresh hay without allowing it to dry out?

Spontaneous combustion also occurs in cities. Interview a firefighter, garage mechanic, or the janitor of a large building. Ask them what materials are most likely to cause this problem, and what steps can be taken to prevent spontaneous combustion from occurring. Write a report on your findings.

Mechanical energy

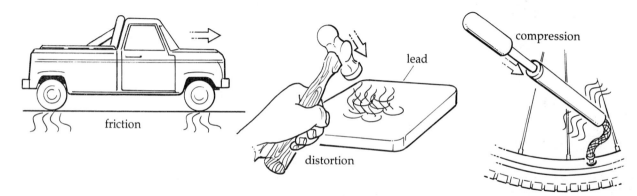

Mechanical energy is the total kinetic and potential energy in a moveable object. Three types of force can be used to convert mechanical energy into heat—friction, compression, and distortion. Of the three, friction is the most common.

Figure 5–5 Mechanical or kinetic energy can be converted to heat as a result of friction, compression, and distortion.

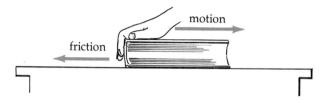
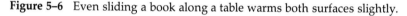

Figure 5–6 Even sliding a book along a table warms both surfaces slightly.

Friction is a force that acts like a brake on most moving bodies. Friction is caused when two surfaces rub against each other. This speeds up the surface molecules, increasing their

How is this girl reducing friction?

Pumping air into a bicycle tire is an example of compression.

kinetic energy, causing both surfaces to become hotter. Suppose that a basketball player trips and then slides across a gym floor. If the player slides to the right, the force of friction acts to the left, slowing his motion. Gradually, friction converts the player's mechanical energy into heat, so that both the player and the gym floor are warmed slightly.

Friction in moving systems can be a problem. First, it wastes mechanical energy meant to make objects move. For example, friction between the tires of a car and the road acts to slow the car down. Second, friction wears out moving parts, such as car tires, so that they must be replaced. Third, friction produces unwanted heat, which can cause serious damage. Car tires that are worn thin from use and warmed up by friction can actually burst from overheating.

But friction can be helpful, too. For example, car brakes depend on friction to bring the car to a safe stop. Sand scattered on icy roadways improves traction by increasing friction. Friction also enables you to pick up your pen, walk to the store, and hold onto your lunch bag.

Try this!

Rub your hands together for 1 min. Then wet your hands with water and rub them together again. Compare the heat produced by friction when your hands were dry and when they were wet. Now try lubricating your hands with substances that are safe for the skin such as vegetable oil or hand lotion. Which substance was most effective at reducing friction?

Machine parts are often lubricated with oil or grease made from petroleum. Can you think of two fuels made from petroleum? What effect do you think using petroleum to produce lubricants has on the supplies available for fuel?

A force of **compression** acts to squeeze matter into a smaller space. Only gases can be compressed to a noticeable extent. The gas becomes warmer as a result of the compression. This is what happens when air is pumped into a car tire. As more and more air is forced into the tire, the temperature inside of it increases.

Figure 5–7 Only a small percentage of the chemical energy from fuel is used by the car in the form of mechanical energy. The rest escapes as heat.

A force of **distortion** causes objects to change their shape. But distortion also produces heat. For example, you can heat up a piece of soft iron by hitting it rapidly and repeatedly with a hammer. The mechanical energy of the moving hammer is converted into heat. The iron becomes so warm that it can be reshaped. Little heat is generated by hammering a piece of steel, however. Steel is so hard that the hammer bounces off of it with hardly any conversion of mechanical energy into heat.

Except to reshape metals, mechanical energy is not usually used as a source of heat. Chemical energy from a fuel is much more practical for most needs. But heat from mechanical energy is very important because society is so dependent on machines. All machines waste some of their mechanical energy by converting it into unwanted heat. In a car, for example, friction in the engine wears out parts and generates heat. This wastes energy that is meant to make the car move. There is no practical way to make use of this heat produced by friction. Much of the energy used in Canada to operate machines is wasted in the form of unwanted heat as the result of friction.

Investigation 2 Sources of heat

PURPOSE
To investigate and identify sources of heat.

MATERIALS
2 wooden sticks
bicycle pump
bicycle tire

MEASURING TOOL
thermometer

paper clip
matches
candle
small bowl
petroleum jelly
disposable cup
cold tap water
spoon
plaster of Paris
disposable stirring stick
safety glasses

PROCEDURE

1. Rub the two wooden sticks together several times. Press them hard as you rub them together. (Feel the rubbed parts with your hands before and after you rub them together.)

2. Pump up a bicycle tire with a bicycle pump. (Feel the tire and the barrel of the pump before and after you pump up the tire.)

3. Quickly bend a paper clip in the same spot. (Feel the point of bending with your fingers before and after you bend the paper clip.)

4. Put on your safety glasses. With your teacher's permission, light a candle and drip a few drops of wax into the bottom of the bowl. Blow out the candle. Press the base of the candle into the pool of wax. Allow the wax to harden and light the candle again.

5. Hold your hand for a few seconds about 10 cm above the flame. Then hold your hand 10 cm to the side of the candle. Repeat this step at distances of 5 cm and 20 cm.

Caution: Only light the candle with your teacher's permission. Make sure the bowl holding the candle is on a level surface. Tie back long hair and keep your clothes away from the flame. Be sure that you don't move your fingers any closer to the flame than you are asked to in Step 5.

Figure 5–8

6. Smear the bottom half of the thermometer with petroleum jelly.
7. Place three or four heaping spoonfuls of plaster of Paris into the disposable cup. Pour two spoonfuls of water into the cup and stir the plaster.
8. Immediately insert the thermometer. Read the temperature every minute until the plaster hardens. (Rotate the thermometer frequently to keep it from sticking.)

OBSERVATIONS
1. Describe any temperature change you observed in Steps 1–3.
2. Record what you observed when you held your hand at various distances away from the flame.
3. Make a chart to record the temperature readings you took while the plaster of Paris hardened.

CONCLUSIONS
What can you conclude about the sources of heat you examined in this investigation?

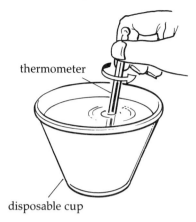

thermometer

disposable cup

Figure 5–9

Discussion questions

1. In which step(s) was mechanical energy used as a heat source? In each case, state the force that converted mechanical energy into heat.
2. In which step(s) was chemical energy used as a heat source? In which case(s) was chemical energy converted into heat by burning? Identify the steps where a different type of chemical reaction occurred.
3. Why do you think that people who drive in remote areas often keep candles and matches in their cars?
4. Which heat source is more practical for heating a building — mechanical energy or chemical energy? Why is one more practical than the other?

Electric energy

Electric energy is widely used as a source of heat for domestic purposes. In the kitchen, it is used to operate toasters, ket-

Do all of these appliances produce heat? Which ones produce more heat than the others? Why?

tles, and stoves. Appliances like these contain heating coils made of materials that resist electric current. As the current moves along, it forces the molecules in the coil to vibrate back and forth faster. The stronger the current, the faster the vibrations and the hotter the element becomes.

Electric energy is often used as a heat source for homes. Baseboard heaters may be installed around exterior walls, and heating coils are sometimes built into walls and ceilings. With electric heating, each room can have its own thermostat, so no energy is wasted by heating unused rooms.

Even when electricity is used for some other purpose, such as running a washing machine, some heat is produced. Scientists and engineers are constantly looking for ways to reduce the production of this unwanted heat, which wastes electric energy needed for other purposes.

Try this!

Find out which kind of lighting unit wastes more electricity. Obtain a lamp with a fluorescent tube and one with an ordinary incandescent bulb. Make sure that the tube and the bulb have the same power rating. For example, both might be rated at 40 W. Turn both lamps on at the same time and allow them to warm up for 5 min. Hold your hand 20 cm away from each lighting unit. Which unit produces more heat? Which one must be producing more light? Which unit do you think wastes more electricity by converting energy into heat instead of light?

Radiant energy

All hot objects give off **radiant energy** in wavelike rays. When you stand near a wood-burning stove, radiant energy causes the molecules in your skin to speed up. As the kinetic energy of these molecules increases, your skin feels warmer. The sun's rays warm your skin and the Earth's surface in a similar way. In fact, radiant energy from the sun is our most important source of heat.

Radiant energy can also be used for other purposes. Many calculators have solar cells that convert radiant energy into electricity. Presently, solar batteries are too expensive to use in large devices. However, the Earth receives so much radiant energy from the sun that scientists in many countries are looking for cheaper ways to collect and convert solar radiation.

A solar-heated house

Try this!

Usually, heat from the sun's rays is too weak for purposes such as cooking. With a little help, however, the sun's radiant energy can be used as a source of intense heat. To see how, place a match on a dry piece of wood. (Be sure to wear safety glasses for this activity.) Use a magnifying glass to focus the sun's rays on the head of the match. What causes the match to ignite? What is the function of the magnifying glass? Do some research to discover which planets receive more intense solar radiation than the sun. How could you use energy from the sun to cook a hot dog? Design a procedure you could follow.

Nuclear energy

Where does the sun get its energy? At one time, scientists believed that the sun was a ball of burning gas. Now they realize that the sun's energy is produced by nuclear fusion. In this type of nuclear reaction, four atoms of hydrogen fuse together to produce one atom of helium. This new atom has slightly less mass than the combined masses of the four

The sun's energy is produced by nuclear fusion.

hydrogen atoms. The small amount of mass that disappears during fusion is converted into energy. The heat produced by just one fusion is enormous. If you imagine a continuous series of millions of hydrogen fusions, then you will understand how much energy it takes to power the sun. The sun's energy is radiated in all directions into space, and the Earth receives a minute amount of this energy.

Nuclear energy can also be produced on Earth by nuclear fission. This type of nuclear reaction causes atoms to split apart and to release a great deal of heat energy. Nuclear energy produced by fission is becoming increasingly important as a source of heat. Hundreds of nuclear power plants have been built throughout the world. There are several nuclear power generating facilities in Canada. They use the reliable CANDU reactor. In fact, about 50% of Ontario's electricity is generated by nuclear power facilities such as the one in Pickering. There are many different types of nuclear plants, but they all generate heat from nuclear reactions. The heat is then used to produce steam to drive turbines that generate electricity.

While heat from nuclear reactions is an efficient way to generate electric energy, there are some people who feel it is too dangerous. Public protests have halted some nuclear projects and delayed others. Many protesters are worried about the danger of radiation leaks, and about the long-term effects of radiation on humans. A second problem is how to store or dispose of the waste from nuclear plants. Nuclear waste remains dangerous for thousands of years. A third problem is how to avoid heat pollution of nearby lakes and rivers. Hot water coming from the reactors' cooling systems can damage plant and animal life in bodies of water.

The Pickering nuclear generating station

Try this!

Today, Canadians obtain most of their heat from chemical energy by burning coal, oil, and natural gas. Many scientists think that these non-renewable energy resources will be gone within 200 years. As these fuels are depleted, we will have to develop techniques to make better use of alternative energy sources. Doing so would also make available fuel sup-

What alternative energy sources do you see in these photographs? Which one do you think is in greater danger of depletion if it is not properly managed? Why?

plies last longer. Look carefully at the photographs on this page. What alternative energy sources can you find? Read about one of these energy sources. Then write a one-page report on it.

Section review questions

1. List five forms of energy that can be converted into heat. Draw a diagram showing an example of how each is used.
2. Which forms of energy are practical heat sources for home use? Explain why the others are not.
3. State an example in which a form of energy produces a great deal of waste heat. Explain why it is called waste heat, and why it is a problem.
4. Fuels such as oil, natural gas, and coal are often burned to heat homes. Why are scientists and engineers trying to develop alternative energy sources?
5. Use the Kinetic Molecular Theory to explain what happens when radiant energy from the sun heats a pond.

Using nuclear energy

Canadians, particularly in Ontario, receive a large percentage of their electricity from nuclear power stations such as the one in Pickering. Nuclear energy is a source of power that is relatively inexpensive. It is also cleaner than burning coal and oil. However, nuclear energy can be very dangerous. Its use requires very sophisticated and expensive technologies. As a result, Canadian scientists and technologists have developed the CANDU nuclear reactor. The CANDU reactor has proven to be very reliable and safe to operate.

What is a nuclear power plant? Essentially, it is a device that transfers the heat generated in a controlled nuclear reaction to a series of high-speed turbines that turn electromagnets in an electric generator. A nuclear power plant uses the same scientific principles to generate electricity as a hydroelectric or thermal-electric facility. The major difference is the original source of energy. Hydroelectric plants rely on the energy produced by falling water. Thermal-electric plants rely on the heat energy produced by burning fossil fuels such as coal or oil. Nuclear facilities rely on the energy released when atoms are split. This process is called nuclear fission.

A section of the CANDU reactor

The electric energy from a nuclear power facility is produced by electric generators that are driven by steam turbines. A nuclear power facility is a complex system. It consists of devices that control and contain a nuclear reaction, and pipes that transfer heated water for the nuclear reactor to the steam-driven turbines. The nuclear reaction that occurs in the reactor vessel generates a tremendous amount of heat. This heat is transferred to a special kind of water, which is called heavy water, that moves through the pipes. This super-heated water produces steam when it leaves the pipes and expands rapidly in a steam chamber. This high-pressure steam passes over the blades of a turbine causing them to spin. These turbines are connected to the electric generators that actually produce the electricity.

The nuclear reactors in nuclear power facilities are designed to meet the most rigorous safety standards in Canada. These reactors are designed to contain and control the nuclear chain reaction of uranium. An uncontrolled nuclear chain reaction would produce too much heat. In fact, it would melt the reactor. At Chernobyl, in the Soviet Union, the control mechanisms of the nuclear reactor failed and the reactor overheated causing a meltdown. When this happened, radioactive waste that would normally be contained in the reactor escaped into the atmosphere. The results were disastrous.

Many people are concerned about the use of nuclear energy. They feel the potential danger from a reactor meltdown outweighs the economic benefits of nuclear power. Scientists and technicians, however, maintain that nuclear energy is a safe source of power in Canada.

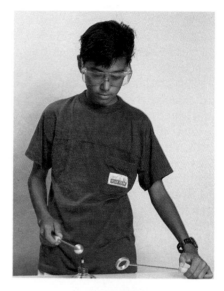

5.3 Heat and changes in volume

Have you ever noticed that construction workers leave spaces between slabs of concrete when they pour them? Do you know why these spaces are important? Investigation 3 will help you to find out.

Investigation 3   The effect of heat on the volume of a solid

PROBLEM
How does heat affect the volume of a solid substance?

MATERIALS
metal ball and ring   cold tap water
bimetallic strip   pail
alcohol burner   safety glasses
matches

HYPOTHESIS
State what will happen to a solid when it is heated and then cooled.

PROCEDURE
1. Try to pass the ball through the ring when the metals are cold.
2. Put on your safety glasses. Light the burner with your teacher's permission.
3. Heat the ball by holding it over the flame for about 1 min.
4. Try to pass the heated ball through the ring.
5. Cool the ball in a pail of cold water. Repeat Step 4.
6. Heat the bimetallic strip over the flame. Observe what happens.
7. Cool the strip in the pail of cold water. Observe what happens.

OBSERVATIONS
1. Draw diagrams to show how heating and cooling affected both the ball and ring and the bimetallic strip. Label the diagrams.

2. Record your observations of Steps 3–7 under each diagram.

CONCLUSIONS
What can you conclude about the effect of heat on the volumes of solid substances?

Discussion questions

1. What would you expect to happen if
   a) you tried to pass a heated ball through a heated ring?
   b) you tried to pass a cold ball through a heated ring?
   c) you tried to pass a heated ball through a cold ring?
2. A bimetallic strip is made by joining two metals—yellow brass and silvery invar. Based on your observations, which metal expanded more when it was heated, brass or invar? How do you know this?
3. Figure 5–10 shows how a bimetallic strip acts as a thermostat to control a bulb connected to a battery. Explain how it works.

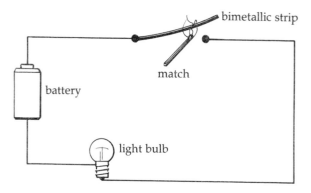

Figure 5–10

Why solids expand and contract

Now you know why construction crews leave spaces between slabs of concrete when they are building bridges, roads, and sidewalks. Without these spaces, the slabs would buckle and break on hot summer days. In winter, cracks form as the concrete contracts. Almost all materials expand when

Why would this sidewalk buckle if there were no spaces between the concrete slabs?

Figure 5–11 The molecules of a solid are held together by forces acting like springs.

heated and contract when cooled. Remembering the Kinetic Molecular Theory will help you to understand why. According to this model, all matter is composed of molecules that are in continuous motion. As a substance is heated, its molecules move faster and bump into each other more often. This makes the molecules spread farther apart, so that the substance expands. However, the molecules themselves do not enlarge, only the spaces between the molecules grow bigger. The opposite occurs when a substance cools.

It is helpful to imagine that the vibrating molecules of a solid are joined by springs. As the solid is heated, the springs stretch and the solid expands. This effect is often called thermal expansion.

Did you know?
Despite lubrication, friction in car engines still produces enough heat to expand metal parts and prevent smooth movement. For this reason, most engines are cooled by a liquid that carries excess heat to the car's radiator where it escapes harmlessly. If the car is driven too hard, however, the liquid could expand and spill out of the radiator. Overflow tubes or containers are connected to radiators to give the fluid more room to expand.

Investigation 4   The effect of heat on the volumes of liquids

PROBLEM
How does heat affect the volumes of different liquids?

MATERIALS
2 large test tubes
2 one-hole stoppers with
   narrow glass tubing
   already inserted
1000-mL beaker or juice
   can
elastic band
tap water at room
   temperature
ethyl alcohol at room
   temperature

MEASURING TOOLS
thermometer
timer

narrow strips of masking
   tape
electric kettle
ice cubes

HYPOTHESIS
State what will happen to different liquids when they are
heated and cooled.

PROCEDURE
1. Fill one test tube with tap water. Fill the other test tube
   with ethyl alcohol.
2. Make the liquid levels in both pieces of tubing the same
   by applying slight pressure to the stoppers. Mark this
   level on both pieces of tubing with strips of masking tape.
3. Put an elastic band around the two test tubes to hold them
   together. Stand the tubes in the beaker. (See Figure 5–12.)

Caution: Alcohol is both poisonous and flammable. Keep it away from sparks, heat, and open flame. Make sure the room you are working in is well ventilated. Avoid breathing the fumes from the alcohol. Keep it away from your mouth and eyes.

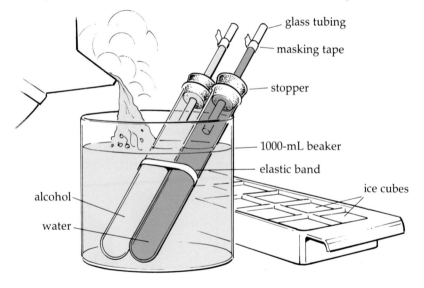

glass tubing

masking tape

stopper

1000-mL beaker

elastic band

ice cubes

alcohol

water

Figure 5–12

4. Pour hot water from the kettle into the beaker until the
   tubes are about three-quarters submerged. Observe what
   happens to the levels of the alcohol and the water.
5. Wait 3 min. Then mark the new liquid levels on both
   pieces of tubing with additional strips of masking tape.
6. Drop ice cubes into the beaker. Wait 3 min. Then observe
   what happens.

Caution: Be careful not to scald yourself when you pour hot water from the kettle into the beaker.

OBSERVATIONS
1. Record what happened when hot water was poured into the beaker.
2. Record what happened when ice cubes were placed into the beaker.

CONCLUSIONS
What can you conclude about the effect of heat on the volumes of different liquids?

Discussion questions

1. Do all liquids expand to the same extent when they are heated?
2. Thermometers contain either liquid mercury or alcohol. Why do you think the level of the liquid goes up or down?

Why liquids expand and contract

If a liquid is heated long enough over high heat, it will start to boil. Until the liquid begins to boil, however, it simply expands. Heat speeds up the molecules in a liquid causing them to spread out. But liquid molecules are farther apart than solid molecules, and the forces that hold liquid molecules together are much weaker. As a result, liquids expand much more than solids.

Heat speeds up the molecules in a liquid causing it to expand.

If a liquid is heated in a wide-mouthed container, the change in volume might be hard to observe. For example, microwaving soup in a wide-mouthed container does not seem to make the soup expand (unless it is allowed to boil). If the container has a narrow neck, however, any change in volume is easily seen.

This is why demonstrations showing how heat affects liquids are done so that all the expansion takes place in a narrow tube. This is also why beverage companies leave space at the top of a soft-drink bottle. Leaving space allows the liquid to expand without forcing the cap off the bottle. Why do you think knowing how much a liquid expands when it is heated is important to manufacturers?

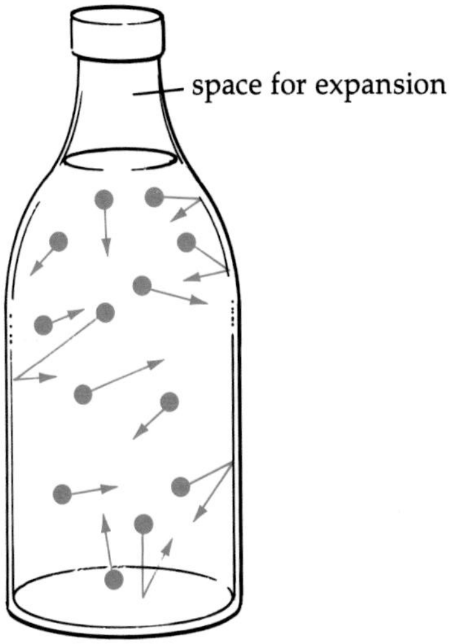

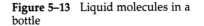
space for expansion

Figure 5–13 Liquid molecules in a bottle

Try this!

Most liquids contract when they are cooled. When liquids freeze, their solid form has a smaller volume. There is one liquid that is an exception to this rule. To understand why, fill a small bottle to the top with water and then put the cap back on. Tie the bottle inside a plastic bag and put it in a freezer overnight. Draw a diagram to show what you see the next morning. Does water contract or expand when it freezes? Why is it important to know how much water expands or contracts when it freezes? What type of bottle should be used to prevent water from breaking it in cold weather if the water freezes? Why should a manufacturer be concerned about glass bottles in cold climates?

Investigation 5   The effect of heat on the volume of
                   a gas

PURPOSE
To demonstrate what happens when a gas is heated and cooled.

MATERIALS   MEASURING TOOL
small flask or soft-drink   thermometer
   bottle
balloon
1000-mL beaker or juice can

tap water
electric kettle

PROCEDURE
1. Fit the uninflated balloon over the open end of the flask.
2. Fill the beaker one-third full with hot water.
3. Grasp the flask by its neck and lower it into the beaker. Hold it there for 1 min.
4. Lift the flask out and allow it to cool.

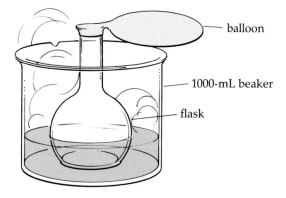

Figure 5–14

OBSERVATIONS
1. Draw diagrams to illustrate the appearance of the balloon a) before heating, b) after heating, and c) after cooling.
2. Record your observations under each diagram.

CONCLUSIONS
What can you conclude about the effect of heat on the volume of a gas?

Discussion questions

1. Make a general statement describing what happens to a gas when it is heated. Use the Kinetic Molecular Theory to explain why.
2. What happens to a gas when it is cooled?
3. Why do you think that cakes shrink after they are removed from an oven?
4. Which expands most when it is heated — a gas, a liquid, or a solid? Which expands least?

Why gases expand and contract

Solids, liquids, and gases all expand when heated for the same reason. Heat energy increases the kinetic energy of the molecules, which speed up and spread out. But the molecules of a gas are even farther apart than those of a liquid and move much faster. This explains why the expansion of gases is much more noticeable than the expansion of liquids or solids. The large gaps between gas molecules make it possible to compress a gas by forcing it into a smaller space such as in a tire or a balloon.

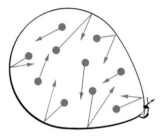

Figure 5–15 Gas molecules in a balloon

Why do you think hot-air balloons rise above the Earth's surface?

The gas in a balloon will expand if it is exposed to increased temperature, so an inflated balloon may burst if you leave it near a window in a constant stream of sunlight. The heat makes the gas molecules in the balloon move faster and push harder on the balloon's walls. The balloon expands and may burst.

Section review questions

1. When telephone wires are put up in the summer, they are allowed to sag a little. Use the Kinetic Molecular Theory to explain why.
2. Why do you think a blacksmith heats the iron rim for a wooden wheel before putting it on the wheel?
3. If a metal lid on a glass jar is stuck, how could you free it?
4. Why do engineers place one end of a bridge on rollers?
5. Concrete and steel have almost the same rate of thermal expansion. Explain briefly why this is important in the construction of tall buildings.
6. Suppose a friend is filling two containers, one with water and one with alcohol. Based on what you know about these two liquids, what should your friend do before tightening the caps? Explain why.
7. A hot-air balloon that is aloft in the sky suddenly moves into the shadow of a cloud. What happens?

5.4 Heat and changes in temperature

Your exhaled breath feels warm on fingers that have just handled ice. The same breath feels cool on fingers that have just picked up a hot poker. Using your senses to estimate how hot or cold something is can be misleading. But you can avoid this problem by using a thermometer. Most common thermometers are made of glass and contain a liquid such as alcohol. They measure temperature in units called degrees Celsius (°C).

Investigation 6   Investigating a liquid-in-glass
                                thermometer

PURPOSE
To investigate the design and operation of a liquid-in-glass thermometer.

MATERIALS   MEASURING TOOL
beaker   thermometer
cold tap water
broken thermometer with fire-polished end (for teacher
    demonstration)
hair

PROCEDURE
1. Examine the scale on your thermometer. Note the lowest and highest temperatures that it can measure. Note how many degrees Celsius can be measured by the whole scale and by one division on the scale.
2. Read the temperature of the room by observing the liquid level when the bulb is held in the air. Record your observations in a chart.
3. Lower the thermometer into a beaker of cold tap water. Observe how quickly the liquid responds to the change. Observe how quickly it comes to rest. Record the temperature of the tap water.
4. Hold the bulb of the thermometer in your hand. Observe how quickly the liquid responds and comes to rest. Record the temperature.

Caution: Be careful when handling thermometers. They break easily, especially at the bulb where the glass is thinnest.

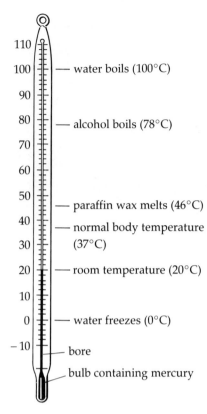

Figure 5–16   A mercury thermometer

Remember that it is important to repeat your experiments and to average your results. Doing so ensures the accuracy of your observations and the validity of your results.

5. Observe while your teacher tries to insert a hair into the bore of the broken thermometer.

OBSERVATIONS
1. Use Figure 5–16 to help you sketch your thermometer. Label the bulb, the bore, and the liquid inside. (The bore is the tube the liquid expands into.)
2. Record your observations in a chart like the one below.

Thermometer Reading	Individual Results (°C)	Class Average (°C)
Temperature of Room		
Temperature of Cold Water		
Temperature of Hand		

3. Record temperature readings for each step from each student on the chalkboard.
4. Determine a class average for each reading and record it in your chart.
5. Record what you observed when your teacher tried to insert a hair into the broken thermometer.

Discussion questions

1. Use the Kinetic Molecular Theory to explain how a liquid-in-glass thermometer works.
2. Describe the actual thickness of a thermometer bore. Explain why the column of liquid in the bore seems so much wider than it really is.
3. Why do you think the bore of a thermometer is made so much smaller than its bulb?
4. Did everyone in the class record approximately the same

temperature for the air in the room, the cold tap water, and their hands? Explain why or why not.
5. If you were measuring the air temperature outside, what variables might affect the measurement?

Temperature and thermometers

You have seen that **thermometers** are instruments that are used to measure temperature. And temperature is another name for heat intensity. Thermometers cannot measure heat energy itself. Most thermometers work on the principle that substances expand when they are heated and contract when they are cooled. There are three main types of thermometers: liquid-in-glass thermometers, gas thermometers, and metal thermometers.

Liquid-in-glass thermometers

Liquid-in-glass thermometers have been steadily improved since they came into use 100 years ago. Early mercury thermometers were large and clumsy compared with ones used today. Mercury has several properties that make it suitable for use in thermometers. Mercury expands about seven times as much as glass does when it is heated the same amount. Mercury also expands uniformly over a wide range of temperatures. Mercury does not stick to glass, has a high boiling point, and a low freezing point.

Look at Figure 5–16 to see how a mercury-in-glass thermometer is constructed. The bulb is made of very thin glass, which allows the mercury inside to respond quickly to surrounding temperatures. The bore the mercury expands into from the bulb is very fine. The narrowness of the bore makes even the slightest expansion of the mercury noticeable.

All thermometers have numbered scales. To calibrate a mercury thermometer, the manufacturer first immerses it in a bath of crushed ice and water. The mercury level falls and the stem is marked where the liquid settles. This point is 0°C. Then the bulb of the thermometer is held in steam from boiling water and the mercury expands. When the mercury expands to its highest point, a mark is made that indicates 100°C. The space between the two temperature indicators is then divided into 100 equal parts. Because they are marked

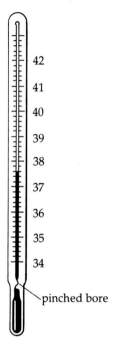

pinched bore

Figure 5–17 A clinical thermometer

in first, 0°C and 100°C are usually called the fixed points.

The scale on a clinical thermometer ranges from 34°C to 42°C. This extremely short mercury thermometer is used by doctors and nurses to measure body temperature. Normal body temperature is about 37.2°C. A reading much higher or lower could be a sign of serious illness, so clinical thermometers are designed to give accurate readings. The bore is pinched just above the bulb. This prevents the mercury column from falling as soon as the thermometer is removed from the patient's mouth. A clinical thermometer must be shaken vigorously to return the mercury to the bulb after a reading has been taken.

Alcohol thermometers work on the same principle as mercury thermometers. Red or blue colouring is usually added to make the alcohol easy to see. Alcohol is cheaper and safer to use than mercury. Another advantage of alcohol is that it can be used at temperatures as low as −114°C, while mercury freezes at −39°C. However, alcohol thermometers can cause problems for measuring very high temperatures. Because alcohol thermometers can contain different kinds of alcohol, and the boiling points of these alcohols range between 78°C and 110°C, alcohol thermometers will burst at these temperatures. Mercury thermometers are better for use in high temperatures, because mercury does not boil until it reaches 357°C.

Another disadvantage of alcohol is that it does not expand as uniformly as mercury. That is why the divisions are closer together at the lower end of the scale on an alcohol ther-

Which type of thermometer would you use to measure the outdoor temperature of each of these locations?

mometer. Alcohol also tends to stick to glass, so it may not always flow easily in the bore of the thermometer.

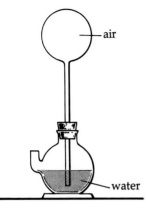

Gas thermometers

Gas thermometers were probably the first thermometers made. Scientists still prefer to use them whenever great precision is required. The advantage of a gas thermometer is that the gas inside it will expand a great deal even for a small change in temperature. Therefore, minute temperature changes can be measured precisely. The gases most commonly used in gas thermometers are air, hydrogen, and nitrogen.

Figure 5–18 A model of the first type of thermometer—a gas thermometer

Metal thermometers

Metal thermometers have a small coil made of a bimetallic strip. Brass and steel are used because their rates of expansion and contraction are quite different. The brass strip is on the inside of the coil. When the coil is heated, the brass expands more than the steel does. This causes the coil to open slightly. The more the coil is heated, the wider it opens.

The free end of the coil has a pointer that moves over a scale. Metal thermometers are often used in ovens because a liquid thermometer might boil and burst.

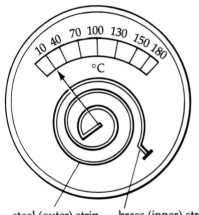

steel (outer) strip   brass (inner) strip

Figure 5–19 A bimetallic oven thermometer

Temperature and amount of heat

Temperature means the intensity of heat, or how hot or how cold something is. Are temperature and **amount of heat** the same thing? No, but for a long time scientists thought they were. It was Joseph Black (1728–1799), a Scottish chemist and professor of medicine at Edinburgh University, who first made a clear distinction between temperature and amount of heat. The following example shows the difference between the two.

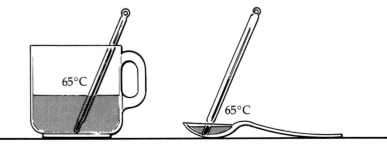

Figure 5–20 Although both the cup of cocoa and the spoonful of cocoa are at the same temperature, the cup contains more heat energy than the spoonful.

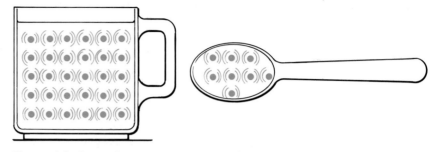

The cupful of cocoa has more molecules, so it has more heat energy.

The spoonful of cocoa has fewer molecules, so it has less heat energy.

Figure 5–21

Suppose you stir a cup of cocoa and then measure its temperature. Wherever you move the thermometer, it reads 65°C. Apparently, every drop in the cup is at the same temperature. If you spilled one spoonful onto your lap, it probably wouldn't cause much harm. Spilling a cupful, however, might cause a serious scald. Even though both are at the same temperature, the cupful of cocoa has more heat energy than the spoonful of cocoa. (See Figure 5-20 on page 263.)

This example shows that ''temperature'' differs from ''amount of heat.'' Remembering the Kinetic Molecular Theory can help you to understand why. According to the theory, the cupful of cocoa has more heat because it has more molecules and more total energy. A spoonful of cocoa, however, has fewer molecules. But they move just as fast and hit a thermometer just as intensely as the molecules in a cupful of cocoa. Therefore, the temperature is the same for both the cupful and the spoonful of cocoa because the average speed of the molecules is the same.

Temperature describes heat intensity and depends on the average kinetic energy of the molecules. Amount of heat describes a quantity of energy and depends on the mass, or the number of molecules, in a substance.

Investigation 7   Mass and temperature change

PURPOSE
To investigate how mass affects temperature change when two different quantities of water are heated in the same way.

MATERIALS
tap water
beaker
alcohol burner
burner stand
matches
safety glasses

MEASURING TOOLS
100-mL graduated cylinder
thermometer
timer

PROCEDURE
1. Measure 50 mL of tap water with the graduated cylinder and pour it into the beaker.
2. Measure the starting temperature of the water. Record this temperature.
3. Place the beaker on the stand over the burner. Put on your safety glasses. Light the burner with your teacher's permission. Heat the water for 4 min. Record the final temperature of the water after heating.
4. Repeat Steps 1, 2, and 3 using 100 mL of water. Record your observations.
5. Calculate any changes in temperature and record them.

OBSERVATIONS
1. Record your observations in a chart like the one below.

Volume of Water Heated	Initial Temperature (°C)	Final Temperature (°C)	Change in Temperature (°C)
50 mL			
100 mL			

Caution: Make sure the alcohol burner is on a level surface. Light the burner only when your teacher tells you to do so. Tie back long hair and keep your fingers and clothes away from the flame.

CONCLUSIONS
What can you conclude about the effect of mass on temperature change when two different quantities of water are heated?

Discussion questions

1. Which quantity of water showed more temperature change?

Remember that it is important to repeat your experiments and to average your results. Doing so ensures the accuracy of your observations and the validity of your results.

2. Which quantity of water received more heat energy from the burner? Explain why.
3. Why was the change in temperature not the same for both quantities of water? Use the Kinetic Molecular Theory to explain your answer.
4. How does this investigation demonstrate that temperature is not the same as amount of heat?
5. If a kettle full of boiling water is poured into a swimming pool, would you expect the pool to warm up very much as a result? Why or why not?

Try this!

The mass of a liquid affects the amount of heat it can absorb or give off. To learn how the *type* of liquid affects the amount of heat, prepare two test tubes as shown in Figure 5–22. Lower them into a hot-water bath. Then observe them closely. When one thermometer goes up by 10°C, read the other thermometer. Which liquid shows more change in temperature? Explain how you know both test tubes received the same amount of heat. If the liquids were heated separately, and the temperatures of both went up by 10°C, which liquid do you think received more heat? Why?

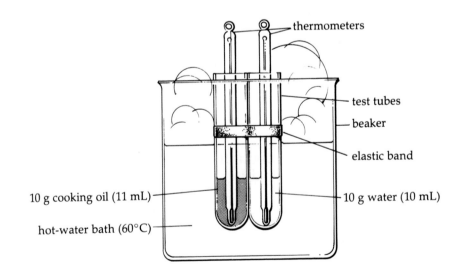

Figure 5–22

Temperature, heat, and changes of state

The three forms in which most substances normally exist are called the three states of matter. They are the solid state, the liquid state, and the gaseous state. In the solid state, molecules stay close together and move very little. When heat is added to a solid, the kinetic energy of the molecules increases and so does the temperature. When a temperature called the melting point is reached, the solid molecules are no longer bound together. The substance changes state from a solid to a liquid. This process is called melting. Once a solid melts, it cannot hold its shape. The resulting liquid must be kept in a container.

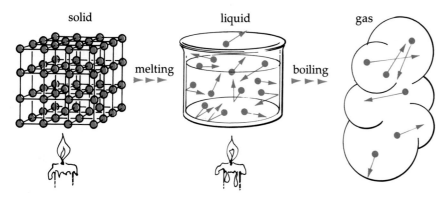

Figure 5–23 Changes of state

Further heating causes the liquid molecules to move faster and faster, increasing the temperature of the liquid. If heating continues until the liquid boils, the substance will change state again. As the liquid becomes a gas, its molecules will speed up and move far apart.

Changes of state are closely related to heat and temperature. You can see this relationship by measuring temperature changes before, during, and after a change of state as you will do in Investigation 3.

Investigation 8   Temperature and a change of state

PROBLEM
Will the temperature increase steadily when heat is added steadily to a quantity of solid water?

MATERIALS
crushed ice
tap water
alcohol burner
burner stand
matches
safety glasses

MEASURING TOOLS
thermometer
timer
250-mL beaker
100-mL graduated
    cylinder

HYPOTHESIS
State how you think the temperature will change as solid ice melts and the resulting water heats up.

Caution: Make sure the alcohol burner is on a level surface. Light the burner only when your teacher tells you to do so. Tie back long hair and keep your fingers and clothes away from the flame.

PROCEDURE
1. Fill the beaker with 250 mL of crushed ice. Measure out 50 mL of tap water using the graduated cylinder. Pour it into the beaker.
2. Record the temperature of the ice-and-water mixture.
3. Place the beaker on the stand over the burner. Put on your safety glasses. Light the burner with your teacher's permission.
4. Heat the ice-and-water mixture and measure its temperature every 30 s as the ice melts.

OBSERVATIONS
1. Record your temperature readings in a chart like the one below.

Time (min)	Temperature (°C)
0.0	
0.5	
1.0	
1.5	
2.0	
2.5	
3.0	
.	
.	
.	

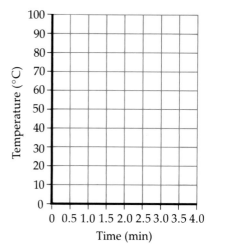

Figure 5–24

2. Use your temperature readings to plot a graph of temperature against time. (See Figure 5–24.)

CONCLUSIONS
What can you conclude about the temperature of a substance
while a change of state is taking place?

Discussion questions

1. What is the melting point of ice according to your graph?
   Is this the accepted value? If not, suggest why.
2. Why didn't the temperature rise while the ice was melting? Where was the added heat energy going if it was not
   being used to raise the temperature?
3. How does this investigation show that heat is not the same
   as temperature?
4. If the water was boiled until it had all changed to steam,
   sketch the graph of the results you would have expected
   to obtain. Explain the shape of your graph.

Section review questions

1. Draw a diagram of a mercury thermometer and explain
   how it works.
2. State two advantages of an alcohol thermometer over a
   mercury thermometer. State two disadvantages.
3. How does a clinical thermometer differ from other liquid-
   in-glass thermometers?
4. Which would take longer to bring to a boil on a hot stove,
   1 L of water at 20°C or 2 L of water at 20°C? Explain your
   answer.
5. Use the Kinetic Molecular Theory to explain how adding
   heat energy causes a solid to change state.
6. Why is ice at 0°C more effective at keeping soft drinks cool
   than the same amount of water at 0°C?
7. Why can you receive a more serious burn from steam at
   100°C than from water at 100°C?
8. The amount of heat a liquid contains depends on three
   factors. One factor is temperature. What are the other
   two?

Natural climate control

These photographs were taken around the same day in the spring. In Victoria, snow had fallen only twice all winter, and it had lasted less than a day each time. Spring flowers had been blooming for several weeks. In North Bay, the ground had been covered with snow for most of the winter, and it would not disappear completely for another month.

Which city do you think is farther south? Would it surprise you to learn that North Bay is about 300 km closer to the equator? How can Victoria stay so much warmer in the winter when it is so much closer to the North Pole?

Large bodies of water have a big effect on climate. In summer, a little heat is enough to make land temperatures rise quickly. But it takes a lot of heat to make the temperature of water increase even a small amount. In winter, water cools very slowly, while land temperatures drop quickly. If warmer water is nearby, winds will carry its heat to the cooler land.

Near Victoria, the Pacific Ocean provides a large mass of warmer water all winter. North Bay also has a body of water nearby called Lake Nipissing. However, Lake Nipissing is shallow. Its mass of water is

Victoria, British Columbia

North Bay, Ontario

small and cannot hold much heat. By late autumn, the lake is as cold as the land and freezes over completely. Lake Nipissing cannot act as a source of heat for North Bay during the winter.

All around the Earth, cli-mates are influenced by large bodies of water. The oceans of the world act like heat storage tanks that keep coastal lands warmer in winter than lands farther inland. In summer, however, large bodies of water keep coastal lands cooler.

5.5 How heat energy is transferred

Heat energy moves naturally from a warm place to a cooler place. This movement is called heat transfer. There are three ways to transfer heat: by conduction, by convection, or by radiation.

Conduction

The Kinetic Molecular Theory explains that molecular collisions cause heat to travel along a metal poker. Beginning at the hot end of the poker, kinetic energy from the fire passes from one molecule to the next. Finally, some of the heat energy reaches your hand. This form of heat transfer is called **conduction**.

The ability of a substance to conduct heat is called **thermal conductivity**. You can compare the thermal conductivity of various substances by studying Table 5.1. Metals are the best conductors of heat, and the best **heat conductor** of all substances is silver. The conductivity of silver is set at 1.00. All other substances are compared with silver. The conductivity of aluminum is 0.48, which means that aluminum is about

Why do you think copper is used to make kettles?

Why do you think some pot handles are made of plastic?

Table 5.1 Thermal conductivity of various substances

	Substance	Thermal Conductivity
Metals	silver	1.00
	copper	0.92
	gold	0.70
	aluminum	0.48
	tin	0.16
	iron	0.14
	nickel	0.14
	mercury	0.02
Non-metals	ice	0.005
	glass	0.002
	water	0.001
	wood	0.0004

one-half as conductive as silver. Except for mercury, liquids are poor conductors of heat. Water, for example, is only 1/1000 as conductive as silver.

No gases are included in Table 5.1. The ability of gases to conduct heat is minimal in comparison with solids and liquids. The molecules in gases are too far apart to transfer heat energy by molecular collisions. Materials that do not conduct heat well are called **non-conductors** or **insulators**.

Investigation 9 Investigating the conductivity of solids

PURPOSE
To compare the conductivity of various solids.

MATERIALS
candle
matches
paper clips
50-cm lengths of copper
    piping, aluminum drapery
    track, glass tubing
4 heavy books
alcohol burner
safety glasses

MEASURING TOOL
timer

PROCEDURE
1. Put on your safety glasses. Light the candle with your teacher's permission.
2. Hold the candle very carefully over the length of copper piping. Allow a few drops of wax to fall onto the piping. Quickly press a paper clip into the wax (see Figure 5–25), and allow the wax to harden.

Caution: Be careful not to drip wax on your hands or clothing.

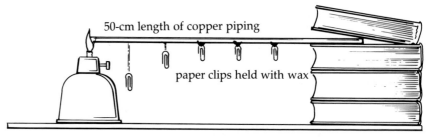

50-cm length of copper piping

paper clips held with wax

Figure 5–25

3. Repeat Step 2 until you have attached six paper clips at 5-cm intervals. (The paper clips should be firmly attached to the copper piping. If they are not, repeat the procedure.)

4. Support the copper piping horizontally using the four books as in Figure 5–25. Set the alcohol burner under the exposed end of the piping.

5. Light the alcohol burner with your teacher's permission. (You should still be wearing your safety glasses.)

6. Record the time it takes the heat to travel to each paper clip and causes it to fall.

7. Repeat Steps 1–6 replacing the copper piping with the aluminum track.

8. Repeat Steps 1–6 replacing the aluminium track with the glass tubing.

Caution: Make sure the alcohol burner is on a level surface. Light the burner only when your teacher tells you to do so. Tie back long hair and keep your fingers and clothes away from the flame.

OBSERVATIONS

1. Record your observations in a chart like the one below.

Distance Heat Travelled (cm)	Time Taken (s)		
	Copper	Aluminum	Glass
5			
10			
15			
20			
25			
30			

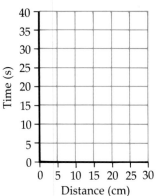

Figure 5–26

2. Based on your chart, plot a graph of time against distance. (See Figure 5–26.)

CONCLUSIONS

Based on your observations, what can you conclude about the ability of copper, aluminum, and glass to conduct heat?

Discussion questions

1. How do your results compare with the information given for copper, aluminum, and glass in Table 5.1 on page 271?

Firefighters wear insulated clothing to protect themselves from heat.

2. Would the amount of wax you used to support each paper clip affect the results of your investigation? Explain your answer.

3. What other factors might affect the results of this investigation?

4. Which variables were controlled in this investigation? Which variables were not controlled?

5. Do you think this investigation was a fair test (a controlled experiment) of thermal conductivity? Why or why not? Describe how you would conduct a completely fair test.

6. Why do you think the outer bottom surfaces of some cookware are coated with copper?

Try this!

Design a controlled experiment to test the insulating abilities of various materials such as wool, sawdust, or sand. Draw a diagram of the equipment you would use and how you would set it up. Which variables might affect your results? Which variables would you control? What measurements would you take? Be sure to write up a procedure for your experiment and have it approved by your teacher.

Convection

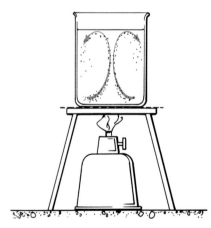

Figure 5–27 Convection currents in water can be seen by adding a little sawdust.

When a beaker of water is heated, the molecules directly above the flame start to move faster and farther apart. The extra space between the molecules makes the warm water less dense than the cool water around it. The warmed water floats upward. The cool water moves in to take its place, but soon it is warmed, too. The result is a continuous upward movement of the water directly above the flame, and a downward movement of water at the sides of the beaker. The moving fluid is called a **convection current**. The current carries heat energy from a warm place to a cool place. Heat transfer by convection occurs only in gases and liquids.

Convection currents occur every day in the Earth's atmosphere. Huge updrafts and downdrafts of air create winds that transfer heat from warm lands to cool lands. Convection currents also circulate heat in the oceans and in other bodies of water.

Convection is important to the life of a lake or a pond.

The surface water in a lake or pond cools during the autumn. This cooler, denser water sinks, and warmer, lighter water rises to take its place. The resulting convection current is important to the life of the pond because oxygen absorbed from the air at the surface is carried to the lower levels. Without this "autumn overturn," deep-water fish could not survive.

Investigation 10   Observing convection currents

PURPOSE
To observe convection currents.

MATERIALS

large beaker	potassium permanganate
tap water	crystals
alcohol burner	chimney apparatus
burner stand	candle
matches	paper
tweezers	safety glasses
glass tubing	

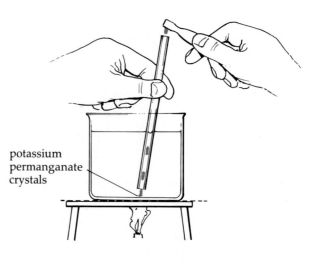

Figure 5–28

Caution: Potassium permanganate crystals can stain your clothes. You may want to wear an apron for this investigation.

Caution: Make sure the alcohol burner is on a level surface. Light the burner only when your teacher tells you to do so. Tie back long hair and keep your fingers and clothes away from the flame.

PROCEDURE
1. Fill a large beaker with tap water. Place it on the burner stand over the alcohol burner. Put on your safety glasses. Light the burner with your teacher's permission.
2. Use the tweezers to drop a few potassium permanganate crystals down the glass tubing into the beaker of water as in Figure 5–28. (The crystals should fall onto the bottom of the beaker directly over the flame.)
3. Hold your thumb tightly over the top of the glass tubing and lift the tubing out of the water.
4. Observe what happens as the permanganate crystals dissolve.

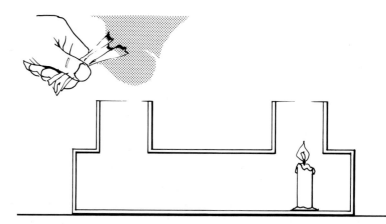

Figure 5–29

5. Secure a candle under one of the chimneys of the chimney apparatus. Put on your safety glasses again and light the candle.

6. After a few minutes, light a piece of paper. Blow it out quickly and bring the smouldering paper close to the top of the other chimney (see Figure 5–29).

7. Observe what happens to the smoke.

OBSERVATIONS

1. Write a description of what you observed when the crystals and the water were heated.

2. Describe what happened when you held the smouldering paper over the chimney.

3. Make sketches to correspond with your descriptions.

Discussion questions

1. Explain why the coloured water moved as it did in Step 4.

2. Explain why the smoke moved as it did in Step 6.

3. If you measured the temperature in a room near the floor and at the ceiling, what would you expect to find?

4. Draw a picture of a room with an electric heater against one wall. Using arrows, show how the air moves in the room when the heater is turned on.

5. Hot-air registers are usually put near the floor, but air conditioners work best when the cold-air registers are near the ceiling. Explain why you think this happens.

Radiation

Heat energy from the sun cannot be transferred to Earth by conduction because there are few molecules in space to act as conductors. For the same reason, there are no convection currents in space between the sun and the Earth. So how does the sun's energy travel 150 000 000 km to reach us? Because heat can also be transferred by **radiation**.

The sun sends out wavelike rays that carry energy. When these rays reach the Earth, some are reflected back into space by clouds. Others are absorbed by the Earth's atmosphere

Energy from the sun is transferred by radiation.

Figure 5–30 Rays from the sun warm up the Earth by increasing the kinetic energy of molecules near the Earth's surface.

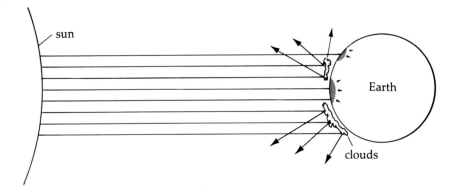

and surface, which warm up from the added energy. Bright and shiny surfaces make good reflectors. Therefore, they reduce heat transfer by radiation. Dark and dull surfaces tend to increase heat transfer by radiation.

Investigation 11   Investigating radiant energy

PURPOSE
To observe how the surface colour of an object affects the absorption of radiant energy.

MATERIALS	MEASURING TOOLS
2 identical empty soup cans	2 thermometers
black paint	timer
paint brush	
tap water	
paper	
heat lamp	

PROCEDURE
1. Paint the outside surface of one can black. Leave the surface of the other can shiny.
2. Fill both cans with cold tap water. Measure the temperature of the water in each can. Covering each can with a lid made of paper will help prevent evaporation.
3. Place the two cans in a sunny window or about 0.5 m from a heat lamp.
4. Measure the temperature of the water in each can every 5 min for about 30 min.

Figure 5–31

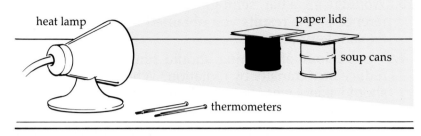

OBSERVATIONS
1. Record your temperature readings for both cans in a chart like the one below.

Time (min)	Temperature of Water	
	Black Can (°C)	Shiny Can (°C)
0		
5		
10		
15		
20		
25		
30		

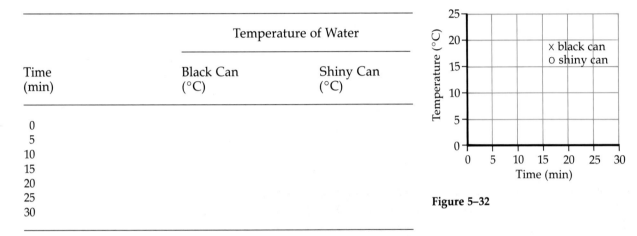

Figure 5–32

2. Use your temperature readings to plot a graph of temperature against time. Plot the data for both cans on the same graph. (See Figure 5–32.)

CONCLUSIONS
What can you conclude about the relationship between the surface colour of an object and the absorption of radiant energy?

Discussion questions

1. In which can was heat transferred by radiation more rapidly?
2. What do you think would happen if you used a can that was painted another colour such as green? State a reason for your answer.

3. Would using a flat, semi-gloss, or glossy paint make a difference to the results you obtained in this investigation? Explain your answer.

4. What colour of clothing should tennis players wear to reduce heat transfer by radiation? What colour of clothing should skiers wear to increase heat transfer by radiation? State reasons for your answers.

5. Why is a layer of aluminum foil often included when the walls of a house are being insulated? Should the shiny surface face in or out?

Heat transfer in the home

Energy for home heating may come from chemical sources such as wood, coal, oil, or natural gas. Other sources include electric energy from nuclear power or hydroelectric plants. Whatever the source, all heating systems depend on conduction, convection, and radiation to transfer heat around a building.

Fuels are normally burned in a furnace. In a hot water heating system, the resulting heat is transferred by conduction to a nearby fluid such as water. Convection currents make

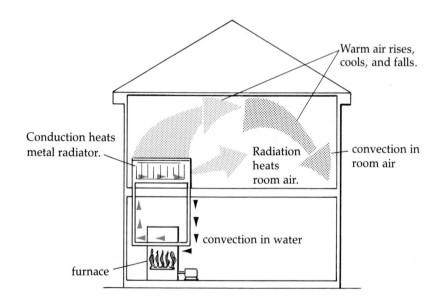

Figure 5–33 A hot-water heating system uses conduction, convection, and radiation to transfer heat.

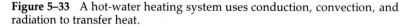

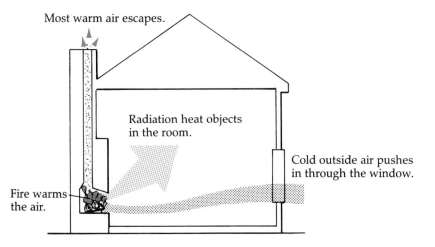

Most warm air escapes.

Radiation heat objects
in the room.

Cold outside air pushes
in through the window.

Fire warms
the air.

Figure 5–34   Open fires waste heat energy.

the hot water rise through pipes to metal containers called radiators. Conduction transfers heat from the hot water to the metal. Radiation transfers heat from the hot metal to the air in a room. As the hot water cools down, its molecules crowd close together. Convection currents then carry the denser, cooler fluid back to the furnace.

Some convection systems use air to carry the heat. An open fire is the simplest of this type of system. However, a fireplace wastes much of the heat it produces. Convection currents carry most of the warmed air straight up the chimney. Modern forced-air heating systems keep the warm air separate from the flame and use pumps to assist the natural convection currents.

Heat from electricity can be transferred by the convection of hot air or water. More often, however, electricity is converted to heat in a metal radiator. The heat is then transferred from the hot metal to the air of a room by radiation.

Preventing heat transfer

There are three main reasons for trying to prevent conduction, convection, or radiation from taking place.

Protection
Unwanted heat transfer can cause burns and fires. Preven-

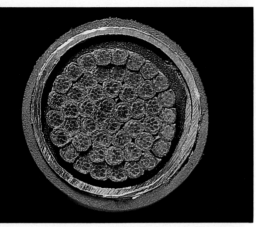

Why do you think the wires in this communications cable are surrounded by a plastic coating?

tion involves the use of non-conductors or insulating materials. For example, plastic or wooden handles on cooking utensils prevent conduction of heat from hot metals. In buildings, very hot pipes or wires could eventually ignite wooden walls. Insulators, such as fibreglass, are used to slow down conduction around hot pipes. Flexible plastic coatings are used around electrical wires.

Economy

Unwanted heat transfers also waste much of the money society spends on home heating. Radiation carries heat away from windows and walls. Convection currents allow heat to escape around doors. Methods to reduce heat loss include using double or triple layers of glass on windows, coating windows with a material that reflects heat back inside a building, adding extra insulating material in the attic and walls, and sealing all cracks and gaps.

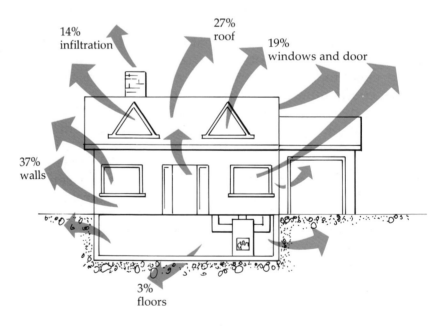

Figure 5–35   Where heat escapes in a typical two-storey home

Pollution control

Heat transfers are also a major cause of pollution. The air above cities stays unnaturally warm all year. In winter, heat escapes from buildings and factories. In summer, air conditioners pump warm air outside. All this excess heat forms huge pockets of warm air. Sometimes the warm air gets trapped for days and blocks normal convection currents. This unnatural weather pattern is called an inversion. While it lasts, smoke and exhaust fumes cannot escape from the city. Air pollution worsens, and babies and people with lung problems can become sick. Better insulation of buildings can help to lessen our dependence on heating and air conditioning systems.

Inversion is a process that traps smoke and exhaust fumes causing air pollution to worsen.

Section review questions

1. State the three methods of heat transfer. For each method, state one example of a wanted heat transfer and one example of an unwanted heat transfer.
2. Explain the difference between a conductor and an insulator. State two good conductors of heat and two insulators.
3. Explain why energy from the sun cannot reach Earth by conduction or convection. How is solar energy transferred to Earth?
4. Explain what causes the autumn overturn in a lake or pond. Why is it important to aquatic life?
5. Explain why solids are much better conductors than liquids or gases. (Refer to the Kinetic Molecular Theory.)
6. Which method of heat transfer is used in your home-heating system? Explain how it works.
7. State two examples of unwanted heat transfers. Describe how these transfers can be prevented. State reasons for your answers.

SCIENCE IN OUR LIVES

Heat radiation and thermography

When you hold your hand near something hot like an iron, you can feel the heat it gives off. The rays of heat that you feel are called infrared rays. Although you cannot see these rays, they can be detected in photographs taken with either a special type of television camera or a film that is sensitive to infrared radiation. Such photographs are called thermograms. Thermography can reveal much information about objects, landforms, oceans, and living things.

In a thermogram, infrared energy is shown by variations in colour and brightness. For example, if you took an infrared photograph of the outside of a house, the heat energy lost around the windows and the doors would appear as brightly coloured areas against a dark background.

Thermograms have many applications in many different branches of science. Through careful study of the colour variations in thermograms taken by satellites, information about acid rain, water pollution, volcanoes, and forest fires can be obtained. Aerial infrared scanners can also show the population distribution in cities and the type of crops being grown

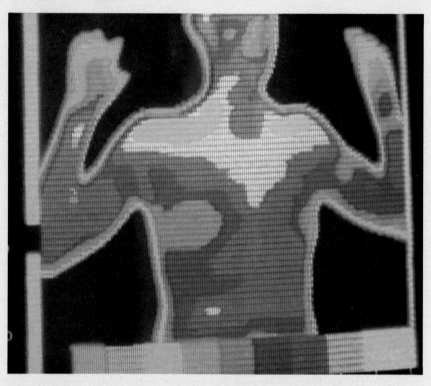

in rural areas.

In industry, thermograms are used to detect construction flaws such as heat leaks or overheated electrical systems in houses.

Thermograms also help doctors to diagnose diseases. A healthy human body gives off heat radiation in particular patterns. If a patient's thermogram shows a difference in the normal pattern of heat radiation, a doctor may suspect a medical problem. The photograph on this page shows a

thermoscan of a person's head, upper torso, arms, and hands. A series of colour bands—blue, dark green, light green, violet, red, and yellow—appears across the bottom of the image. Blue reveals the most amount of heat transfer and yellow indicates areas where heat radiation is less. Based on this scale, which areas of the human body radiate the most heat? Which areas radiate the least? Can you think of other ways to use thermography?

Should we turn municipal waste into energy?

The standard of living of Canadians is one of the highest in the world. Canada has large amounts of energy that can be used to power factories that shape raw materials into finished goods. Today, especially in large urban centres, Canadians consume huge amounts of goods and produce large quantities of waste material. A great deal of energy is needed to produce this waste. However, this energy is essentially lost if the products it is used to manufacture are eventually buried in landfill sites.

Some people believe that municipal waste is a potential source of energy. They think that facilities to burn this waste should be constructed in order to produce the heat energy necessary for the operation of electric generators. This process would recycle some of the energy originally used to produce the products that we discard and reduce the volume of waste material that is disposed of in landfill sites. Converting waste into energy is also an alternative to burning fossil fuels or using nuclear power.

Critics of this scheme are concerned that waste products harmful to the environment would still be produced and

A landfill site

released into the atmosphere. They also point out that waste disposal is not completely eliminated. Ash left over from the conversion process would still have to be buried.

Explore the issue

Working with a partner, research the possibility of constructing a waste-burning facility to produce electric energy in your community. Try to obtain information about the amount of waste produced in your community, the methods used to dispose of it, and the cost of disposal. Research the technology of waste-recovery facilities and the costs associ-

ated with them. Try to obtain information about the cost of producing electric energy by burning waste. Compare this cost to that of other methods of producing electricity. You may also want to assess the potential impact of such a facility on the environment of your community. Based on your research, would a waste-burning facility be feasible in your community? Why or why not?

If a facility is already operating in your area, ask the company officials for information like that above and determine whether it is a good idea to have this facility in your community.

Meet Barbara McPhail

Barbara and her husband have their own business as consultants in the architectural conservation field. As a technologist, her specialty concerns the scientific principles of architecture and energy conservation in older buildings.

Q. What led you to this field?
A. I came to it from the historical rather than the scientific end. I took an honours history degree at Trent University in Peterborough and became interested in the conservation of architecture. Then I went to St. Lawrence College in Brockville and took a three-year course to get a "restoration technology diploma."

Q. What courses did you take?
A. The courses dealt with scientific subjects such as structural design, soil mechanics, timber design, building materials, and architectural history.

Q. Where do people with this diploma usually work?
A. Usually for the government. I worked for the Ontario government as a conservation officer.

Q. How long did you stay at this government job?
A. About four years. Then I decided to go back to university to do a masters degree in conservation studies. I went to England to do this.

Q. Did you start your own company after your studies?
A. Yes. My husband and I have had our own company for just over a year. Our clients are mainly government clients, both municipal and provincial. We have just finished doing a series of lectures on heritage energy conservation, which was aimed at owners of older homes.

Q. What was your message in these lectures?
A. We were trying to get across that most older buildings were built with an energy system relying on natural sources, or passive energy sources, such as radiant heat.

The prevailing-wind side of an old house was built with no windows to keep heat in. On the sun-facing side, there were large windows to collect the heat from the sun. Usually, there were interior and exterior shutters on the windows that were part of the natural ventilation system. This system helped to keep the house warm in the winter and cool in the summer. Exterior and interior vestibules helped to contain heat and to reduce drafts. Small rooms with many doors were also ways to control interior heating.

Q. What do you recommend to renovators of old houses?
A. Looking at the heating and cooling system before putting insulation into the walls. Certain other measures can make a big difference and be much more cost effective. For example, caulking and weatherstripping around doors and windows cuts out drafts. Caulking the baseboards around exterior walls can also make a big difference.

Q. What can students do to prepare for work in your field?
A. It's important to keep up with mathematics and sciences because most of the concepts you work with in building technology have a scientific basis.

Chapter review

Words to know

Write a brief definition for each of the terms listed below. The location of these terms is indicated by the section number in the brackets.

- chemical energy (*Section 5.2*)
- electric energy (*Section 5.2*)
- heat conductor (*Section 5.5*)
- heat energy (*Section 5.1*)
- insulator (*Section 5.5*)
- kinetic energy (*Section 5.1*)
- Kinetic Molecular Theory (*Section 5.1*)
- mechanical energy (*Section 5.2*)
- non-conductor (*Section 5.5*)
- nuclear energy (*Section 5.2*)
- radiant energy (*Section 5.2*)
- temperature (*Section 5.4*)
- thermometer (*Section 5.4*)

Questions

A. Indicate whether each of the following statements is true or false. Explain why the "false" statements are not true.

1. Thermograms are photographs taken using ultraviolet light.
2. In the seventeenth century, many scientists believed that heat was a fluid called "caloric."
3. Heat is due to the motion of molecules in a substance.
4. The energy of the sun is produced by burning gases.
5. The Earth has a plentiful supply of non-renewable energy that will last for hundreds of years.
6. When solids and liquids are heated, they expand more than gases.
7. Alcohol thermometers work better than mercury thermometers in the far North.
8. Different sized glasses of water at the same temperature hold the same amount of heat.
9. The amount of heat contained by a substance depends on the type of substance, its mass, and its temperature.
10. Heat travels upward.

B. Choose the best answer for each of the following.

1. The methods of heat transfer are
   a) radiation and convection
   b) conduction and convection
   c) conduction, radiation, and convection
   d) radiation and conduction
2. a) Wood is a better conductor than mercury.
   b) Water is a better conductor than tin.
   c) Glass is a better conductor than nickel.

d) Copper is a better conductor than aluminum.

3. a) Air-conditioning registers work better when they are installed near the floor.
   b) Convection currents in air help gliders to get lift.
   c) Convection currents in air cause cold air to rise.
   d) Hot air registers are usually put near the ceiling.

4. a) Tennis players should wear dark colours on a hot day.
   b) For comfort, it doesn't really matter what colours your clothes are.
   c) Dark-coloured clothing keeps you warmer on a cold, sunny day.
   d) Infrared and ultraviolet waves are visible rays.

5. When ice is heated, its temperature
   a) falls then rises
   b) immediately begins to rise
   c) starts to fall
   d) stays the same until all the ice has melted

C. Write full answers to each of the following.

1. List all the sources of heat in your school and your home. Classify them according to the form of energy used to produce the heat.

2. How could you demonstrate that molecules in a liquid are in continuous motion?

3. State examples of five types of energy that act as sources of heat.

4. Use the Kinetic Molecular Theory to explain expansion and contraction.

5. State two examples each of expansion in solids, liquids, and gases.

6. Draw a diagram to help you explain how a thermostat with a bimetallic switch works.

7. Examine Figure 5–35 on page 282. If you were living in this house, what could you do to help reduce the heat loss?

8. Examine Figure 5–36 of a thermos bottle. What is the function of each of its features? Be sure to state how each feature helps to reduce heat transfer.
   a) cork
   b) glass bottle
   c) vacuum
   d) silvered surfaces
   e) spring
   f) plastic case

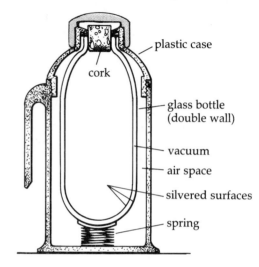

Figure 5–36

9. The excess heat produced by factories and by electric generating stations can cause thermal pollution of large bodies of water. Use the resource centre in your school to investigate the following. Write a report on your findings.
   a) the effects of thermal pollution on fish and other aquatic life
   b) what can be done to make use of this heat energy and help protect the environment

Science challenge

1. You are given a mercury thermometer without a scale on it. Describe the steps you would take to calibrate it.

2. Find out about Galileo's thermometer and write a clear explanation of how it worked.

3. Like plaster of Paris, freshly mixed concrete gives off large amounts of heat. If the heat cannot escape, thermal expansion may cause the concrete to crack and lose its strength. How do you think the engineers who design dams prevent this problem? Draw a sketch to describe how you think this could be done.

4. Suppose you had a quantity of water vapour at 110°C that was cooling at a constant rate, causing it to change to a liquid, and finally to a solid. Suppose you also were able to read the temperature of the water every minute. Draw a graph of temperature against time. Explain the changes of state that are shown on your graph.

Science projects

1. Design and perform an experiment to determine the effect of distance from a source of radiant energy, such as a light bulb, on the temperature change in a container of water. Be sure to control variables such as the amount of water, the shape and colour of the container, the wattage of the bulb, and the exposure time. Plot the values of temperature and distance on a graph to help formulate a conclusion.

2. Investigate the effect of a ceiling fan on the temperature in different parts of a room. List the variables that need to be controlled.

3. Do a research project on microwave ovens. Try to find answers for the following questions. How does a microwave oven work? When are microwaves dangerous? How does food cooked in a microwave oven compare in taste and appearance with food cooked in a conventional oven? Are there different types of microwave ovens?

Adaptations

You may have seen dinosaur exhibits in a museum, or looked at illustrations of dinosaurs in books. But have you ever wondered what it must have been like when dinosaurs lived on Earth and why they no longer exist?

Dinosaurs were plant- and flesh-eating reptiles that lived on Earth 225 to 65 million years ago. They lived on land, in the air, and in water. Dinosaurs varied greatly in size, appearance, and habits. From the study of plant and animal fossils, scientists have inferred that dinosaurs thrived in a mild, moist climate that supported lush forests and many types of flowering plants. But the existence of dinosaurs was unknown until fossils were discovered in the late eighteenth and nineteenth centuries.

One of the most recent fossil discoveries took place in Alberta, where seven dinosaur nests were uncovered. Scientists hope that the study of the eggs found in these nests will reveal important information about the development and functions of dinosaurs' bodies, enabling them to learn more about why dinosaurs disappeared.

Why do you think dinosaurs disappeared? Why do you think plants and animals look and act the way they do? This chapter will help you to find out.

6.1 What are adaptations?

The world teems with life. Organisms survive on land masses from the hot regions of the equator to the frigid regions of the Arctic. They survive in water from small ponds, inland lakes, and rivers to the depths of the huge oceans that cover most of the Earth's surface.

Have you ever wondered why some orchids grow on trees and obtain their food and moisture from the air? Why does sphagnum moss, which makes up muskeg, grow so well in the thawed layers of soil above the Arctic permafrost, and why do caribou survive in the harsh Arctic environment? Why do monkeys live in the dense vegetation of the tropics and camels in the desert?

Life is varied in its form, size, and characteristics. Plants and animals exhibit very different characteristics. You are different from other mammals, and mammals are different from fish and insects. Plants themselves exhibit tremendous variety. Perhaps the greatest debate among life scientists is why this is so. Scientists believe that the great variety in the characteristics of living things is related to how individual organisms carry out their life functions in diverse and ever-changing environments. However, no one species is capable of living everywhere on Earth. Adaptation is the ability of organisms to survive because they have the characteristics that suit them to a particular environment.

Try this!

Look carefully at Figure 6–1. Write a description of the external characteristics of the fish in the illustration. Describe the environment shown in the illustration. Which characteristics do you think best suit the fish to live in water? Describe the characteristics of a plant that could survive in the environment illustrated in Figure 6–1. Explain why the plant should have these characteristics.

Fish possess characteristics that suit them for survival in water. You have characteristics that suit you for surviving on land and for breathing air. **Adaptation** is the ability of an organism to survive because it has the characteristics that suit

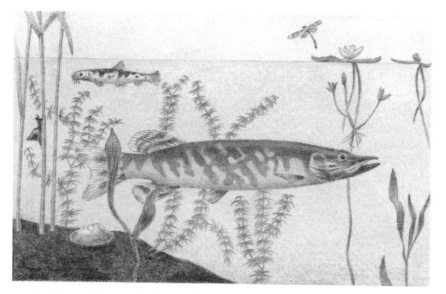

Figure 6–1

it to a particular **environment**. The different environments on Earth are made up of living things, such as animals, plants, fungi, and protists; and non-living things, such as water, air, soil, light, and temperature. The adaptations of a living thing determine how successfully its characteristics will enable it to live in a certain environment. Fish have fins, gills, and sleek bodies. These characteristics are adaptations that suit fish to live in water. Mammals have limbs and lungs, which are adaptations that suit them to life on land.

What adaptations do you think the animals in these photographs have that would help them to survive in their environments?

Try this!

Identify a water or land environment to investigate near your home. Carefully observe the surroundings. Make notes or a sketch to describe what you observe. Find two plants and two animals in the environment you have chosen. Describe the characteristics of each organism, and infer how these characteristics suit the organism to the environment. Organize your observations and inferences in a chart like the one below.

Organism	Characteristics	Reason for Characteristics
Dandelion		
Grasshopper		
Maple Tree		
Squirrel		
. . .		

What characteristics do cacti have that suit them for life in the desert?

In unique ways, each species is suited for its way of life in its natural environment. The characteristics of animals and plants enable them to carry on the life functions necessary for their survival in the physical conditions of their particular environments.

The response of a plant to the stimulus of light, water, heat, or gravity is a characteristic that suits a plant to its environment. This characteristic is an adaptation that scientists call **tropism**. In Investigation 1, you will discover how plants respond to an environmental stimulus.

This bean sprout is responding to the stimulus of light. What do you think would happen if it were turned away from the light?

Investigation 1   Plant tropism

PROBLEM
How do the roots of germinating seeds respond to water?

MATERIALS   MEASURING TOOL
16 bean seeds   ruler
tap water
8 test tubes
cotton batting
masking tape
marker
tweezers
aluminum foil tray
rectangular pieces of sponge

HYPOTHESIS
State how you think the roots of germinating seeds will respond to the stimulus of water.

PROCEDURE

1. Soak the bean seeds in lukewarm tap water for 24 h.
2. Fill all of the test tubes with loosely packed cotton batting. Use the masking tape and the marker to label the test tubes A, B, C, D, E, F, G, and H.
3. Use the tweezers to place two bean seeds into each test tube, 10 cm away from the mouth of the tube. Make sure the seeds are on opposite sides of each tube and in the positions shown in Figure 6–2. (Label the seeds #1 and #2 for each tube by placing a small piece of masking tape on the tube under the seed.)
4. Cut four semicircles along one side of the aluminium tray as shown in Figure 6–2. Fill the tray with water to a depth of 2 cm. Place the tray on a flat surface in a sunny location.
5. Submerge the mouths of test tubes A, B, C, and D in the water tray. Make sure each test tube is in a vertical position.
6. Position the mouths of test tubes, E, F, G, and H in the

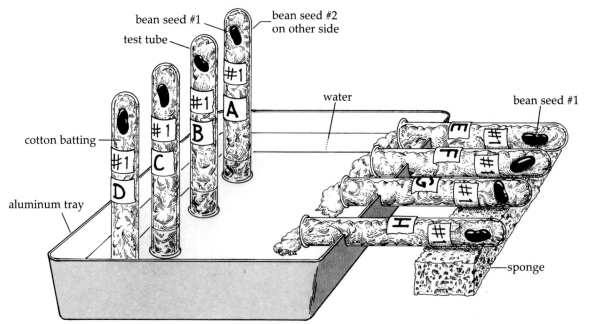

Figure 6–2

semicircles you cut out of the tray. Support each test tube with a piece of sponge to keep it horizontal. (Make sure that some of the cotton batting touches the water.)

7. Add water to the tray daily to keep the water at a depth of 2 cm.
8. Observe the growth of each seed and measure the length of each seed root over a two-week period. Record your observations.

OBSERVATIONS
1. Observe the changes that take place in each bean seed on days 1, 5, 10, and 14. Record your observations in charts like the ones below.
2. In what direction are the roots of each bean seed growing?
3. Measure the length of the roots of each bean seed and record your measurements in your charts.

Response of Roots in Vertical Test Tubes

Test Tube	Seed #	Day	Observed Changes	Direction of Growth	Length of Roots (cm)
A					
B					
C					
D					

Response of Roots in Horizontal Test Tubes

Test Tube	Seed #	Day	Observed Changes	Direction of Growth	Length of Roots (cm)
E					
F					
G					
H					

CONCLUSIONS

What conclusions can you make about the way the roots of germinating seeds respond to water?

Discussion questions

1. Which variables essential for plant growth did you control in this investigation?
2. Do you think gravity has a greater influence on the growth of roots? How would you design an experiment to test the effect of gravity on root growth?

Types of adaptations

Organisms must have adaptations that meet the challenges of their environment. They are affected by temperature change, precipitation, wind, and light. Organisms are also affected by the space they live in. They must have enough room to build a nest, dig a burrow, spread their roots, or grow branches. They must be able to obtain enough food to grow and reproduce. And they must deal with the threat to their survival from parasites, predators, and diseases.

A rainforest on the Queen Charlotte Islands, British Columbia

A penguin and its nest

Adaptations may be in the structure, the behaviour, or the function of an organism. Let's look at these types of adaptations.

Structural adaptations

You know that ducks have webbed feet to help them swim in the water. You know that robins lay eggs and cats have kittens. The trees in your neighbourhood have sturdy trunks that help them to stay upright and roots that help them to obtain moisture. These physical characteristics of animals and plants are structural adaptations that enable them to survive in their environments.

Structural adaptations are related to the way an animal moves, obtains its food, defends itself, builds its home, and reproduces.

Table 6.1 Structural adaptations of living organisms

Adaptation	Name of Organism	Use and Reason for Adaptation
• has spinerettes that produce silk thread	• spider	
• can hover in all directions; rapidly beating wings make a humming sound		• feeding and locomotion
• has downward pointing hairs on funnel-shaped leaves	• Venus fly trap	
• has incisor teeth that continue to grow throughout its lifetime		• feeding and habitat construction
• makes food in its stem because it doesn't have leaves	• cactus	
• has internal ink sac that is used to squirt black fluid into water		• distracts enemies and obscures their vision
• has sharply barbed quills in the skin on its back, sides, and tail	• porcupine	

Try this!

Different organisms have different structural adaptations. These adaptations help organisms to perform the life functions necessary for their survival. Use the descriptions of the structural adaptations of the organisms in Table 6.1 on page 299 to help you complete the table. Infer the name of each organism, the use, and the reason for the adaptation described. (Some have already been done for you.) After completing the table, compare your inferences with those of your classmates. Why might some inferences differ? Why do you think it is important for scientists to study the structural adaptations of plants and animals?

Camouflage is an example of an important structural adaptation. Many organisms rely on camouflage based on shape or colour for survival. Camouflaged animals sometimes look like plants, soil, rocks, or other animals. Camouflage helps to protect organisms from predators and occurs in animals in most habitats of the world.

Colour camouflage often takes place when the seasons change. The polar bear and the snowy owl, for example, shed their old coats and replace them with a new growth of white feathers or fur that blend in with their winter environment.

The camouflage used by fish is called counter-shading. The backs of fish are usually darker in tone than their undersides. When a predator looks down into the water, the darker tones seem to make the fish merge with the blue-grey colour of the water. Predators that live in the water often cannot distinguish the paler tones of the underside of a fish from the background of the sky.

A chameleon

A polar bear

Try this!

Make two teams of some of your classmates or friends. Give each team 250 toothpicks: 50 each of red, blue, yellow, green, and beige. In separate locations of a field or a large lawn, stake out two 5-m × 5-m areas. Each team will distribute their toothpicks in their own area, making sure that the toothpicks are hidden in the grass. Then the teams will exchange their areas. At a ''go'' signal, each team should try to retrieve as many toothpicks as possible in a 2-min period. Count the number of each coloured toothpick for each team. Which colour of toothpick was easiest to find? Which colour was most difficult? What type of colouration do you think would suit organisms to a grassy environment? Why?

Behavioural adaptations

Behavioural adaptations are the ways an organism acts to increase its chances of survival when it moves, feeds, mates, or carries out other life functions. The behaviour may be inherited, or it may be learned as the animal grows.

Instincts are inherited behaviour patterns that help animals to survive in their environments. Insects, birds, fish, amphibians, and reptiles depend mainly on instinctive behaviour.

The way a spider spins its web or a bird builds its nest is an example of instinctive behaviour. Mating calls, sexual displays, and chemical releases are also instinctive behaviours.

Some animals, such as the opossum, play dead to deter their enemies. Other animals bluff a predator by inflating parts of their bodies, or by spreading out their feathers or their fur to look bigger and more threatening.

The way a frog feeds is called a **reflex action**. A frog considers any small, moving object it can see to be its prey. When a frog sees something move, its tongue darts instinctively in the direction of the moving object.

The migratory urge of birds, fish, insects, and mammals is an important instinctive behaviour. Animals are unable to

Did you know?
Some animals, such as the monarch butterfly, contain poisonous chemicals that cause predators to vomit. The vivid red, orange, and yellow colour of the monarch butterfly is called warning colouration. Other animals are ''warned'' by this colouration to avoid eating insects and animals that contain poisons.

What instinctive behaviours are the kitten and the spider demonstrating?

Did you know?
Ethology is the study of an animal's behaviour in its natural habitat. Ethologists suggest that animals act in certain ways because they have inherited these instincts. But behavioural psychologists suggest that animal behaviour is learned in response to external stimuli.

Did you know?
Research about migratory animals suggests that they respond to internal clocks or biological rhythms, co-ordinate their flight patterns with the sun, the moon, and star patterns, or rely on landscape features or ocean currents for direction.

Canada geese

Did you know?
Atlantic salmon migrate almost 3200 km from the ocean to spawn in the freshwater streams where they were born.

control their environments the way humans can. During migration, animals move from one place to another to find the physical conditions necessary for their survival.

Investigation 2 Migratory adaptations of animals

PURPOSE
To compare the migratory patterns and adaptations of monarch butterflies, caribou, salmon, Canada geese, and whales.

MATERIALS
library resource materials:
  encyclopedias
  textbooks
  newspaper articles
  magazines
  films
  videos
  maps

PROCEDURE
1. Ask your teacher to divide your class into four groups. Each group should then select one animal to research.
2. Use the subject reference section in your library or resource centre to help you find information about the animal your group has selected.
3. As a group, identify the summer and winter locations of the animal. Note the distances the animal travels. Infer reasons why the animal migrates. Research how the animal migrates. List the adaptations of the animal that suit it for migration.
4. As a class, compile the information gathered by each group and set up a chart to record the results of your research. (See Table 6.2.) Information about the monarch butterfly is provided as an example.
5. Make a larger map of the world to plot the migratory routes of all the animals researched. Use a different colour for each animal and be sure to include a colour-coded legend or key for the map.

Table 6.2 Migratory adaptations in animals

	Monarch Butterfly	Caribou	Salmon	Canada Goose	Whale
Starting Point	• Canada and United States				
End Point	• California • Mexico				
Distance Travelled	• 3000 km (going) • 3500 km (return) • 6500 km (total)				
Reasons for Migration	• response to shorter days and decreasing temperatures • instinctive behaviour to move to locations where climate is cool, moist, and temperatures remain above 0°C				
How Animal Migrates	• uses sun as a guide • relies on inner clock • is drawn by Earth's magnetic field				
Adaptations	• last generation of summer, so do not mate because reproductive organs do not mature until spring • magnetic material present in head and thorax • chemical ingested from milkweed plant provides protection against most birds				

CONCLUSIONS
What conclusions can you make about the migratory patterns and adaptations of the animals researched in this investigation?

Are these porpoises exhibiting learned or instinctive behaviour? Why?

Did you know?
Imprinting is a special type of conditioning. Konrad Lorenz, an Austrian biologist, discovered that goslings hatched in an incubator followed him around. He showed that newborn geese, ducks, and other birds are imprinted to respond to objects that move and make sounds as though they were their mothers.

Discussion questions

1. Why do you think migration is necessary for the survival of some animals and not for others?
2. Are there any human activities you think might interfere with the migration of the animals you researched? Explain how and why.

The behaviour of animals can be changed by experience. This is called **learned behaviour**. An important type of learning is called **conditioning**. Ivan Pavlov (1844–1936), a Russian psychologist, observed that a dog instinctively produces saliva (response) when it is given food (stimulus). If a bell is rung just before food is given, the dog will eventually produce saliva at the sound of the bell. That is, the dog learns to respond to the bell in the same way it responds to food.

Learned behaviour can be reinforced. Positive reinforcement rewards a behaviour, and is frequently used in the training of circus animals or working dogs. Negative reinforcement uses an unpleasant stimulus to discourage an unwanted behaviour.

Functional adaptations

Functional adaptations are related to the life functions of organisms such as breathing, reproduction, and metabolism. For example, some animals hibernate because they are not structurally or behaviourally adapted to survive in cold weather. They lack the thick, insulating fur of a polar bear or the instinct of a monarch butterfly to migrate to a warmer climate. To survive, these animals hibernate.

Hibernation is a functional response to seasonal change. When temperatures drop and food becomes scarce, some animals go into a state of deep sleep. Their body temperatures drop and their body processes, such as breathing and metabolism, slow down. Hibernating animals survive on food stored in their body fat. When their environment again becomes favourable, they wake up and their life functions return to normal.

Carnivorous plants, such as the Venus fly trap, make their own food through photosynthesis. So the trigger mechanism they have to trap insects is a functional adaptation based on the need for nutrients and not for food.

If the trigger hairs of a Venus fly trap are touched, the lobes and spikes of the plant interlock for four or five days while the insect is digested. However, if you were to "trigger" the plant's response with a pencil, you would discover that a Venus fly trap has an adaptation that enables it to recognize what is an insect and what is not. When something other than an insect is trapped by the plant, its leaves will reopen in less than 30 min.

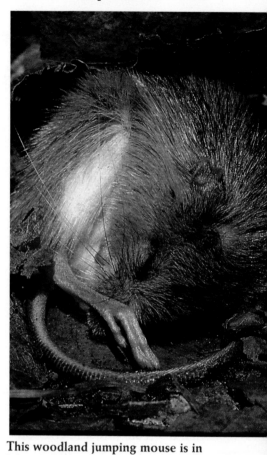

This woodland jumping mouse is in hibernation.

Section review questions

1. Define adaptation. Why is adaptation important to living organisms?
2. Match the three types of adaptation with their definitions.
   a) behavioural
   b) functional
   c) structural

   • the physical characteristics of a living organism that help it to survive in an environment
   • the way an organism responds to stimuli in its environment
   • adaptations related to the life functions of living organisms such as breathing
3. Why are structural adaptations important to plants and animals? List and explain four examples.
4. State two types of plant tropism. How do plants respond to the stimulus of water?
5. What is the difference between instinctive and learned behaviour? State one example of each.
6. Explain why some animals migrate.
7. Why is hibernation in animals a functional adaptation?

Did you know?
Estivation is a type of summer hibernation. Some animals, such as the snail, go into estivation to escape heat and dryness.

Human adaptation

The most important human adaptation is intelligence or intellect. The ability of humans to observe, think, and understand things about their living and non-living environment has enabled them to populate a wide variety of environments on Earth.

In fact, intellect has led to the creation of devices that can enable humans to live and function in the environment of space beyond the Earth's atmosphere.

Space is a hostile environment that will not support life as we know it on Earth. To overcome this difference, scientists and technologists have had to create artificial environments that will support humans in space. Humans need to be protected against extremes in temperature, radiation, and the effects of being weightless. Special methods have been developed to maintain nutrition, waste management, breathing, hygiene, exercise, and mental health.

Scientists and technologists have developed spacecraft that will allow humans to travel to and from space safely. Special space suits have been designed to help astronauts adapt to different environmental conditions. Scientists have used the Skylab and *Mir* orbiting space

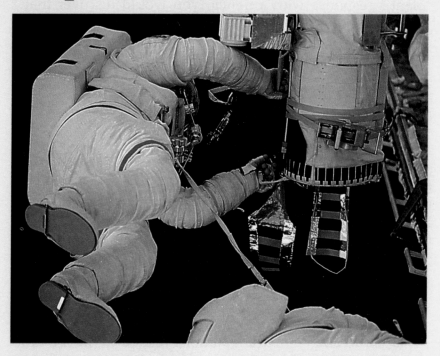

laboratories to monitor the effects of weightlessness on the bodies of astronauts. They discovered that the astronauts' backbones lengthened causing them to grow slightly taller. The astronauts' faces flattened as body fluids moved upward, their hearts shrank slightly, and their blood lost 14% of its red-blood cells.

To help astronauts adjust, scientists have devised exercise programs for use in space. They have also developed ways for astronauts to move efficiently while being weightless. To maintain good health, astronauts adjust to regular

menus prepared from dehydrated foods. Waste management is critical, so a special waste collector operated by suction has been developed.

To cope with the conditions of space and the technology needed to ensure their survival, astronauts receive special training on Earth under simulated conditions. With the help of science and technology, humans are finding ways to adjust to life in an environment that would have been impossible to survive in 50 years ago.

6.2 The physical environment and the basic needs of organisms

You don't really think about what to wear on a cold, snowy day. You know that to survive during the winter you must keep yourself warm. So you wear warm clothing to keep in the heat. Cold temperatures, shorter days, snow, and the duration of winter are features of the physical environment you live in. You can think of the way you dress during the winter as a kind of behavioural adaptation that suits you for survival in your environment.

You have seen that adaptations in structure, behaviour, and function help organisms to survive in their particular environments. In this section, you will learn more about different environmental conditions and the basic needs of organisms for survival. Knowing about environmental conditions and the physical necessities of organisms will help you to understand why adaptation is so important to the survival of living things.

Figure 6–3

A terrestrial environment

An aquatic environment

The physical environment

The physical environment of Earth varies from place to place, but all environments have certain things in common. They all have climates, which are determined by the length of daylight, temperature range, rainfall patterns, and seasonal change. These factors combined with physical features, such as soil type, water, air, and mountain, plain or coastal location, form specific environments. **Terrestrial environments** include deserts, grasslands, forests, and arctic regions. **Aquatic environments** include oceans, lakes, rivers, ponds, and streams.

Each environment has characteristic plants and animals that are suited to live in its physical conditions. Living and non-living things together make up an environment. Many organisms would die if removed from their habitat such as a fish out of water. The environment must provide the essential needs of living things: food, shelter, and suitable conditions for reproduction. Using aquariums and terrariums in the classroom can help you to study the adaptations of living organisms in their habitats.

Investigation 3   Constructing a natural habitat

PURPOSE
To design a procedure for constructing a natural habitat for living organisms.

MATERIALS
list based on research

PROCEDURE
1. Ask your teacher to divide your class into four groups. (Two groups will design aquatic environments and two will design terrestial environments.)
2. Depending on the habitat your group is to design, research how aquariums and terrariums are constructed.
3. List all of the materials you will need for the construction of your natural habitat.
4. Write down all of the steps you will follow to construct your natural habitat. (This will be your Procedure.) Be

Figure 6–4 Constructing an aquarium

sure to consider the type of container, soil, water, heat, light, and any plants and animals you want to include.
5. Find an appropriate location for your display. Include this information in your Procedure.
6. When your group has completed the Procedure for the investigation, ask your teacher to approve it.
7. Follow the steps of the Procedure to construct a natural habitat.

Caution: Some people have allergies to certain plants or animals. If you have allergies, or if your eyes and nose become irritated during this investigation, be sure to inform your teacher immediately.

OBSERVATIONS
1. Make written notes about the living and non-living components of your natural habitat.
2. Design a chart to record your observations of the adaptations of the plants and animals in your habitat.
3. Design another chart to compare your observations with those of another group. (Choose a different habitat for this comparison.)

Discussion questions

1. Describe the relationship between the living and non-living things in your habitat.
2. Identify and explain the adaptations of the plants and animals in your habitat.
3. Why do you think it is important to preserve natural habitats?

A tornado can cause a sudden change to an environment.

The physical environment of Earth is always changing. Usually, these changes are very gradual. The transformation of a marsh to a forest takes hundreds of years. But sometimes the physical conditions of an environment may change very quickly. Sudden changes may be caused by earthquakes, floods, forest fires, or diseases. Human activity also influences the rate at which environmental change takes place.

Sudden changes to an environment often kill many of the organisms that grow and reproduce there. When living conditions change, organisms with the greatest abilities to adapt survive. Gradual changes, however, give animals and plants a chance to move or develop characteristics that will help them to survive in a changed environment.

In this section, you will learn about desert, pond, and forest environments.

The desert environment

If you were asked to think of an environment scorched by the sun, having little rainfall and extreme temperatures, you would probably think of the desert. Deserts cover 14% of the Earth's surface and receive less than 25 cm of rainfall annually. Deserts have a variety of appearances. They may have vast areas of shifting sand dunes, or rocky slopes where wind erosion carves strange shapes.

Torrential rainfall sometimes creates shallow lakes that evaporate quickly. Deserts receive 90% of all available solar energy, causing scorching heat during the day. At night, desert temperatures become extremely cold. The cloudless sky and dry air provide poor insulation, and heat is lost rapidly from the land.

British Columbia, for example, has a mini-desert of sand dunes, sagebrush, and prickly pear cactus. Long hours of sunshine and less than 20 cm of rainfall annually created this environment, which is unique in Canada. Rattlesnakes, marmots, pygmy horned toads, bats, swifts, wrens, and nighthawks make their home in this desert region.

In deserts, water is in short supply. Plants that live in deserts must have adaptations that are designed to help them use every drop of water.

The pond environment

Ponds are often the result of depressions formed by glaciers, or are constructed by animal engineers such as the beaver.

The Walhachin desert in British Columbia

Did you know?
Deserts have very high temperatures during the day. A record high temperature of 56.6°C was recorded at Death Valley desert in California.

Some ponds are made by humans to supply water for irrigation, to attract waterfowl, to control erosion, or for recreational uses. A wide variety of aquatic plants and animals, such as the water lily and the otter, live in a pond environment.

Water quality is important to the survival of aquatic organisms. The variables that control water quality include temperature, concentration of gases, nutrients, sediment, and pH levels. The temperature range in a pond is usually less than that in the air above it, and is determined by shade, depth, and speed of water flow.

Concentrations of dissolved gases in pond water are determined by temperature and water turbulence. A good supply of dissolved oxygen is necessary for most aquatic organisms. The amount of suspended sediment in pond water is determined by how fast the water flows. Too much sediment cuts down on light penetration, which can affect the breathing of organisms. Sand, mud, and silt on the floor of a pond contain nutrients required by plants, and can also affect the pH of the water. Most organisms have a range of pH tolerance beyond which they are unable to survive.

Hundreds of species of plants grow in or near freshwater ponds and possess adaptations that enable them to live there.

A freshwater pond in Ontario

The forest environment

Canada is well known as a country of forests, having one-third of its area covered with trees. Although the dominant vegetation in forests is the tree, forests are complex systems of non-living and living things. Animals, such as squirrels, foxes, bears, deer, and beavers, and plants such as mosses, wildflowers, ferns, fungi, and shrubs grow in Canada's forests. Coniferous, or needle-bearing, trees dominate Canadian forests.

Coniferous forests are found across northern Canada and have temperatures that range from $-30°C$ to $20°C$. Northern forests have a short growing season and long, cold winters. Low annual precipitation of 50 cm is concentrated during the summer. Poor drainage conditions create water-logged, acidic, and nutrient-deficient soils. The forest floor is covered with a dense cushion of fallen needles.

Deciduous, or broad-leaf, trees are found in forests in the eastern half of North America where the climate is less severe. Temperatures in these forests range from $-12°C$ to

A forest in New Brunswick

27°C, and there is a longer growing season. Annual precipitation of 75–125 cm is evenly distributed throughout the four seasons. Deciduous forests are more humid during the spring growing season.

The soil found in deciduous forests is described as "brown earth." The forest floor is usually covered with leaves that decompose quickly to provide a renewed supply of soil nutrients for the next growing season.

Cows eat plants to survive.

You need to eat plants, too.

Try this!

Look at the organisms in Figure 6–5. Can you predict the type of habitat each one requires? State whether they are terrestrial or aquatic environments. Make inferences about how each organism is adapted to its environment. Use a chart to organize your answers. Include the headings Organism, Habitat, and Adaptations.

Basic needs of plants and animals

All living things require food, oxygen to breathe, space to build their nests and burrows or spread their roots, and the proper conditions for reproduction. From their physical environments, living things obtain gases, nutrients, food, and water, all of which support their life functions. Plants make their own food from carbon dioxide, water, and sunlight. They also depend on soil conditions to obtain nutrients and to give them support. Animals need to eat plants or other animals in order to survive, so they must have adaptations that help them to obtain these necessities. Many animals cannot alter their immediate environments the way humans can, so they often move from place to place to obtain food. You are dependent on both plants and animals for the necessities of life such as food, clothing, and shelter.

Figure 6–5 Plants and animals from different environments

Try this!

We are distinct from other living organisms because of our intelligence. We can solve problems and change the way we meet the challenges of our environment. These characteristics enable us to live anywhere on Earth for certain periods of time. For example, humans manipulate the environment by domesticating plants and animals and by using raw materials for agriculture and industry. We also alter the landscape by cutting down forests and building dams. We consume many processed and preserved foods. We change our clothing to adjust to climate conditions. We also construct a variety of shelters for protection. Today, many people think that we consume natural resources beyond what we need to survive. As a result, these resources are in danger of being depleted. Make a list of your basic needs for a 24-h period. Then make a list of what you eat, wear, or do to meet these needs in the same time period. Compare both lists. Are there any differences that might suggest a reason why people are concerned about the depletion of natural resources and global pollution?

Light

Different places on Earth receive different amounts of light. The duration of sunlight varies with geographic location and seasonal change, while the intensity of light depends on the time of day or the season. These differences in light conditions affect the distribution of plants.

Light is essential to plants for photosynthesis and flower formation. The duration of light controls the flowering of many plants. Some plants flower at night, while others only flower during the day.

Did you know?
Red algae are adapted for photosynthesis. They contain a red pigment that traps light and transmits the energy to cells containing chlorophyll for photosynthesis.

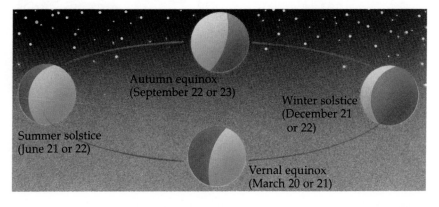

Figure 6–6 Seasonal change and the length of daylight

Autumn equinox
(September 22 or 23)

Winter solstice
(December 21 or 22)

Summer solstice
(June 21 or 22)

Vernal equinox
(March 20 or 21)

What differences can you see between these two environments and the amounts of light they receive?

In environments where light is unable to penetrate, vegetation is limited to organisms such as fungi (moulds and mushrooms), which do not contain chlorophyll but are nourished by organic matter.

In aquatic environments, light decreases with the depth of the water, so plants that have chlorophyll live only in the surface regions. There are no plants below a certain depth of water.

Light allows animals that are active during the day to see. Vision enables these animals to locate food, construct nests or burrows, mate and care for their young.

Temperature
Temperature influences the important processes of photosynthesis, respiration, flower formation, and seed production of plants. Most plants are adapted to survive in a specific temperature range. Temperatures below 0°C or above 43°C result in injury or death to most plants unless they have special adaptations. In cold regions, conifers develop frost-resistant needles with a waxy coating and are capable of withstanding temperatures well below the freezing point. In warmer regions, deciduous trees shed their leaves and

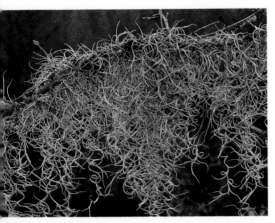

Spanish moss needs warm temperatures to survive.

Animals could not survive without water.

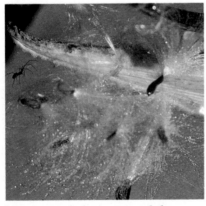

Moving air helps to spread the seeds of this milkweed plant.

become dormant during the winter. Other plants die down but grow again the following spring from dormant roots or seeds.

Temperature also affects animals. Temperature changes can cause some animals to moult or change colour. Temperature also affects migration, metamorphosis, hibernation, and the incubation of eggs.

Water

Plants and animals could not survive without water. Where moisture is abundant, foliage is dense and animal populations are large. Plants such as orchids and Spanish moss have aerial roots that can absorb moisture directly from the air in the humid tropics. Besides having roots to absorb moisture, plants have adaptations that help them to conserve moisture in dry regions, or to live completely or partly submerged in aquatic environments.

Some animals live in and obtain oxygen from water. Other animals, such as the beaver, use water for transportation and as a means of keeping clean.

Soil

Soil is a mixture of rock particles, minerals, air, water, and organic matter known as humus. Soil provides anchorage, nutrients, and air. Soil varies in type. Clay, loam, and sand are examples of different soils. Depending on their chemical composition, some soils can be alkaline, neutral, or acidic. Most plants survive best in neutral soils that obtain moderate amounts of air and water. Some plants, such as the blueberry, are adapted to grow in acidic soils, while cacti prefer alkaline soils.

Soil is also important to burrowing animals for shelter. Soil provides food in the form of organic matter for organisms such as the earthworm. Many animals bury their eggs in soil during reproduction. Others use soil for camouflage, food storage, hibernation, and waste disposal.

Air

The atmosphere contains oxygen, nitrogen, carbon dioxide, and water vapour necessary for living things to carry out their life functions. Plants have structural and functional adaptations to acquire, use, and expel these gases during respiration, transpiration, and photosynthesis. Moving air also helps plants to spread pollen, seeds, and spores. Too much wind, however, may cause plants to dry out, distort their shape, or uproot them.

Many animals breathe air to obtain oxygen.

Try this!

The next time you go to a zoo, investigate the different kinds of indoor exhibits. How are these different environments created? Why are some humid and hot, and others dry and cold? Did you see aquatic and terrestrial environments? What types of animals and plants did you find in each environment? Find out how the conditions in each environment are monitored. Make a report to your class.

Section review questions

1. What features are common to all physical environments?
2. State two main types of environments on Earth. List three examples of each.
3. State five characteristics each of a desert environment, a pond environment, and a forest environment. List several plants and animals that live in each environment.
4. How does the physical environment provide the basic needs for survival for plants and animals?
5. Explain why light, temperature, water, soil, and air are important to plants and animals.

An indoor exhibit at the Metro Toronto Zoo

Human impact on the Arctic environment

When you think of the Arctic, you probably think of a vast region of ice and permafrost. Although the Arctic does have long, dark winters with strong winds and very low temperatures, it also has short summers of continual sunshine and moderate temperatures.

Lichens, mosses, shrubs, and many other plants cover most of the Arctic's low, swampy plains. Arctic plants have adaptations that enable them to conserve heat and moisture. For example, some Arctic plants have fuzzy stems for insulation. Others have branching roots that enable them to obtain moisture and leathery leaves that help them to reduce water loss.

Many animals are also adapted to survive in the Arctic environment. Insects, for example, thrive in the summer. Many species of migratory birds nest in the Arctic, eating these insects and taking advantage of the constant daylight. Polar bears, caribou, seals, and wolves are some of the larger animals that live in the Arctic.

But the Arctic environment is a fragile one, and human activity in this region threatens

to upset the Arctic's delicate balance. As accessible deposits of fossil fuels, such as oil, coal, and natural gas, are depleted, the oil industry has turned to offshore drilling and Arctic exploration to find new deposits.

Many people are concerned about the impact of these activities on the Arctic environment. The Inuit worry that oil spills will threaten the land and marine life necessary for their economic survival. The construction of oil wells, pipelines, and roads may affect the calving grounds and migratory routes of caribou, seals, and

whales. Petroleum refining and ore smelting produce sulphur dioxide, resulting in pollution that kills lichens, an important food source for caribou.

To ensure that the development of the North does not threaten the Arctic environment, more knowledge is needed about the adaptations of Arctic organisms and how change can affect them. Lessening the destructive impact of human activity in a fragile environment like the Arctic will help to preserve the many organisms that grow and reproduce there.

6.3 Adaptations of plants

Plants are essential to the existence of all living things. Plants are unique because, unlike animals, they are able to manufacture their own food, and they form the basis of the food chain. You depend on plants, and on animals that eat plants, for your food. Plants grow on land, in oceans, in tropical rain forests, on rocks, and even on other living things.

Like animals, plants must compete for the basic needs of their survival. They must have special adaptations that suit them to their particular environments, enabling them to obtain air, light, water, nutrients, and space to grow. Without these special adaptations, they would be unable to survive.

In this section, you will discover some of the unique adaptations that suit plants for survival in the three environments you examined in Section 6.2.

These plants are suited to grow on rocks.

Adaptations of desert plants

In Section 6.2, you learned that the desert environment receives little rainfall and has temperatures that range from very hot to very cold. Plants that live in deserts must have adaptations that help them to conserve water.

Cacti have adaptations to reduce water loss. Cacti come in a variety of shapes from pin cushions to thorny trees. Some cacti are soft and squishy; others are woody and hard. Their stems contain large chambers made up of tissue that can take in and hold large amounts of moisture. Water stored in the stem of the barrel cactus enables it to live for more than a year on a single load of water. Prickly spines and thick, waxy, waterproof skins are structural adaptations cacti have to help them reduce water loss. The spines also protect cacti from being eaten by animals. You will learn more about cacti in Investigation 4.

Other desert plants obtain moisture from the dew that condenses on their surfaces during the cold desert nights. Some trees, such as the acacia and the mesquite, have roots that can grow to 30 m in length, enabling them to reach underground water sources.

Some desert plants have short life cycles, so they can complete their growth and reproduction cycles in the brief, rainy

Saguaro cactus

Hedgehog cactus

Did you know?
The saguaro cactus is a living accordion that swells to store water and contracts as its water supply is reduced.

periods between droughts. Short life cycles are functional adaptations that help desert plants to survive. When their seeds are exposed to rain, new plants grow, mature, are pollinated by insects, and produce seeds in just a few weeks.

Other desert plants reduce water loss by becoming dormant during periods of drought. Dormancy is another example of a functional adaptation.

Investigation 4 Adaptations of desert plants

Did you know?
Not all cacti are leafless. Some types sprout tiny leaves for a brief period, while others grow leaves that can be seen only under a microscope.

PROBLEM
How do the structural characteristics of cacti adapt them for survival in a desert environment?

MATERIALS
several different specimens of cacti
magnifying glass
microscope
glass slide
cover slip
red food colouring
small spoon
water
eyedropper
tweezers

MEASURING TOOL
ruler

HYPOTHESIS
State how the structural characteristics of cacti help them to survive in a desert environment.

Caution: Be careful not to scratch yourself on the spines of the cactus when you are handling it.

PROCEDURE
1. After your teacher has divided your class into groups, choose one cactus specimen for your group to observe.
2. Remove the potting soil to expose the root system.
3. Using the magnifying glass, carefully observe each structural characteristic of the cactus your group has chosen. Record your observations.
4. Use the ruler to measure the spines, stem, and root of your specimen where possible. Record your measurements.

5. Make a wet-mount slide by removing a small portion of the skin of the cactus with the tweezers. Place the skin specimen in the centre of the glass slide. (See Figure 6–7.)
6. Make a stain by adding one drop of red food colouring to a small spoonful of water. (The stain makes the specimen easier to see.)
7. Use the eyedropper to add a drop of stain to the specimen on the slide. Use the tweezers to lower the cover slip over the specimen.
8. Observe the specimen under the low-power objective of the microscope. Record any additional observations about your cactus plant in your chart.

OBSERVATIONS
1. Record your observations of the cactus in a chart like the one below.

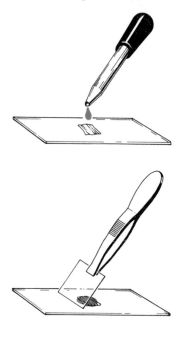

Structural Characteristic	Description
Colour	
Spines (shape, number, size)	
Roots (type, structure, size)	
Breathing Pores (location)	
Flower	

Figure 6–7 Preparing a wet-mount slide

2. Record the colour of your specimen. Are there any variations in the colour of your cactus?

CONCLUSIONS
What can you conclude about how the structural characteristics of cacti adapt them for survival in a desert environment?

Figure 6–8 Common plants adapted to the pond environment

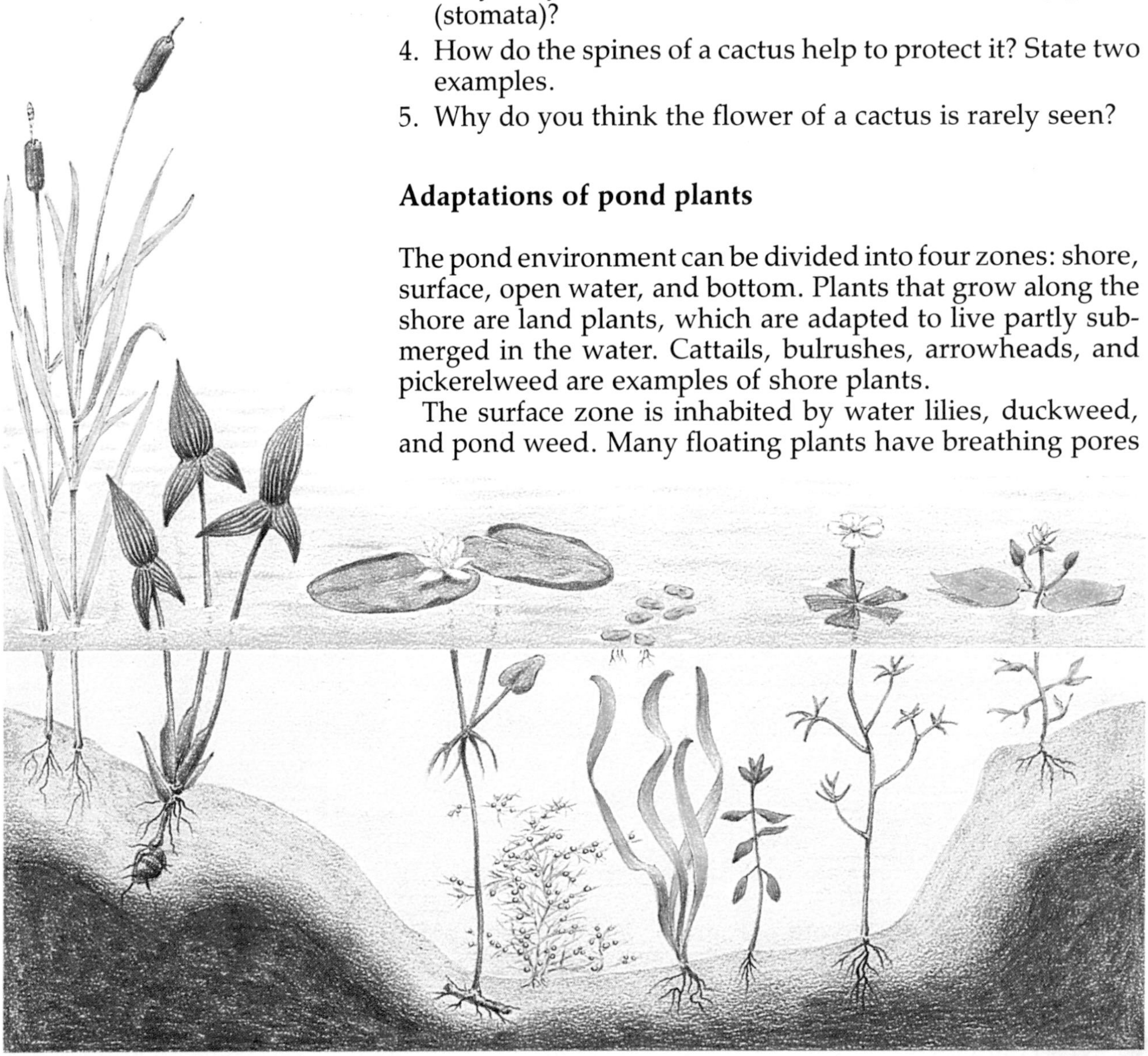

Discussion questions

1. Which adaptations help cacti to conserve water? Why?
2. How does the root system of a cactus help it to survive in the desert?
3. Why do you think cacti have so few breathing pores (stomata)?
4. How do the spines of a cactus help to protect it? State two examples.
5. Why do you think the flower of a cactus is rarely seen?

Adaptations of pond plants

The pond environment can be divided into four zones: shore, surface, open water, and bottom. Plants that grow along the shore are land plants, which are adapted to live partly submerged in the water. Cattails, bulrushes, arrowheads, and pickerelweed are examples of shore plants.

The surface zone is inhabited by water lilies, duckweed, and pond weed. Many floating plants have breathing pores on the upper surface of their leaves. Other structural adaptations include water-repellent surfaces, air cells in leaves and stems to keep the plants buoyant, and broad leaves for maximum exposure to sunlight. Some surface plants have flexible stalks to keep them rooted in favourable growing locations. Free-floating plants do not have anchors. They have thickly branching roots instead.

The open water and bottom zone contain algae and submerged plants such as waterweed and watercelery. Submerged plants have soft, feathery foliage. Sometimes they produce aerial flower stems to enable the flowers to reach the air for pollination and reproduction. The water crowfoot is an example of this adaptation. In Investigation 5, you will investigate the adaptations of the water lily that help it to survive in a pond environment.

The shore of a pond

Investigation 5   Adaptations of a water lily

PROBLEM
How do the structural characteristics of a water lily adapt it for survival in a pond environment?

MATERIALS   MEASURING TOOL
water lily obtained   ruler
  from a pond
aquarium filled with
  pond water
magnifying glass
Vaseline

HYPOTHESIS
State how the structural characteristics of a water lily help it to survive in a pond environment.

PROCEDURE
1. Carefully observe the structural characteristics of the water lily. Use the magnifying glass and the ruler to improve the accuracy of your observations. Record your observations.
2. Cover one-quarter of the plant's leaf surface with Vaseline. Place the water lily in the aquarium. Observe the changes that take place in the plant over a seven-day period.

Figure 6–9

OBSERVATIONS
1. Record your observations of the water lily in a chart like the one below.

Structural Characteristic	Description
Leaf (colour, shape, effect of Vaseline)	
Stem (colour, length, flexibility)	
Roots (type, structure, size)	
Flower	

2. Record any changes you observed in the plant after it was covered with Vaseline.

CONCLUSIONS
What conclusions can you make about the adaptations that suit a water lily for life in an aquatic environment?

Discussion questions

1. Which adaptations help to keep the leaves of the water lily buoyant?
2. Which functions do the roots and the stalk of the water lily perform?
3. After observing the effects of the Vaseline on the leaves of the water lily, what can you infer about the location and function of its breathing pores?
4. How do you think the water lily reproduces? Support your inference.

Adaptations of forest plants

Conifers, such as spruce, pine, fir, balsam, and tamarack, have needles with waxy coatings and few breathing pores. These are structural adaptations that reduce water loss and help the trees to withstand freezing temperatures. Conifer needles are shed gradually, so the trees can carry out photosynthesis throughout the year. Since the soil that conifers grow in is often water-logged, acidic, and lacking in nutrients, their root systems are shallow and branch out widely. Conifers produce seeds and pollen in cones, which are adapted for pollination by the wind. The tall angular shape of conifers and their flexible branches are adaptations that enable them to withstand heavy snow and strong winds.

Deciduous trees, such as oak, chestnut, beech, and maple, also have many structural adaptations that help them to survive in the forest. These broad-leaf trees have fibrous root systems that extend deep into the soil to obtain moisture and nutrients.

The leaves of deciduous trees vary in form and arrangement. This helps them carry out photosynthesis during the growing season. Some trees have spiral, lobed, fringed, or alternating leaf arrangements that allow light to filter through to all of their leaves.

Giant sequoias

Did you know?
Conifers are the world's oldest, tallest, and biggest trees. In California, the oldest known specimen is 4600 years old. The tallest conifer is a coastal redwood that is 111.6 m high. The biggest conifer is a giant sequoia that measures 24 m in diameter at its base and is 24 m high.

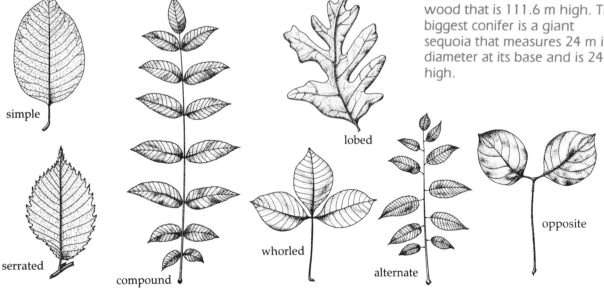

Figure 6–10   Various leaf structures

In the autumn, deciduous trees no longer produce chlorophyll, which is why their leaves change colour and fall off. Deciduous trees are dormant in the winter, which is a functional adaptation, surviving on stored food until the spring.

Shade-tolerant trees, shrubs, bushes, herbs, and flowering plants complete their reproductive cycles before the leaves of deciduous trees form. This functional adaptation allows them to grow before they are shaded by the leaves of deciduous trees. Shade-plant adaptations include thin, broad leaves with stomata on both sides and dull surfaces that help to absorb light.

Investigation 6   The effect of light on a fern

PROBLEM
How does varying the intensity of light affect the structural characteristics of a fern plant?

MATERIALS
2 healthy ferns of similar size
2 rectangular peat pots
masking tape
marker
potting soil
cardboard box
scissors
water

HYPOTHESIS
State how varying the intensity of light will affect a fern plant.

PROCEDURE

Be careful when removing any plant from its natural habitat. Make sure that you do not injure its root system or disturb other living things around it.

1. Carefully dig up two ferns from their natural habitat.
2. Observe the structural characteristics of both ferns. Record your observations.
3. Plant each fern in a rectangular peat pot using 5 cm of potting soil. Using the masking tape and the marker, label one pot Plant A and the other pot Plant B.
4. Place both plants in a sunny location.
5. Prepare a sun shield by removing two sides from a cardboard box (see Figure 6–11). Place the box over Plant B to prevent it from receiving direct sunlight.

6. Leave Plant A exposed to direct sunlight.
7. Water both plants daily with 20 mL of water.
8. Observe both plants every five days for one month. Record your observations.

OBSERVATIONS
1. Record your observations of the structural characteristics of the ferns in a chart like the one below. (Fronds are the leaf-like structures on the fern.)

Structural Characteristic	Description	
	Plant A	Plant B
Fronds (shape, colour upper surface, lower surface)		
Stem (type, colour shape)		
Roots (type, number)		
Spore Capsules (location, colour)		

cardboard box

2. Record your observations of the effect of light on the ferns in a chart like the one below.

Time	Effect of Light on Plant A	Effect of Light on Plant B
Day 5		
Day 10		
Day 15		
Day 20		
Day 25		
Day 30		

Figure 6–11

CONCLUSIONS

What can you conclude about the effect of light on fern plants?

Discussion questions

1. Identify the variable you tested in this investigation. Which variables did you control?
2. Infer why the spore capsules are located on the lower surface of the fronds rather than on the upper surface?
3. For what type of environment is a fern best suited?
4. What are the adaptations that suit a fern to life in that environment?

Section review questions

1. Explain four adaptations of desert plants caused by limited water supplies in the desert.
2. What are the four zones of a typical pond? List one plant found in each zone and explain how it is adapted to this zone.
3. Explain and compare the adaptations of coniferous and deciduous trees to their environments.
4. Why would a cactus be unable to survive in an aquatic environment?
5. Could the drainage of wetlands cause the extinction of water lilies? State reasons to support your opinion.

SCIENCE IN OUR LIVES

Cloning and plant breeding

Since the beginning of agriculture, people have been trying to breed better plants. Today, most cultivated crops in North America are the result of the efforts of early farmers. As the world's population increases, the need for more efficient food production grows. Plant-breeding programs play an important role in agricultural development throughout the world.

Plant-breeding programs are designed to develop characteristics that will suit crops to a particular environment. This research is very important for crop development in environments that have harsh climates.

Cross-breeding, or hybridization, is a traditional plant-breeding technique. Recently, however, biotechnologists have developed another breeding technique called cloning. Cloning is a method of reproduction where a single plant cell develops into an identical plant to the one from which the cell was taken. Microscopic bits of tissue are taken from superior plant breeds and placed in a solution of nutrients, vitamins, and growth regulators. Shoots are removed as they grow, making it possible to produce one million identical plants from an original plant.

The Orono Nursery in Orono Provincial Forest uses cloning to produce Norway spruce seedlings.

Nova Biotechnology, a research company in Nova Scotia, uses cloning to produce 32 different kinds of fruit bushes, plants, and herbs. They are grown in disease-free, climate-controlled greenhouses. The Canadian National Research Council also employs many scientists in the biotechnology field to improve the quality and yield of crops. They have developed cold-resistant strains better suited to the cold Canadian climate.

Cold-resistant strawberries have been developed and cloned. Plants with natural defences against insects have also been developed and could reduce the need for chemical spraying. Research continues with canola, wheat, barley, and sunflowers.

The widespread use of cloning techniques could have a positive effect on world agriculture through the development of better-adapted, higher-yielding crops.

6.4 Adaptations of animals

The environment an animal lives in is directly related to its ability to provide the necessities of life. Animals must have the adaptations that enable them to acquire and compete for these necessities. The method an animal uses to breathe (diffusion, gills, lungs, skin) is an adaptation to its environment (air, land, water, soil). The same is true for the way an animal moves, obtains food, defends itself, and builds its home.

In this section, you will examine the adaptations that suit animals to desert, pond, and forest environments.

Adaptations of desert animals

Can you remember the characteristics of a desert environment and the kinds of plants that grow there? Most deserts contain a wide variety of animals, including insects, spiders, reptiles, mammals, and birds.

Some animals have functional adaptations that help them to avoid extreme light, heat, and dryness. Some of them burrow beneath the sand to create a cooler micro-climate. These animals usually have structural adaptations that help them to burrow. Some reptiles have upturned nostrils, and some lizards have large shields that hang over their eyes to protect them from the sand.

Hordes of flies, beetles, ants, wasps, and locusts can be found in a desert. Their small size enables them to avoid the spines of cacti, so they can feed on desert plants, or drink the drops of moisture that condense on the plants' surfaces. Insects, whose bodies are composed mostly of water, provide moisture for lizards, spiders, and scorpions.

Many desert animals have functional and structural adaptations that help them to conserve moisture. The kangaroo rat's body system, for example, functions efficiently on the small amount of water contained in its food, so it never needs to drink. Reptiles, such as lizards and desert tortoises, have thick outer coverings that reduce water loss from the surface of their bodies.

Small desert mammals are able to cool the air in their noses, causing the moisture in their breath to condense so that it is not lost as water vapour when the air leaves their nostrils.

How is this lizard adapted to survive in the desert?

green plants

camel

falcon

lizard

dung beetle

Figure 6–12   Plants and animals in a desert environment

Gazelles and other grazing animals can survive indefinitely on the small amount of water they obtain from the plants they eat. Camels can drink large amounts of water at one time and are able to retain water for long periods of time. Their body temperatures can fluctuate to reduce the moisture lost through sweating and panting.

The most common types of birds found in the desert are insect-eaters. Very few hawks and birds of prey live in the desert. Most desert birds live within flight range of a water source. Their reproductive cycle, which is a functional adaptation, is linked to the arrival of rains and a plentiful food supply. During droughts, many desert birds produce fewer young or do not breed at all.

Most desert-dwelling animals are structurally adapted by colour camouflage. What advantages do you think camouflage would have for desert animals? Pale sandy tones can also act as a cooling system because lighter colours reflect more of the sun's rays. The colour of some lizards changes with daily temperatures. These animals are darker in the morning and the evening, but paler during midday.

Because these dromedary camels have long legs, they can run at fast speeds. What advantage do you think this might give them in the desert?

Did you know?
Some seed-eating rodents have adaptations to help them to conserve water. During the day, they plug the entrances of their burrows with seeds. The moisture lost while the animals sleep is absorbed by the seeds, then regained by the rodents at night when they eat the seeds.

Did you know?
Frogs have adaptations that suit them to life on land and in the water. They are members of a group known as amphibians.

Try this!

Sketch and label the desert regions on a map of the world. Collect pictures of desert animals and try to identify the structural adaptations that enable them to live in the desert environment. Research the kind of food they eat and how they are able to obtain it. What is "desertification"? Why does it concern people who live near deserts? Research why deserts are spreading in many parts of the world. Is any action being taken to prevent desertification? Write a report about your findings.

Adaptations of pond animals

Ontario has many lakes, rivers, streams, and ponds. These areas provide a natural environment for numerous species of animals. Earlier in this chapter, you examined the physical characteristics of the pond environment and the adaptations that suit certain plants to that environment. The animals that survive in the pond environment also exhibit interesting adaptations.

Most animals that live in or near a pond are quite small. Many of these animals are species of insects such as mosquitoes and dragonflies. The adult dragonfly lays its eggs in the pond, and the larvae obtain oxygen through breathing gills. Whirligig beetles have water-repellent bodies that ena-

A water strider

A leopard frog

ble them to skitter across the surface of the pond. Water beetles trap air beneath their wings to help them return to the surface after they dive into the pond. You can learn a great deal by visiting a local pond. Investigation 7 will give you an opportunity to conduct your own field trip to a pond.

Investigation 7   Observing animal adaptations in a
                             pond environment

PURPOSE
To collect animals living in or near a pond and to observe their structural adaptations.

MATERIALS
clipboard
paper
pencil
4 collecting jars with lids
masking tape
marker
butterfly net
dip net
kitchen strainer
pail
paper towels
tweezers
magnifying glass
nature guidebook on pond animals

PROCEDURE

PART A
1. This investigation involves leaving your school on a field trip. Before you leave, ask your teacher to divide your class into four investigating teams. Each team should prepare a checklist based on Steps 2 and 3 below. Attach the checklist to a clipboard and use it as a guide for this investigation.
2. The first heading on your checklist should be Materials. List each item you will need to conduct this investigation. (The list of materials above is a good place to start.) Before leaving your school, make sure that your team has everything it needs.

Caution: Be sure that you are familiar with water safety rules before starting this investigation. Learn how to identify poisonous plants such as poison ivy, poison oak, and poison sumac. If you suffer from allergies to certain plants or animals, be sure to inform your teacher.

Try not to disturb the pond environment too much while conducting your investigation. Remove everything you have used after the field study and leave the pond in its original condition.

Figure 6–13

3. List the steps you should follow to investigate the animals living in or near the pond. Use the steps in Part B as a guide. Your teacher may have other suggestions for steps you might follow.

PART B

1. When you reach the pond, sit quietly for 5-10 min and observe the characteristics of the environment. You may want to make a sketch of the location.
2. Select a spot you would like to investigate. If you have sketched a map, mark your spot on the map with a circle.
3. Move to that location and follow Steps 4–7 to collect your specimens.
4. Pass a butterfly net through the plants growing along the shoreline. Place any specimens in a collecting jar and use the masking tape and marker to label it Shoreline. You should repeat this step three to five times.
5. Skim the surface of the pond with a dip net. Place any specimens in a collecting jar and label it Surface. You should repeat this step three to five times.
6. Dip the kitchen strainer completely under the surface of the water, then move it in an arc in front of you. Place any specimens in a collecting jar and label it Open Water. You should repeat this step three to five times.
7. Use the strainer to scoop up some muck from the bottom of the pond. Using the pail, carefully pour water through the strainer to remove the muck. Place any specimens in a collecting jar and label it Bottom. You should repeat this step three to five times.

PART C

1. Remove the specimens from the Shoreline collection jar and place them on a paper towel.
2. Use the tweezers and the magnifying glass to examine the specimens carefully. Use the nature guidebook to identify each organism. Count how many specimens you have collected of each species. Note any structural adaptations and infer their purpose.
3. When you have completed Steps 1 and 2, return the organisms to their original locations.
4. Repeat Steps 1–3 for the other three collecting jars.

OBSERVATIONS
1. Before you go to the pond, copy the following chart onto a sheet of paper and attach it to the clipboard. Record your team's observations from Part C in the chart.

Location	Name of Specimen	Number Found	Description	Adaptation	Purpose of Adaptation
Shoreline	• • •				
Surface	• • •				
Open Water	• • •				
Bottom	• • •				

2. When you have returned to school, copy the chart onto the chalkboard. As a class, record all the information collected by each team. Compare your team's observations with this chart.

CONCLUSIONS
What can you conclude about the structural adaptations of animals that live in a pond environment?

Discussion questions

1. Why was it necessary to repeat Steps 4–7 in Part B several times?
2. Which adaptations were shared by animals living in each of the four zones?
3. Which species was the most abundant? Which was the least? Why?
4. Which zone had the largest number of different species. Can you suggest a reason why this might be so?

A black bear

A mule deer fawn

A beaver

5. Why would conservationists argue that the preservation of the pond environment is important?

Adaptations of forest animals

Forests are very complex environments. They support many animals such as deer, wolves, porcupines, racoons, muskrats, skunks, birds, waterfowl, and a large number of insect species. All of these animals have adaptations that enable them to survive in the forest. Some have adaptations that help to protect them from larger animals. For example, the porcupine has sharp quills and the skunk releases a spray when it is threatened. The woodpecker has a specially shaped beak that enables it to eat insects from the bark of trees. Ducks use their flat bills to strain small, water-dwelling animals from streams, ponds, and lakes. Bees and ants live in highly organized communities that enable them to gather food.

Try this!

The beaver is a fascinating forest animal. It has many adaptations that enable it to survive in the forest environment. Unlike many animals, the beaver is able to change its environment to increase its chances of survival. Beavers build dams to create small ponds or streams that run through forests. This ability helps the beaver to survive the harsh winter months and to protect them from larger animals in the forest. Beavers have sharp claws, long, sharp front teeth, thick water-repellent fur, and large, flat tails. These structural adaptations help the beaver to cut down small trees, and to arrange them with mud and stones to construct a dam. The dam causes the stream to back up and overflow its banks creating a pond. In this pond, the beaver builds a lodge of sticks, mud, and stones. The beaver makes two holes in the lodge near the bottom of the pond. The water at the bottom of the pond does not freeze during the winter, and the beaver is able to leave the lodge to collect food. The following chart lists a number of the beaver's structural adaptations. Copy the chart into your notebook. Try to complete the chart by inferring a reason for each adaptation based on the information given.

Body Part	Structural Adaptations	Reason for Adaptations
Body	• compact, pointed head and rounded back produces a streamlined shape	
Fur	• rich golden-brown colour • outer layer of guard hairs • underfur has interlocking barbed hooks that form a thick, dense mat	
Front Legs and Feet	• small, short with long, sharp claws and five toes • uses like hands to perform complex tasks	
Hind Legs and Feet	• short, with large, blunt claws • five toes, fully webbed • inside two claws on feet move like pliers	
Tail	• flat, muscular, flexible, and strong • broad, paddle-shaped • covered with leathery scales and coarse hairs	
Teeth	• four long, self-sharpening incisors with a hard, orange enamel coating • sharp, bumpy molars • teeth grow constantly • mouth shuts behind incisors	
Eyes	• small, covered with transparent eyelids	
Ears	• excellent hearing • have valves that close under water	
Nostrils	• acute sense of smell • have valves that close under water	

Did you know?
Researchers have discovered that nerve endings in the beaver's nose trigger a reaction that sends blood to vital organs that may suffer oxygen depletion when the beaver dives under water. At the same time, the beaver's heart rate slows down due to this reduced need for oxygen. Since humans have similar nerve endings in their noses, researchers are studying the beaver's underwater swimming adaptations to improve the procedure for open-heart surgery.

The beaver also has many behavioural adaptations. Research these adaptations using your library or resource centre. Write a one-page report on your findings.

Section review questions

1. Why is the environment an animal lives in directly related to its ability to provide the necessities of life? State reasons for your answer.
2. List a desert animal and state the adaptation it has that enables it to survive for the following conditions.
   a) avoiding extreme light and heat
   b) conserving moisture
3. Why are insects the most plentiful desert animal? Why are they an important link in desert food chains?
4. List the four zones of a typical pond. Identify one animal that lives in each zone and explain how it is adapted for survival.
5. How is the beaver structurally adapted to build its dam and lodge?

6.5 The role of adaptation

In this chapter, you have seen that adaptation is the ability of an organism to survive in a particular environment as a result of its special characteristics. The Earth contains over one million known species of animals and 350 000 species of plants, all of which are suited to live in their particular environments.

Structural adaptations in plants enable them to obtain enough air, light, moisture, and nutrients to survive. For example, plants breathe through breathing pores, or stomata, and reproduce by methods such as cell division, pollination, seed production, and spore formation.

Adaptations protect plants from extremes of temperature and light, and help them to compete with other plants. Adaptations also protect plants from disease, and discourage animals from eating them. Adaptations allow plants to fulfill their basic needs and ensure the continuation of each species.

Why are maple keys an important structural adaptation of the maple tree?

Many animal adaptations are related to finding and consuming food, such as special mouth parts, sense organs, camouflage, and ways of moving. Adaptations for breathing include diffusion through membranes, gills, spiracles, and lungs.

The role of adaptation in animal reproduction ensures the existence of each species. Adaptations for reproduction include cell division, egg laying, or live birth. Adaptations in plumage, colour, odour, communication, or behaviour activate mating. The number of offspring, the amount of space, and the kind of parenting also influence survival.

Animals must be able to feed and reproduce. Animal adaptations for defence against predators or adverse environmental conditions may include the structural adaptations of mouth parts, limbs, body coverings, and sense organs. Other adaptations include chemicals, camouflage, hibernation, the way an animal builds its home, and how it moves.

Adaptation allows organisms to survive in ever-changing environmental conditions. Organisms that do not have the adaptations that suit them to their environments cannot survive.

Can you now infer why dinosaurs no longer live on Earth? Scientists believe that dinosaurs were victims of changes in their environment. The characteristics that suited dinosaurs to live in lush forest conditions allowed them to flourish as long as those conditions did not change. However, scientists suspect that gradual changes in the Earth's climate led to drastic changes in the dinosaurs' temperate forest environment. The characteristics of dinosaurs that suited them to

How do fish scales enable fish to survive in an aquatic environment?

What kind of parenting behaviour is necessary for the survival of hatchlings?

What is the role of a skunk's spray?

these conditions did not suit them to the new conditions.

Dinosaurs passed into Earth's history leaving fossil records of their long-ago presence. The lush forests that were home to dinosaurs became the great oil and coal deposits that we use for fuel. Why do you think scientists call these sources of energy fossil fuels?

Try this!

Conduct a library and laboratory research project to determine the role of adaptation in the survival of these organisms: ants, perch, gulls, polar bears, and maple trees. Ask a librarian to help you choose the appropriate reference materials and remember to use recent magazine articles, too. Describe the environment each organism lives in. Examine live or preserved specimens where possible, and record your information and observations in a chart. Investigate the adaptations used by each organism to feed, breathe, reproduce, and defend itself. What are the similarities and differences of the adaptations of each organism? Write down your conclusions about the role of adaptation in the survival of each organism.

Try this!

Many human inventions reflect the adaptations of specific organisms. For example, bats, dolphins, and porpoises produce squeaks that bounce back from solid objects telling them the location and distance of these obstacles. Radar is a human invention that simulates this adaptation. Can you think of any other examples where human invention reflects a particular adaptation? Research the adaptations of several organisms such as hummingbirds, ducks, crabs, ray fish, and water spiders. Make a chart listing an adaptation of each organism and the human invention that corresponds to it. Cut out pictures from magazines to illustrate your chart.

A bat

The danger of extinction

Fossil remains reveal that many plant and animal species have become extinct due to natural events, such as a change in global climate. The changes that led to the **extinction** of dinosaurs were probably very gradual. Changes that alter environments and affect the survival of organisms can also occur on a smaller scale. Often these changes are caused by humans. For example, southern Ontario was once home to large numbers of timber wolves. Native Canadian folklore often centres on legends of the wolf, a creature feared and respected by native peoples.

Today, there are no timber wolves in the forest tracts that remain in southern Ontario. A variety of factors led to their disappearance. When settlers cut down trees for lumber, or removed them to create farms, the forest environment changed. Over the decades, the number of areas that could support wolves has decreased. Another factor in the decline of wolf populations was the hunting of wolves for bounty. People misunderstood the wolf and the part it played in the forest environment. They thought the wolf was a vicious killer that threatened human settlements, so people were paid to kill wolves.

Today, there are only 33 000 timber wolves left in Canada. Hardly any of them live in southern Ontario. Fortunately, timber wolves are now protected, and, unless there is a change, they should avoid extinction. Other species have not fared as well.

A timber wolf

Endangered species

The forces of natural selection eliminate organisms unable to compete with other organisms that are better able to survive in a particular environment. Today, four out of five species that are **endangered** were adapted to thrive in their natural environment. However, due to rapid changes in their environments, they face extinction.

Many factors contribute to wildlife becoming endangered. As human populations increase, competition for living space takes place and natural habitats are lost. Forests are shrinking because of the space required for urbanization, agriculture, and transportation. Wetlands are drained for similar reasons.

A bald eagle   An eastern cougar

Shorelines and inland beaches are used for home and cottage development. Prairie grasslands have been converted for domestic crop production. Even the fragile Arctic is undergoing changes due to resource development and oil exploration. Other factors also contribute to the increase in endangered wildlife, such as pollution and unregulated hunting and fishing.

Increased awareness of endangered species has led many people to try to solve some of the problems that threaten them. International agreements have been developed to protect endangered species by preventing trade in certain products. Fishing and hunting regulations have also been developed for use in international waters. Many provinces have an endangered species act that protects flora or fauna threatened with extinction in those provinces. The government has established national parks and wildlife reserves to provide breeding grounds. Some animals are bred in captivity and reintroduced into natural habitats. Hunting regulations limit the number of animals killed per year, and poachers are heavily fined if they are caught. Through public education and government action, it is possible to preserve the variety of life by maintaining a stable environment.

Table 6.3   Some animals in danger of extinction

Animal	Description	Natural Habitat	Reason in Danger of Extinction
Mammal			
• Right Whale (Other whales: Bowhead, Blue, Beluga, Humpback)	• large, black whale lacking a dorsal fin • 20 m in length • wart-like projection at tip of snout	• temperate and cool oceans • off the coasts of Canada	• whaling industry
• Eastern Cougar	• medium to dark colour, tawny or greyish-brown • lion-like head • predator of white-tailed deer	• Ontario, Quebec, Maritimes	• clearing of eastern hardwood forest • human killing
• Sea Otter	• 1.5–3.0 m long • fine, soft, dense fur; reddish brown to black with silvery guard hairs	• coastal waters (Alaska to Vancouver Island)	• commercial hunting for pelts
• Marmot	• resembles woodchuck	• Vancouver Island • Rocky Mountains	• environmental change
• Wood Bison	• large, dark, woolly	• Saskatchewan to Rockies • arid plains to coniferous forests • Elk Island National Park (protected)	• commercial hunting • disease
• Northern Kitfox	• big ears, grey back, and creamy legs	• southern Alberta and British Columbia • short, grassy plains and shrubby deserts	• habitat loss • predators
• Northern Rocky Mountain Wolf	• large, light-coloured	• forest and foothills of Rockies	• loss of habitat • human killing
Reptiles			
• Timber Rattlesnake	• stout body, narrow neck, triangular head • black tail, pits between eyes and nostrils • V-shaped bands • pale and flecked underbelly • poisonous	• Niagara escarpment to Manitoulin Island • rocky, limestone ledges	• human killing • harsh temperatures
• Blue Racer	• blue-grey back, pale underbelly • long, slender body • non-poisonous • 1.2–1.5 m long	• prairie grasslands and open woodlands • Pelée Island in Lake Erie	• change in habitat due to agriculture • human killing

Table 6.3 Some animals in danger of extinction

Animal	Description	Natural Habitat	Reason in Danger of Extinction
• Lake Erie Water Snake	• light-grey skin; lacking body markings • 1 m long	• rocky shores of Lake Erie • limestone rocks	• human killing • loss of habitat by shoreline development • den flooding
Birds • Bald Eagle	• white plumage on head and tail • 1 m long and wing span of 2 m	• lower Great Lakes to tree line • forest with tall trees near lakes and rivers	• habitat disturbed by urbanization and logging hunting • pesticide contamination producing thin-shelled eggs
• Eskimo Curlew	• brown-and-cinnamon plumage • arrow-shaped breast markings • 30–35 cm tall • short, slightly curved bill	• McKenzie District (Northwest Territories) • grassy tundra • wintering grounds in South America	• hunting • cultivation of cereal crops in South America
• Kirkland Warbler	• small, yellow-bellied songbird	• north-central Michigan • low branches of jackpine in dense areas with good ground cover	• human cultivation of mature red pine and hardwood forests • parasites
• Peregrine Falcon	• black moustache • slate-grey and narrow tail • buff-white breast with black spots and bars	• Arctic, United States, South America, Europe, Asia • cliff-nesting sites	• D.D.T. pesticide contamination produced thin-shelled eggs
• Piping Plover	• sandy-grey, black with white underparts • black collar and black band across brow	• lower Great Lakes, St. Lawrence, north to Georgian Bay • high-water mark on undisturbed shorelines	• hunting • loss of habitat by cottages, trails, roadways • eggs eaten by gulls
• Greater Prairie Chicken	• barred plumage • short, rounded tail • clump of feathers over sac on each side of neck	• prairies and southern Ontario • Atlantic seaboard • Manitoulin Island	• loss of habitat to agriculture
• Whooping Crane	• long legs, long neck • white plumage, long, black beak • crimson face, yellow eyes, black patch on head and back	• Canada's Wood Buffalo Park • migrates to Texas, Arkansas Wildlife Refuge • marshes	• habitat destruction • hunting

Are humans changing the global environment?

An increasing human population and the growth of technology often produces serious problems for other organisms and the environment.

The pollution of air, land, and water has a harmful effect on all parts of the environment. Most air pollution comes from the combustion of fossil fuels in industry, homes, and vehicles, causing smog, acid rain, and sometimes climatic changes like the greenhouse effect. Air pollution also reduces the amount of sunlight available to plants for photosynthesis, and harms the respiratory systems of many organisms.

Water pollution is caused by oil spills, industrial chemicals, fertilizers, pesticides, and sewage. The action of bacteria that decomposes the waste, depletes the oxygen in the water. An increased growth of algae also depletes the oxygen supply. Waste hot water from hydroelectric dams causes thermal pollution. This kind of pollution reduces the amount of fresh water. Thermal pollution may kill organisms unable to adapt to temperature increases.

Soil pollution affects a thin layer of fertile soil that took thousands of years to develop naturally. The heavy use of chemical fertilizers and pesticides interferes with the natural

A guillemot covered with oil from an oil spill

Water pollution threatens the survival of many organisms.

cycle of decomposition. The removal of the natural cover of vegetation for farming, urbanization, and road construction often results in erosion and depletion of soil nutrients, robbing organisms of a suitable habitat and food supply.

Try this!

Research some of the actions taken by government, agriculture, industry, and your community to reduce environmental pollution. Collect newspaper and magazine articles about pollution and its effect on the environment. Are there any natural habitats, such as a pond or a marsh, that are threatened by pollution in your community? Which organisms are at the greatest risk? What recommendations would you make for controlling pollution in these areas?

Section review questions

1. Outline the role of adaptation in plants which allows them to fulfill their basic needs for survival.
2. Describe some of the adaptations necessary for defence and reproduction in animals.
3. State the causes and effects of air, water, and land pollution on natural habitats.
4. State three factors that cause wildlife to become endangered.
5. What steps have been taken by governments to protect endangered species?

SCIENCE IN SOCIETY

Should we use pesticides on food crops?

Grain and corn fields are complex environments that often support a variety of organisms. Because farmers want to harvest these crops for our use, they try to control insects and other pests that eat or harm these food crops.

To control micro-organisms, such as bacteria and fungi, scientists have used selective breeding techniques to create plant varieties that are resistant to these micro-organisms. Scientists have also produced chemicals called herbicides that can be sprayed on crops to protect them from bacteria and fungi.

Insects however, pose a more difficult problem. Insects eat plants as food. In this way, they compete with us for the food produced by the plants. If not controlled, insects, such as grasshoppers, can destroy crops quickly. Farmers have tried to control insects with insecticides. Herbicides and insecticides are called pesticides.

Farmers spray insecticides on their crops, which effectively alter the environment that insects are adapted to. The changes introduced into the insects' environment result in the death of insects that are not adapted to the changed environment. However, there

are always a few that have adaptations enabling them to survive. They are said to be resistant to the insecticide. Because insect life cycles are so short, these survivors reproduce new generations with adaptations that help them to survive in an environment that has been treated with insecticides. As a result, farmers are always struggling to control insects.

However, the chemicals that are sprayed onto crops can be carried by the wind to locations beyond the crop fields. These chemicals can also accumulate in the soil and be spread by water and wind erosion. As water runs through the soil, it dissolves these chemicals and carries them into streams, rivers, and lakes. Here the chemicals enter the environment of other organisms who may not be able to adapt to these environmental

changes. The result is a steady accumulation of toxic substances in a variety of environments that endanger both wildlife and human populations.

Explore the issue

The environmental damage caused by the extensive use of insecticides concerns naturalists and environmentalists. These people advocate the development of alternatives to the use of insecticides. Divide your class into four groups. Each group will explore and prepare a report on one of the alternative approaches to pest control listed below.

- Continue to use chemical insecticides
- Develop new plant breeds that repel insects or are resistant to attack
- Introduce more insect predators, such as birds, to the environment
- Develop new strains of bacteria and viruses that destroy insect populations

Each group should analyze its option in terms of costs and benefits, then make conclusions about the value of the alternative approach. Each group should examine economic and environmental costs.

Meet Christine Fraser

Christine works as a nature interpreter at the Humber Arboretum, which is a tree museum located on 120 ha of land next to the Humber River. The building is shaped like a tree and outside there are forests, ponds, and meadows that support a wide variety of plants and animals. Christine runs the nature study programs, mostly for groups of school children.

Q. Have you always been interested in the outdoors?
A. Ever since I can remember. It was a family interest. We camped and spent a lot of time outdoors when I was a child.

Q. When did you start working at the Humber Arboretum?
A. I started with a summer job the year I graduated. I was hired to do a summer program in nature studies. That was in 1982 and the programs here were just beginning. I guess I really established the program here. I was really in the right place at the right time. It was a unique situation with a new, young staff, and we were able to create what we wanted.

Q. What are your goals here?
A. Our main focus is to stimulate children to appreciate the outdoors. We have groups of school children coming here every day, and we offer a "hands-on" experience. We don't just talk about insects. We go out to the meadow to observe them in their habitat. We want each child to have fun while learning.

Q. Do all the children respond to these studies?
A. Almost always. We've had some interesting cases. One little boy came here recently who was an expert on insects. He had all the books and knew everything, but when I took him to the meadow he was terrified. He had never actually seen a live insect. We had to break down the barriers to get him involved.

Q. How do you examine insects?
A. We have magnifying boxes for observation. And we use a white sheet to lay on the meadow so all the insects can be seen. We tell the kids that they are in the insects' home, and explain how insects fit into the balance of nature and why we must respect them.

Q. What is a typical day like in your job?
A. Well, four days out of five we have school groups for the entire day. The other day is spent on planning and meetings. The children arrive by bus in the morning. We begin with an introduction to the arboretum and explain why it's a special place for trees. Then they see a video—a different one for each season— that describes what they'll see on their walk.

Q. So much of your time is spent outdoors, even in winter?
A. Yes. We go out for a nature walk for about two hours. We emphasize that we are part of nature. It's not just something you go to see. We do activities that make the children observe more by using their senses.

Q. What part of the job do you enjoy most?
A. I enjoy the children and the teaching. Since we're a community project, we offer all kinds of extra events throughout the year. It's nice to feel you're contributing to a community.

Chapter review

Words to know

Write a brief definition for each of the terms listed below. The location of these terms is indicated by the section number in the brackets.

- adaptation (*Section 6.1*)
- behavioural adaptation (*Section 6.1*)
- conditioning (*Section 6.1*)
- endangered species (*Section 6.5*)
- environment (*Section 6.1/Section 6.2*)
- extinction (*Section 6.5*)
- functional adaptation (*Section 6.1*)
- instincts (*Section 6.1*)
- learned behaviour (*Section 6.1*)
- reflex action (*Section 6.1*)
- structural adaptation (*Section 6.1*)
- tropism (*Section 6.1*)

Questions

A. Indicate whether each of the following statements is true or false. Explain why the "false" statements are not true.

1. Biologists involved in conservation work think unlimited hunting is a good way to keep environments balanced.
2. Tropism is how a plant manufactures its food.
3. Structural, behavioural, and functional adaptations enable organisms to survive in their environments.
4. Camouflage is a structural adaptation that helps an animal conserve moisture.
5. Migration is an important instinctive behaviour.
6. Terrestial environments are better for plants and animals to live in than aquatic environments.
7. Sudden changes to an environment may destroy many of the organisms that live there.
8. All organisms need air, water, food, and suitable temperatures in order to survive.
9. Pond environments are not much different from forest environments.
10. Erosion and the depletion of nutrients in the soil can rob organisms of a habitat and food supply.

B. Choose the best answer for each of the following.

1. The structural adaptation that allows a praying mantis to change its body colour from green to brown to match a blade of grass or a tree twig is called
   a) counter-shading
   b) mimicry
   c) protective colouration
   d) warning colouration

2. The variables that affect the water quality of a pond environment are
   a) light, temperature, pH levels, and sediment
   b) concentrations of gases, pH levels, sediment, and light
   c) sediment, temperature, concentration of gases, and light
   d) temperature, concentration of gases, nutrients, sediment, and pH levels

3. The most important factor responsible for an increase in the number of endangered species in Canada today is
   a) environmental pollution
   b) the loss of natural habitat
   c) the process of natural selection
   d) unregulated hunting

4. The branch of science that studies an animal's behaviour is called
   a) paleontology
   b) ornithology
   c) ethology
   d) biotechnology

5. An adaptation of cacti to conserve water in the desert environment is
   a) to become dormant
   b) to store moisture in their stems
   c) to close their stomata
   d) to develop waterproof spines

6. Organisms lacking the adaptations for survival in their environment will
   a) decrease in numbers
   b) change their environment
   c) become extinct
   d) change their physical characteristics

7. Many pond plants that float in the water have
   a) breathing pores on the upper surface of their leaves
   b) inflexible stalks
   c) leaves that are completely submerged
   d) flowers that keep them afloat

8. Most air pollution is the result of
   a) reduced sunlight
   b) the respiration of plants and animals
   c) the combustion of fossil fuels
   d) oil spills

C. Write full answers to each of the following.

1. State a definition, an example, and a reason for structural adaptation, behavioural adaptation, and functional adaptation.

2. Explain how and why animals migrate. State three examples in your answer.

3. What conditions are necessary for humans to survive in a space station? What technology might be used to enable them to survive?

4. Why are light, temperature, water, soil, and air important to plants and animals? State two reasons for each.

5. Why might plants be less able to tolerate changes in their environments than animals? State reasons for your answer.

6. Describe the Arctic environment. State two examples of plant adaptations to the Arctic environment. Why is some human activity a threat to this environment?

7. Compare the structural adaptations of a fern, a cactus, and a water lily. Explain the major differences in these adaptations and state reasons for your answers.

8. How are plants in coniferous and deciduous forests adapted for survival during different seasons? State examples in your answer.

9. State and explain four factors that contribute to wildlife becoming endangered.

10. Are there alternatives to the use of pesticides? Explain what these alternatives are and how they could be used.

Science challenge

1. The behavioural adaptations of animals enable   certain species to be trained by animal behaviouralists to help disabled people. Research which species of animals are used for this purpose, how they are trained, what tasks they perform, and who will benefit from this training.
2. Conduct a research investigation to discover how the use of infrared film in aerial photography is making it more difficult for some animals to rely on camouflage for protection. What suggestions would you make for the continued protection of these animals?

Science projects

1. Some species of plants have the basic properties of plants, but they are also consumers of animals. Choose one of the following carnivorous plants: a) Venus fly trap, b) sundew, or c) pitcher plant. Design an investigation to discover the structural adaptions the plant has that enable it to consume animals. What condition in the plant's environment necessitates this behaviour? Compare the carnivorous plant you have chosen with a non-carnivorous plant. Design a chart for your comparison. Collect pictures from magazines and include them in your chart.

Science Project

As a student, you have probably taken on many projects. Some of these were essays, some were research papers, and some involved building things. When we use the word "project" in science class, it usually means something special and fun. Science projects are practical, hands-on investigations into the nature of our universe. They can be simple, such as the *Try this!* activities, or more elaborate, like the *Investigations*. They can also be complex, taking many weeks or longer to complete.

Carrying out a science project can be a lot of fun. You design the project so it lets you explore an area of science of your choice. This could be a topic that has always interested you, perhaps related to a hobby or a sport. While doing your project, you experience some of the excitement (and maybe some of the frustration) of being a practising scientist. Many scientists chose their careers because of the good experiences they once had with science projects in school.

In this chapter, you will discover how to choose a topic for your project and how to plan it. You will learn how to devise and conduct an experiment, how to write a laboratory report, and how to present your project in a science fair.

Science fairs, whether at the school, local, provincial, or national level, will give you an opportunity to show off your accomplishments and to see what other people are doing. **353**

7.1 Planning a science project

The scientific method

Chapter 1 discusses the scientific method in more detail. You may want to review the text on pages 4–27.

The best science projects follow the **scientific method**. As you probably remember from Chapter 1, the first step in following the scientific method is to ask a question. The second step is to make a **hypothesis** about what you would expect to happen when you test a variable. The third step is to design an experiment to test your hypothesis. During the experiment, you make observations, and from these observations you draw a conclusion. Even if the conclusion does not support your hypothesis, you have gained valuable knowledge. You can put this knowledge to use by coming up with a new hypothesis and testing it. The final step in the scientific method is to look for ways in which your conclusions can be put to use. These are known as **applications**.

Does all this sound familiar? It should. You have been using the scientific method in the *Investigations* throughout this book.

Of course, the outcome of any experiment depends on **variables**. Variables are things that could change during an experiment. So the effect of the variables can be evaluated, scientists often do **controlled experiments**. In these experiments, only one variable is allowed to change at a time.

You should also divide your test specimens into two groups for most experiments. In the **experimental group**, you adjust a selected variable. You do nothing special to the **control group**. Then if something changes in your experimental group but not in your control group, you can assume that the change is a result of the variable that you adjusted. However, if the same change occurs in both groups, you can assume that the change would have happened anyway. You would then choose a new variable to test and repeat the experiment.

Choosing a topic

Choosing a suitable topic for your project is probably the most important step. It should be one that is interesting to you, but will not be too difficult or too time consuming.

Many students make the mistake of choosing topics that

Science books and science magazines are two sources you can use for project ideas.

would be more appropriate for a social studies class, such as building a model of an early Indian village, or making a map showing population densities at various distances from the centre of a city. Don't be one of these students.

Instead, choose a science topic that you can investigate in a scientific manner using the scientific method. Here are some sources for ideas.

- science books
- encyclopedias
- science magazines
- educational TV programs
- newspapers
- visits to zoos, science centres, aquariums, planetariums, and museums
- members of the local business community
- talks with teachers, doctors, nurses and veterinarians.

Your teachers, adults at home, and neighbours can all help to spark your imagination. Perhaps your science teacher will arrange for you to visit a local high school. There you may find other teachers who will be happy to talk over research possibilities with you. If you live near a university or a college, you could talk to some of the science professors there, too.

As you have seen, science affects all aspects of your life. So project ideas can be related to hobbies, crafts, and even

Visiting a museum may also give you an idea for a science project.

Choose a topic that is related to a special interest, a hobby, or a community concern.

to sports. For example, a student who raises tropical fish may want to explore the factors that contribute to the growth of algae in an aquarium. A skater might want to find out if air temperature affects the hardness of ice.

Make sure you don't bite off more than you can chew. Select a simple topic that relates to your home or community. Don't pick something that will require too much research before you can even get started. For instance, determining the most effective insulation material for a house is probably easier than trying to find out how to keep the heat inside the house from getting out.

Planning the project

The Youth Science Foundation in Ottawa lists five categories or ''levels'' for science projects. In general, the higher the level, the more advanced the project. At the higher level, projects require greater scientific thinking and technique.

As you can see from the descriptions below, the first two levels are quite easy. Most grade 7 and 8 students will want to try a project from Level 3 or higher.

Level 1

Higher-level projects require good scientific thinking skills.

These projects consist of a diagram, copy, illustration, table, or other display of scientific information already available in printed or non-printed material. Such a display should include some written comments from the presenter or presenters.

Level 2

These projects consist of a chart, illustration, collection, specimen, or outline that is the result of a first-hand investigation. Some written comments should be included.

Level 3

These projects provide a working model or other demonstration of a scientific phenomenon or principle. One example would be a project that illustrates the life cycle of a mealworm. To do this project, you would care for the mealworm and take photographs of it at each stage in its life cycle from egg to beetle. Another Level-3 project might have you make a working model of an electromagnet from instructions given in a book. Yet another project might have you demonstrate how a beam of light shining on a triangular glass prism comes out as a rainbow or a spectrum.

Level-3 projects should include a statement of the scientific principle or phenomenon you are demonstrating. They should also include a report that outlines the purpose of your investigation, the materials used, the procedures you followed, and your observations and conclusions. Your report would probably include diagrams or photographs.

Level 4

These projects require an experiment designed by you. The experiment must attempt to answer a question or a hypothesis for which you must control one or two variables. Your project should be accompanied by a report.

Some typical Level-4 projects might be the following.

A: You decide to investigate the effects of plant food on the growth of geranium plants. To do this, you vary the amount of plant food given to each plant and control the amount of water. You could raise this project to Level 5 by controlling other variables such as the amount of sunlight, the type of plant food, and the soil temperature.

B: You might attempt to find what effect the length of a vibrating air column has on the pitch of the sound it makes. To do this, you pour water to different depths into bottles that have the same shape. You then strike each bottle above the water line with a wooden mallet. To raise this project to a Level 5, you could also pour water to the same depth in bottles of various shapes and different opening sizes to investigate the effect of these variables.

Did you know?
A good Level-2 project may be awarded only 10 points for scientific thought. On the other hand, a good Level-5 project could receive 25 points because it involved greater scientific thinking. If you do decide to participate in a science fair, try to find out what the judges will be looking for. Having this knowledge will help you pick an appropriate project.

Level 5

These projects also require an experiment designed by you. However, a Level-5 experiment must attempt to answer a question for which you have controlled all of the important variables. Such a project is recognized as the peak of scientific work. (Many science fair participants have won with Level-5 projects.) Here is an example.

Suppose that you want to investigate the effects of pollution from an industry located on a river. In particular, you want to know what effect the industry's pollution has on the different varieties of snails and the number of snails living in the river. Although you cannot control things such as the weather, you can still control the location, timing, and size of your samples. To make your study more complete, you could test the water's temperature and its clarity. You could also carry out chemical tests to determine the water's acidity, and so on.

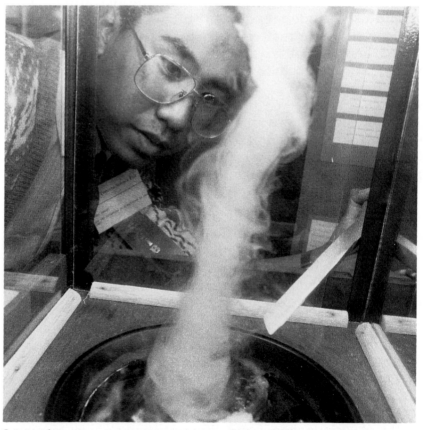

Science fairs give you an opportunity to design challenging experiments.

Try this!

Several science projects are described below. Read the descriptions and decide to which of the five levels each project belongs.

1. In this project, a student tries to find out which type of fabric keeps a container of water warm the longest. No attempt is made to keep the thickness of the fabrics the same.
2. For this project, an experiment is performed to demonstrate the factors that affect the time of swing of a pendulum. (The experiment is found in a textbook.)
3. This project consists of a diagram showing a cross-sectional view of an ant colony, along with a page of explanation. The material was copied from the *Encyclopaedia Britannica*.
4. For this project, a student builds a working model of a solar collector on a model house. Everything in the project is based on the student's own design.
5. In this project, a student investigates the effect of changes in the concentration of a sugar-and-water solution on the bending of light passing through the solution. All major variables are controlled.

How could each of these projects be improved? For those that are not already Level-5 projects, what could be done to raise their level?

Investigation 1   A science project

PURPOSE
To choose a suitable topic for a science project.

MATERIALS
references such as
library books and textbooks
slides, filmstrips, films, video recordings
magazines
newspapers

PROCEDURE
1. Decide whether to work alone or with a partner.
2. Visit your school's library or resource centre and go through reference materials such as those listed above.
3. Look through this textbook and others for interesting topics.
4. Consult your relatives, neighbours, adults at home, and others who have science as a hobby, interest, or career.
5. Make a list of several possible projects, using a chart like the one below. Indicate both the project's *topic*, or area of science it deals with, and the project's *investigation*, or activity you would undertake to learn more about that topic. Also note the reference material or person who suggested your project idea.

Project	Topic	Investigation	Reference Material
1.			
2.			
3.			
4.			
5.			
6.			

Discussion questions

1. Which one of the topics you listed is most likely to make a good science project? Which is least likely? Why?
2. Is it better to choose a topic that you know a lot about or one that you only know a little about? Why?
3. Many science fairs allow teams of two people to work on the same project. What are the advantages of doing a project with a partner? What are the disadvantages?

Who may help

Regardless of whether you do a science project for your class, or because you want to enter a science fair, feel free to consult your teachers, adults at home, and other people for ideas. They can give you advice on organizing the investigation of your topic. They can suggest designs for the experiments, or perhaps even propose an alternative approach. Once you have their advice, however, the project must be your own. So you should build your own model, collect your own data, draw your own graphs, and reach your own conclusions with little or no assistance from others.

Devising an experiment

Writing a good question that provides the basis of a good hypothesis and experiment is the most important part of a science project. These four steps will help you come up with such a question.
1. Choose your topic. An example might be plant growth.
2. Second, identify the variables that may influence plant growth (for example, type of soil, amount of moisture, and temperature).
3. Third, identify the things you will measure and/or observe. For plant growth, these could be height, number of leaves, and leaf colour. Make a chart using your variables as row headings down the side. Write the things you will measure and/or observe as headings across the top. For plant growth, the chart could look like the one below. Can you think of any other variables?

Variable	Height	Number of Leaves	Leaf Colour
Type of Soil			
Amount of Moisture			
Temperature			

4. The chart should now suggest questions such as, ''What is the effect of soil, moisture, or temperature on the height of the plant. How do these variables affect the number or colour of a plant's leaves?''

5. This question, in turn, suggests several hypotheses. One hypothesis is ''If the temperature increases, the height of a plant will increase.'' If you choose to investigate this hypothesis, you would vary the temperature, but keep the amount of moisture and type of soil the same. (That is, moisture and soil would be controlled.)

What are some of the other possible hypotheses suggested by the question about plant growth?

Suppose you choose ''Batteries and How They Work'' as your topic. As part of your project, you may want to make a lemon cell by making two cuts in a lemon and inserting a small piece of aluminum foil into one cut, and a clean, copper penny into the other. (See Figure 7-1.) The citric acid in the lemon reacts with the two metals. You can find out if you have made a battery by connecting the two metals to a galvanometer, an instrument used to detect small currents. This demonstration will lead to other questions for investigations, such as ''If you use different pairs of metals in a lemon cell, what will this do to its strength?'' or ''What will happen when you make a cell out of different fruits such as an apple, an orange, a lime, or a grapefruit?'' or ''What effect does changing the surface area of the metals in the fruit have?'' or ''How does changing the distance between the two inserted metals affect the strength of the cell?'' Each of these questions suggests variables that will have to be controlled as you perform your experiments. Can you think of other variables that could affect the strength of your lemon cell?

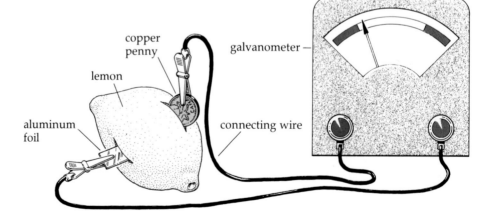

Figure 7-1 A lemon cell

Investigation 2   The project experiment

PURPOSE
To devise an experiment for your project.

MATERIALS
references such as
  library books and textbooks
  slides, filmstrips, films, video recordings
  magazines
  newspapers

PROCEDURE
1. Using the topic you chose in Investigation 1, develop a question that you want to answer.
2. Make a hypothesis.
3. Briefly outline the experiment you will do to test your hypothesis. You could use a plan like the one below.
4. Ask your teacher to approve your proposed project.

Science Project Plan

Name:
Topic:
Question:
Hypothesis:
Equipment:
Procedure:
Safety Considerations:
Variables to be Controlled:
Level of Project:
Applications:
Time Schedule:

Discussion questions

1. Explain which controls you plan to use in your experiment.
2. To which of the five levels does your project belong? If it is not Level 5, what would you have to change to bring it up to that level?
3. Do you feel excited about getting started on your project? If so, good! If not, discuss the reasons with your teacher.

Section review questions

1. What is a hypothesis?
2. What is a controlled experiment?
3. What is a variable?
4. What is the scientific method?
5. A student collects fossil plants and makes a map showing where they were found. What level is this project at? What is the topic of this project?
6. A student investigates the effects of water temperature on algae growth, but some important variables are not controlled. What is the level of this project? What is the hypothesis being investigated?
7. Do you agree or disagree with the following statement? ''Science projects do not have to have any practical value.'' Explain your answer.

Jennifer Louise Haysom and Sanjay Shankla

Throughout this book, you have learned about many adults who are involved in science. Science-fair projects allow students to participate in fascinating scientific inquiries at the school board, provincial, and national levels. In 1987, Jennifer Louise Haysom and Sanjay Shankla won gold medals at the National Science Fair in Mississauga, Ontario.

Jennifer Louise, who is from Halifax, Nova Scotia, wanted to find out if plants would grow in an artificial environment in outer space. This was a challenging problem as there were a number of variables involved. She narrowed her question to find out if plants could grow without atmosphere. She chose chlorilla (an algae), mustard plants, and pea plants as her subjects. She placed the plants in a "vacuum dessicator" with a solution of water and chemicals that were substitutes for the carbon dioxide and oxygen the plants usually acquired from the atmosphere. She found that the plants continued to grow in this artificial environment, and she is now planning to conduct further investigations.

Sanjay Shankla, who is from Medicine Hat, Alberta, chose a different problem to investigate after reading an article on teenage suicide. Sanjay wanted to know if teenagers suffer more from depression than adults do. He commented, "It is generally agreed that the teenage years are the most stressful and confusing times of life. Being a teenager myself, I was interested in seeing if physical, emotional, social, and mental changes, as well as the struggle with one's independence and identity, predisposes the teenager to a higher prevalence of depression." Sanjay developed and used a questionnaire to gather the data he required. Roughly 1046 students and 146 adults participated. He analyzed the data with a computer program. He found that 11% of the students and 10% of the adults displayed similar signs of depression. However, his results indicated that the teenagers were more likely to be more affected by depression than the adult group. Among the teenagers, Sanjay found that 13 and 14 year olds had a higher incidence of depression. Sanjay's investigation made use of some very sophisticated techniques. In fact, the judges were so impressed they awarded him the Rockwell International Canada Limited Award for Best in Fair.

Scientists conduct their research in laboratories.

7.2 Conducting an experiment

Your teacher will approve your science project if it is safe for you to try and is worth doing. Once you have received approval for your project, you can prepare to conduct your experiment. In this section, you will explore some of the considerations you will want to bear in mind during this stage of your project.

Try this!

Scientists set up laboratories to do their research in. In the same way, you should look for a place in your home where you can do your experiment. Think of it as your ''lab.'' If you live in a house, perhaps a table in the basement would do. Perhaps you could use a spare room or just a corner in your bedroom. Much will depend on how messy the materials are that you will be using. You may also have baby brothers, sisters, or pets that you will want to protect from your project (and vice versa). Make sure that you get an adult's permission before you set up your work space.

Keeping a log book

Each day, make brief notes explaining what you did on your project. Write about your failures as well as your successes. Scientists do the same thing. Here's how your log book might read.

Monday, January 20: Today, I put together the pieces of my model solar house. I used glue, nails, and a hammer. The solar panel was attached to the house with screws and wire. I set up an old gooseneck lamp to simulate the sun.

Tuesday, January 21 (after dinner): Today, I started the water flowing through the solar panel. It travelled from a can through a hose, then through the solar panel, and then into my model swimming pool. I measured the temperature of the water in the can and in the pool to see if it had warmed up. The results were:

Temperature of water in can: 19.0°C
Temperature of water in pool: 19.5°C

I found these results disappointing. Tomorrow, I will use a brighter bulb to see if it helps. I will also try bringing the lamp closer to the solar panel.

Monday January 20th
Today, I put together the pieces of my model solar house. I used glue, nails, and a hammer. The solar panel was attached to the house with screws and wire. I set up an old gooseneck lamp to simulate the sun.
Tuesday January 21 (after dinner)
Today, I started the water flowing through the solar panel. It travelled from a can through a hose, then

Figure 7-2

Try this!

Taking good notes requires practice. For one week, record the outside temperature in the morning and at night in a log book. Make notes each time describing the weather conditions as well. At the end of the week, compare your notes with those of your classmates. See if your observations agree with those made by your friends. See if you can agree on what were the most important things to record. Could your notes be used to help predict the weather during the same week next year? Explain your answer.

Safety

In any venture, it is important to both make and follow safety precautions in order to avoid injury to yourself and others. Here are a few safety tips.
1. Protect your eyes by wearing safety glasses whenever you use heat, chemicals, or need to strike things.
2. Tie back long hair and loose clothing when using heat or any moving machinery. Also remove your watch and any jewellery.

3. Make sure all plug-in electrical equipment is approved by the Canadian Standards Association. A sticker on the equipment reading "CSA Approved" will indicate this. For many experiments, six-volt (6-V) batteries can be used as a source of power. They are much safer to use than the electric current from a wall outlet.
4. **Consult your teacher if you have any question or doubt about the safety of an experiment.**

Animals

Many successful biology projects involve experiments with lower forms of life such as fungi, protozoa, and insects. If you want to do an experiment involving animals, these should be your first choice.

Experiments with live vertebrate animals should only involve observing their normal living patterns in the wild, in a park, or at a zoo or an aquarium. You can also report on the normal living patterns of pets and farm animals. Do not harm animals in any way! If you do experiment with animals, you *must* be supervised by a teacher or another adult. Many science fairs have rules against exhibiting live animals in projects. Photographs of animals are a good alternative.

If your project involves live vertebrates, observe them in their natural habitat or at a zoo.

Experimental controls

Suppose you want to discover the effect that a certain plant food has on the growth of bean plants. To conduct this experiment, you buy a package of bean seeds, some potting soil and plant food, and at least 12 small pots or cups. You then divide the pots or cups into two groups. In the control group, you plant a bean seed in each of the six pots of soil. You do the same in the experimental group, but you add varying amounts of plant food. Here is an example.

Experimental Group
Pot A: 1 g of plant food
Pot B: 2 g of plant food
Pot C: 3 g of plant food
Pot D: 4 g of plant food
Pot E: 5 g of plant food
Pot F: 6 g of plant food

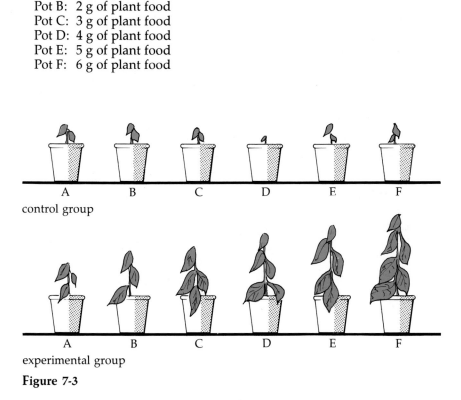

Figure 7-3

This could be an excellent experiment, but there are many variables that still must be controlled. For example, you must make sure that each bean gets the same amount of water. Can you name three other variables that must be controlled if this experiment is to be meaningful?

This naturalist is using binoculars to help him observe distant objects more accurately.

Making observations

Your senses can be used to make observations. In one project, you might see that some plants have grown bigger than others. In another, you might note that one container feels warmer than another. In a third project, you might observe that a test material gave off an odour similar to rotten eggs. In a fourth, you might hear that the song made by a species of wild bird changes with the seasons.

These kinds of observations are called **qualitative observations**. They describe something in terms like bigger, warmer, unpleasant, different. Qualitative observations can lead to misunderstandings. For instance, many students may disagree with an adult about what "loud" means when referring to music coming from a stereo. In the same way, what you call "warm" your friend might call "hot."

Science progresses by sharing experimental results. So it is usually better to have an exact measure of some value instead of a general description. If you can report that sprouting bean plants treated with plant food grew an average of 3.5 cm taller than those not treated, you will have communicated your findings more precisely. Observations that involve measurements are called **quantitative observations**.

To make quantitative observations, you must rely on measuring tools and scientific instruments. You are already familiar with some some of these, including the ruler, balance, and graduated cylinder. Other scientific instruments can help you stretch your senses beyond their normal limits. A microscope, for example, will let you observe details on an insect's leg that would normally be too small to see. A telescope allows you to observe surface details on the moon. A stethoscope allows doctors to hear soft sounds such as your own heartbeat.

Keeping records

It is important to record your observations accurately. Sometimes words are not the most efficient or effective way to do this. You may prefer to take photographs, or make a video or audio recordings. However, you cannot present these alone in your science project. They must be accompanied by written notes and explanations. For example, you could present your observations about the effects of plant food on beans in this way.

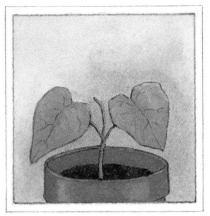

Photograph 1

January 8

Control Group
All but one bean plant is growing taller each day

Experimental Group
All these plants are growing taller and the leaves look greener than those in the control group

Pot	Height (cm)
A	1.2
B	1.3
C	1.1
D	0.3
E	1.4
F	1.3

Pot	Height (cm)
A	2.1
B	2.9
C	3.4
D	4.1
E	4.7
F	5.4

Photograph 2

Here are two photographs I took. Photograph 1 shows a typical plant from the control group. Photograph 2 shows a typical plant from the experimental group. As you can see, the plant in Photograph 2 is larger and has darker leaves. To this date, the plants in the experimental group grew between 1.8 and 5.2 cm taller than those in the control group, with the average being 3.4 cm taller.

Analyzing results

As shown above, your observations should be organized in a chart. To analyze the observations, it is sometimes best to display them in a graph, too. Figure 7–4 on page 372 displays the growth data recorded on January 8 in a bar graph. Graphs often give you a better picture of your results. They can help you to compare your control results with the ones from your experimental group. This comparison will help you to make a conclusion.

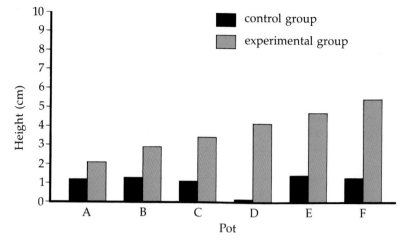

Figure 7-4

Making conclusions

After you have completed your observations and made graphs, the next step is to come to a **conclusion**. Your conclusion should relate to your original hypothesis. Perhaps your hypothesis was "The use of plant food increases the rate at which plants grow." If your experiment supported this idea, then your conclusion could be the same as your hypothesis. If your experiment did not support your hypothesis, then your conclusion might turn out to be the opposite of the hypothesis. "The use of fertilizer does not change the rate at which plants grow." Don't consider your experiment a failure if it ends up disproving your hypothesis. A negative finding is often just as valuable as a positive one. Above all, be honest. Don't try to fake your figures just so you can come up with a tidy conclusion.

Sometimes you will be able to make more conclusions, besides those that agree or disagree with your hypothesis. For instance, if you had tried varying amounts of plant food, you might be able to make a secondary conclusion. "Too much fertilizer will kill a plant."

The need for repetition

You must do an experiment more than once. After all, the results you get the first time could be accidental. Before scientists draw conclusions, they repeat their experiments over and over. Notice that in the control group on page 371, six beans were planted. This is similar to doing the experiment six times. If one bean doesn't grow, you can still make a generalization because five others did grow. **Repeat your own experiment at least three times**. If your project involves plants or animals, use as many specimens as possible. If you get the same results each time, you can probably draw a conclusion.

Sources of error

It is a good idea to list any possible sources of error. For example, not all bean plants grow straight up. This fact could let an error of 1 cm or more creep into your measurements. You could also measure the amount of plant food you used incorrectly.

Figure 7-5

Practical applications

The final thing you should ask yourself is ''What practical applications do my conclusions suggest?'' In other words, what can you do with your findings? The results of the experiment with the beans and the fertilizer is easy. It could tell a farmer or a backyard gardener that using plant food can make a tremendous difference in his or her crop of beans. It might even indicate the right amount of plant food to add. It could also tell this person that too much plant food is not only wasteful, but it may destroy the plant.

Societal implications

Scientists often seek to apply the findings of their research to solve practical problems. One such scientist was Alexander Graham Bell. Bell applied new scientific knowledge to create a large number of inventions. His most famous, and probably his greatest invention in terms of how it changed people's lives, was the telephone.

Bell was born in Edinburgh, Scotland, on March 3, 1847. When he was 23 years old, he moved with his family to Brant-

Alexander Graham Bell

ford, Ontario. In the nineteenth century, scientists had made many discoveries about electricity and machines. Bell met and worked with a young mechanic named Thomas Watson. Together, they applied this new knowledge about electricity and machines to create a working telephone. In 1876, Bell patented his invention in the United States. Later he invented the photophone, which transmitted sound on a beam of light, and the graphophone, which was a practical device to record sound. What impact do you think these inventions have had on our society?

Section review questions

1. Which is better, an experiment that provides results agreeing with your hypothesis, or one that disagrees with your hypothesis?
2. Is it safe to make a conclusion after conducting an experiment only once? Why or why not?
3. Identify each of the following as either a qualitative or a quantitative observation.
   a) the moon has many craters
   b) the temperature increased
   c) the temperature increased 8°C
   d) the beaker got very hot
   e) the specimen had a mass of 10 g
4. You measure the temperature of snow at the same time each day. What are possible sources of error in your observations?

7.3 Writing the report

After you have completed your experiment, you should write a report. It is a good idea to write a rough draft first. Then you can make any necessary changes before writing a polished final copy. Be sure to check carefully for spelling and grammatical errors. What follows are descriptions of the separate parts of a report.

Title page

Your title page should display the title of your project just above the centre of the page. Your name, school, and grade should be in the lower right corner.

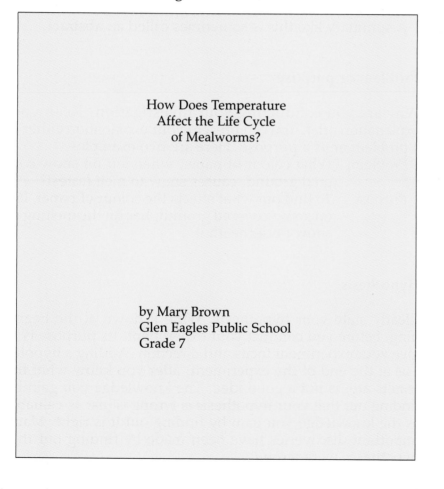

Summary or abstract

When you are searching through reference books in the library, you want to be able to find what you want quickly. Scientists also look through research papers, like the one you are going to write. They want to find out quickly what a research paper is about. So you will want to include a summary right at the beginning of your report. A summary gives your readers an overview of what you tried to do, how you did it, and what you found out. It also serves as a good introduction to your report.

It is a good idea to split the summary into three paragraphs of about 50 words each. Each paragraph should be devoted to one of the following topics.
   a) Purpose
   b) Procedure
   c) Results and Conclusions
A summary like this is sometimes called an **abstract**.

Problem or purpose

Why are you conducting your investigation? Keep your explanation brief. You can present your explanation either as a problem or as a purpose. Here are two examples.

Problem: What colour of paper, when left on snow-covered ground, causes snow to melt fastest?

Purpose: To find out what effects the colour of paper, left on snow-covered ground, has on the melting of snow underneath it.

Hypothesis

Clearly state your hypothesis. Write it down at the beginning, before you conduct your experiment. Its purpose is to give your experiment focus and direction. Adding a hypothesis at the end of the experiment, after you know what the results are, is not a good idea. The knowledge you gain by finding out that your hypothesis is wrong is just as valuable as the knowledge you gain by finding out it is right. Many important discoveries have been made by finding out that hypotheses were wrong.

Materials

So that other scientists can repeat your experiment to verify your results, you must provide a complete list of all the tools, objects, and substances that you used. If possible, give a description and the amounts of each item. For example, "1.5 m of bare copper wire" is better than just listing "some wire."

Procedure

Provide a complete list of all the steps that you took, in the order that you took them. This list should be so complete that someone else could easily duplicate your experiment by following your procedures. Be sure to include cautions and safety notes for any dangerous activities. Here is an example.

"**Caution**: Be sure to have a fire extinguisher standing by and use safety glasses when you heat the substance over the open flame."

Diagrams and photographs often help to explain the steps that you took. Also, they can make your report more interesting to read. Remember the old saying, "A picture is worth a thousand words." Make clear, colourful, labelled diagrams on separate sheets of paper. Put captions under all diagrams and photographs.

Observations

Clearly state what you observed. It is a good idea to use charts for recording data. Photographs help show sequences such as "before" and "after." Draw your graphs carefully. Be sure to label each axis and to include a title.

Conclusions

Discuss the results of your experiment and relate them to your hypothesis. With graphs, explain what your results show and how they support your conclusion. If your hypothesis turns out to be wrong, state this fact clearly. There is nothing wrong with having an incorrect hypothesis. Practising scientists often work through many incorrect hypotheses in order to find the right one. Finally, explain ways in which you or other researchers could expand on your work.

Sources of error

Openly discuss how reliable or accurate your results are. If you measure temperatures only to the nearest degree, this is a possible source of error that could affect your conclusions. Sources of error become more significant when one measurement is multiplied by another. For example, when finding the volume of a box by multiplying the length by the width by the height ($V = l \times w \times h$), your answer is affected by three measurements. If each measurement has a possible error of 3%, then your answer will triple this error. As a result, you could be in error by over 9%.

Applications

Science should be of benefit to us by making things better in some way or by improving our standard of living. Use your imagination to come up with some applications for the results of your experiment. Suppose, for example, that you experiment with various colours of paper placed over snow on sunny days. You would conclude that darker colours absorb more heat from sunlight and cause snow to melt faster. Choosing dark-coloured clothing to keep warm on cold, sunny days is an application of this conclusion.

Bibliography

A **bibliography** is a list of books and other reference materials. Your bibliography should contain all the recorded sources of information that helped you research your topic. The standard format for a bibliography is to list each source alphabetically.

Author's last name, first name, initial, *Title of Book*, where published: name of publisher, year of publication.

If you used this textbook as a source, you would enter it in your bibliography like this.

Flanagan, Frank J., *Focus on Science 8*, (Second Edition), Toronto: D.C. Heath Canada Ltd., 1989.

Acknowledgements

An **acknowledgement** is a statement of recognition and thanks to those people who gave you helpful advice and ideas. A short paragraph should be enough for this purpose.

Checklist

Here is a checklist of the items that should appear in your report.
• Title Page
• Table of Contents
• Summary or Abstract
• Purpose
• Hypothesis
• Materials
• Procedure
• Observations
• Conclusions
• Sources of Error
• Applications
• Bibliography
• Acknowledgements

Section review questions

1. Comment on this statement. ''The purpose of a summary or abstract is to spark your reader's interest so that he or she will want to read the rest of your report.''
2. Should you develop your hypothesis before or after your experiment is completed? Why?
3. Galileo once did an experiment to investigate whether objects would fall to the ground at the same speed even if they had different masses. Supposedly, his procedure called for two metal balls with different masses to be dropped from the top of the tower of Pisa. What are some sources of error in this experiment?
4. Suppose you used a book by John Robert Colombo, entitled *1001 Questions About Canada*, as a reference. That book was published in 1986 by a company called Doubleday Canada, which has its headquarters in Toronto. Write the bibliography entry you would use for this book.

The responsibility of science

Scientists in industrialized nations are currently investigating the effects of chemical pollution on the atmosphere. One recent development concerns the ozone layer. Ozone is a pungent, slightly bluish gas. In the last two decades, scientists have observed and recorded a decrease in the level of ozone in the stratosphere. For example, they have recorded a 4% drop in ozone levels over Toronto. Using high-altitude research balloons, scientists discovered ''holes'' in the ozone layers over Antartica and the Arctic. There is now a great deal of concern in the scientific community about ozone depletion.

About 90% of the Earth's ozone is found in the frigid upper reaches of the atmosphere—the stratosphere. This layer of ozone is a natural filter that protects all living things from the sun's damaging ultraviolet rays. These rays are responsible for sunburn and skin cancer. Scientists believe that a serious depletion of ozone in the upper atmosphere will result in severe health problems for humans. It would also cause extensive damage to the world's cereal crops, wheat, rice, corn, and soybeans.

Through careful scientific research, the primary cause of ozone depletion has been traced to the use of industrial chemicals called CFCs (chloro-

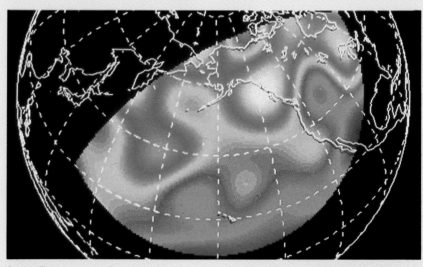

A satellite image of ozone concentrations. The blue areas indicate the least concentrations of ozone.

fluorocarbons). During the 1970s, these chemicals were used as the propellant gas in aerosol containers. Vast amounts of these CFCs were sprayed into the lower atmosphere where they are environmentally safe. But as they spread to the upper atmosphere, the sun's ultraviolet light broke them down. This introduced large quantities of chlorine into the ozone layer. Chlorine destroys ozone. With this new knowledge, governments around the world passed legislation restricting or banning the use of CFCs in aerosol containers. Today, very few CFCs are found in aerosol containers. However, CFCs are still found in insulated foam containers, refrigerators, and air conditioners.

In September 1987, Canada

and 23 other countries pledged to reduce the use of CFCs by 50% by 1990. This agreement is known as the ''Montreal Protocol on Substances that Deplete the Ozone Layer.'' Scientists in industry are now developing substitute chemicals and processes that will reduce the need for CFCs. For example, fast-food packagers are turning to the use of paper products to replace insulating foam.

Scientists and technologists are keeping a watchful eye on the ozone layer. Having created a problem through the development of new technology, scientists and technologists seek to develop new technologies that will be less harmful to the world's environments.

7.4 Presenting your project

Doing a science project is only part of the fun. It can become even more exciting when you are called on by your teacher to share your project with your classmates or with others. You can also choose to present your project to the judges of a science fair. For either of these presentations, you should know how to make an attractive display board, and how to make an interesting oral presentation.

Display board

A display board is a stand-up unit that will hold your graphs, charts, and photographs. It should be as attractive as possible. One way to make a display board is to put together three pieces of plywood with screws and hinges. An easier way is to make two bends in a large piece of cardboard (Figure 7-6). The Canada-Wide Science Fair places the following limits on how big your display board can be.

Dimension "A" must be less than or equal to 3.5 m.
Dimension "B" must be less than or equal to 0.8 m.
Dimension "C" must be less than or equal to 1.2 m.

Once the board is made, it can be painted or covered with backing paper. Try not to make it too elaborate. The board should not distract your audience from the charts, diagrams, graphs, and photographs you may want to mount on it.

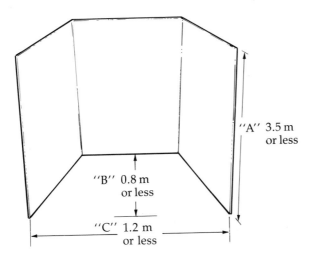

"A" 3.5 m or less

"B" 0.8 m or less

"C" 1.2 m or less

Figure 7-6

Do all of your lettering very carefully. Models or equipment can be placed in front of the board, along with your notebook and log. The notebook should contain the part of your report that may be too long to mount on your display board.

Don't display anything hazardous, such as flammable liquids, dangerous chemicals, bare electrical wires, hot surfaces, or open flames. If your experiment involved living animals, you should not display them either. In general, it is safer, cleaner, and more humane to use photographs of animals instead.

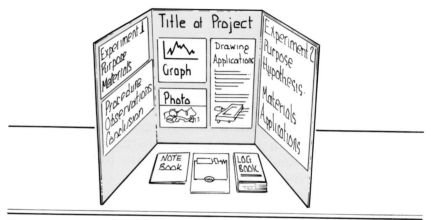

Figure 7-7

Oral presentation

You may be asked to give an oral report on your project. If so, here are several points to keep in mind.

- Present a good appearance by combing your hair and wearing attractive clothes. This will give you confidence that you look sharp, just like your project.
- Stand up straight, smile, and speak loudly. Try not to speak too fast.
- Let the audience sense your interest and enthusiasm. You acted as a young scientist and now you are enjoying talking about your research.
- Begin by telling your audience the purpose of your project. Don't assume they have read it from your display board. Try saying something like this. ''Hello, my name is _____. My project is about _____ . I was trying to find out what would happen if _____ .''

- Next, tell them why you chose this topic and why you are interested in it.
- If you have a partner, make sure that you both have a chance to speak.
- Discuss the same points you did in your written report. For example, talk about the materials you used, your hypothesis, and your procedure. (You may want to demonstrate your project at this point.) Mention the safety precautions you took, and the observations you made (show the audience your graphs and charts). End your discussion with your conclusions and the practical applications of your work.
- Tell your audience what you could do to extend your research if you had more time.
- Ask them if they have any questions. If they do, try your best to answer them.
- Finally, say "thank you" to your audience for taking the time to listen.

Here are a few other tips.

- Get your audience involved by asking them to try something or to look through your notes.
- Write out all the things you plan to say and practise saying them to members of your family or to a friend.
- Another way to practise is to make a tape recording of what you plan to say and play it back to yourself. Keep practising until you feel satisfied that you know the main points you want to make and in what order they should go. Don't memorize your speech word for word.

Section review questions

1. Why is it important to make an attractive display board to present your project? What would you include on your display board?
2. Is it a good idea to display live animals when you set up your project at a science fair? Why or why not?
3. What can you do to make an oral report on your project interesting? How would you get your audience involved?
4. Is memorizing your speech a good way to prepare for giving a report? What are some other ways to prepare?

SCIENCE IN OUR LIVES

The National Research Council

Many people believe that scientific research is critical to the economic prosperity of modern society. In 1916, the Canadian government established the National Research Council (NRC) to help Canadian scientists in their research. Since its beginning, the NRC has funded and provided research facilities for thousands of scientists. Today, the NRC is recognized as one of the world's most important supporters of important scientific research.

Caesium clock

The activities of the NRC are many, and they cover a wide range of scientific inquiry. Usually, the NRC supports research in areas not investigated by industry. Several projects have been created to help handicapped Canadians lead more rewarding lives. For example, the modern pocket calculator is a wonderful tool that helps in mathematical computations. Thanks to the NRC, this device can now be used by blind people. The calculator looks and works like any ordinary calculator, but its output allows the blind to use their sense of touch and hearing to ''read'' the results of the operation.

The NRC was a major contributor to the development of the Canadarm for NASA's space shuttle program. The NRC has also investigated the use of solar energy to heat buildings and homes. Physicists at the NRC developed the Caesium clock, the world's most accurate timepiece.

One very unusual project directed by the NRC concerned the problem birds created near large airports. An aircraft can be seriously damaged if it hits a bird while taking off or landing. At Vancouver International Airport, people tried to scare the flocks of shore birds away by setting off fire crackers and gas cannons. Neither of these methods worked. Finally, a radio-controlled model of a falcon was developed. Real falcons prey on shore birds. When the shore birds saw the falcon, they immediately took flight.

Now you can understand why the involvement of the NRC has been so important to scientific research in Canada.

Chapter review

Words to know

Write a brief description for each of the terms listed below. The location of these terms is indicated by the section number in the brackets.

- applications (*Section 7.1*)
- conclusion (*Section 7.2*)
- control group (*Section 7.1*)
- controlled experiment (*Section 7.1*)
- experimental group (*Section 7.1*)
- hypothesis (*Section 7.1*)
- qualitative observations (*Section 7.2*)
- quantitative observations (*Section 7.2*)
- scientific method (*Section 7.1*)
- variables (*Section 7.1*)

Questions

A. Indicate whether each of the following statements is true or false. Explain why the "false" statements are not true.

1. A hypothesis is the same as a topic.
2. If your hypothesis is not supported by the results from your experiment, you must start your science project over.
3. If three out of four specimens in an experiment show the same changes, you do not have to mention the fourth specimen in your report.
4. Quantitative measurements are usually preferable to qualitative observations.
5. It is not necessary to be precise and complete when listing the materials and procedures used in your experiment.
6. Small sources of error can usually be ignored.
7. It is not necessary to be a scientist to have a science-related career.
8. A bibliography is a list of books and other reference materials.

B. Choose the best answer for each of the following.

1. In an experiment three cactus plants are watered daily and three other cactus plants are not watered at all. The water is the
   a) control
   b) hypothesis
   c) material
   d) variable
2. In a Level-4 science project
   a) all variables are controlled
   b) some variables are controlled
   c) no experiment is performed
   d) the control group is the same as the experimental group
3. "This experiment was designed to _____. First, I _____ . I found that _____." These phrases might be part of a science project's
   a) hypothesis
   b) conclusion
   c) procedure
   d) summary or abstract

4. A summary or abstract
   a) goes at the end of your report
   b) goes at the beginning of your report
   c) should be at least six pages long
   d) should only be prepared if requested

5. Any experiment should be repeated at least
   a) three times
   b) once
   c) six times
   d) eight times

6. Which of the following is a good description of a material used in an experiment?
   a) a large can
   b) fourteen tiny nails without heads
   c) a 3-cm length of nylon rope 6 mm in diameter
   d) a bucket of cold water

7. Applications for the results of your experiment
   a) should be left to practising scientists and technicians
   b) are an important part of any science project
   c) are normally beyond the scope of young students
   d) can only be uncovered after years of research

C. Write full answers to each of the following.

1. Pick a topic that interests you. Describe five science projects related to that topic, one for each of the five levels.

2. In January 1986, the space shuttle *Challenger* exploded shortly after launch. All seven people aboard died. Afterward, it was discovered that rubber sealing rings on the shuttle's solid rocket boosters had failed because they had become too cold before the launch. Describe an experiment that could have been done before the launch to determine if the rings were safe. The space shuttle has millions of parts. Would it be possible to test them all before every launch? Would you fly in a space shuttle today if given the chance?

3. Imagine if Christopher Columbus had entered his experiment to determine if the world is round in a science fair. Write the summary, observation, and conclusion sections that might have appeared in his science-fair report.

4. An experiment shows that an object swinging back and forth on the end of a string always takes the same time to complete one swing, even if the width of the swing decreases with time. What are some practical applications of this conclusion?

5. Much of science is based on observation rather than experimentation. For example, in 1985 and 1986 astronomers observed the arrival of Comet Halley. Since Comet Halley is no longer visible, the findings of these scientists cannot be verified by repeating their observations. Suggest some ways to ensure that such observations are accurate and reliable.

Science challenge

Visit your school's library or resource centre and read about some famous scientific experiments. One famous one has already been mentioned in this chapter. Galileo's investigation to determine if objects of different masses fall to the ground at different speeds. You might also research Newton's experiments with prisms and light. See if you can repeat one of these famous experiments.

Science project

Here is a list of possible topics for science projects.
- What is the best way to make compost?
- How well do preservatives preserve?
- How does the greenhouse effect change a city?
- How do water waves cause erosion?

- How can you prevent erosion?
- How does the shape of a transport truck affect its air resistance?
- How can you build a better bridge using popsicle sticks?
- How can you build and test the efficiency of different windmills?
- What can be done with garbage?
- What are the effects on plants of the depletion of the ozone layer?
- Do plants grow the same in polarized light and in regular light?
- Hydroponics versus plant growth in soil—a comparative study
- How do several foods differ in energy output?
- Why does a stream of water often meander?
- Which sunscreen works best?
- How accurate is your ability to recognize sounds of different pitch?
- How can you compare the strengths of different adhesives?
- Design and construct a better solar-powered car.
- What common substances can glue be made from? How well do they adhere?

- How does rock salt affect concrete?
- Which taste bud is used most often?
- What causes corrosion of metals?
- How can you protect iron from erosion by acid rain?
- How can paper chromatography be used to identify dyes?
- How can you make the best crystals?
- How do you compare the hardness of woods?
- Which solar blanket works the best?
- How can you make dye from plants and use it to colour cotton fabric?
- How can you make a mini-water treatment facility?
- Investigate the effect of different soils in your community on the growth of different plants.
- What is the effect of different fertilizers (natural and synthetic) on plant growth?
- How can you compare the thermal expansion of different metals?
- Are some plants actually carnivorous?
- What is the effect of a landfill site on a surrounding ecosystem?

Index

Photo credits

Chapter 1 Investigating Living Things

2, Birgitte Nielsen; **4,** NASA; **6,** Ontario Ministry of Natural Resources; **8 (left),** MILLER COMSTOCK INC.; **8 (centre),** Kennon Cooke/VALAN PHOTOS; **8 (right),** Bill Ivy; **10,** CANAPRESS; **11 (top, bottom),** National Museums of Canada; **12,** Department of Regional Industrial Expansion; **13,** NASA; **15,** University of Toronto Archives; **16 (left, right),** Department of Regional Industrial Expansion; **17,** J.A. Wilkinson/VALAN PHOTOS; **19, 20 (top, bottom),** Birgitte Nielsen; **21,** Federation of Ontario Naturalists; **23, 25,** Birgitte Nielsen; **26,** Warner-Lambert Canada Inc.; **28,** CANAPRESS; **29, 31, 34,** Birgitte Nielsen; **37, 45,** Department of Regional Industrial Expansion; **52,** Douglas E. Walker/MASTERFILE; **55,** McGill University Archives; **57,** Birgitte Nielsen.

Chapter 2 Solutions

62, 64 (top, bottom left), Birgitte Nielsen; **64 (bottom right),** Province of British Columbia; **65,** Mark Tomalty/MASTERFILE; **70,** Ontario Ministry of Agriculture and Food; **71 (top, bottom), 73, 76,** Birgitte Nielsen; **77,** Athlete Information Bureau and Canadian Olympic Association; **78 (top),** S.S.C. Photo Centre; **78 (bottom),** Birgitte Nielsen; **79,** Pollution Probe; **81, 82, 85,** Birgitte Nielsen; **88,** Warner-Lambert Canada Inc.; **89, 93, 94,** Birgitte Nielsen; **95,** Ontario Ministry of Natural Resources; **96,** National Archives of Canada/c-7516; **97, 98, 99 (top, bottom),** Birgitte Nielsen; **101 (top),** J.A. Kraulis/MASTERFILE; **101 (bottom),** Hans Blohm/MASTERFILE; **103,** Birgitte Nielsen; **105,** Kodak Canada Inc.; **106,** Ontario Ministry of Natural Resources; **107,** Birgitte Nielsen; **108 (left, right), 109 (left),** Pollution Probe; **109 (right),** E.B. Eddy Forest Products Ltd.; **110,** Ontario Ministry of Agriculture and Food; **111,** Ontario Ministry of Natural Resources; **112,** Hamilton Harbour Commissioners; **113,** Walter Hodges/MASTERFILE; **114,** Birgitte Nielsen.

Chapter 3 Force, Work, and Energy

118, Jurgen Hingsen/MASTERFILE; **120,** Birgitte Nielsen; **124,** NASA; **125 (top),** Birgitte Nielsen; **125 (bottom),** Thomas Ives/MILLER COMSTOCK INC.; **126,** Birgitte Nielsen, **127,** CANAPRESS, **129, 137,** Birgitte Nielsen; **140,** NASA; **143, 145 (top),** Birgitte Nielsen; **145 (centre),** West Virginia Governor's Office; **145 (bottom), 147,** Ontario Hydro; **149,** Birgitte Nielsen; **153,** Fitness Slide Library, Athlete Information Bureau; **154 (left),** Department of Regional Industrial Expansion; **154 (centre),** Athlete Information Bureau and Canadian Olympic Association; **154 (top right),** Birgitte Nielsen; **154 (bottom right),** Dennis W. Schmidt/VALAN PHOTOS; **155,** Department of Regional Industrial Expansion; **156,** Athlete Information Bureau and Canadian

Olympic Association; **157,** Birgitte Nielsen; **158,** Ontario Ministry of Natural Resources; **159,** Department of Regional Industrial Expansion; **166 (top),** National Archives of Canada/PA-129684; **166 (bottom),** Department of Communications; **167,** General Motors of Canada; **168,** Bombardier Inc.; **169,** Ford Motor Company; **170,** Birgitte Nielsen.

Chapter 4 Soil and Plant Ecology

174, 176, Ontario Ministry of Agriculture and Food; **177,** Birgitte Nielsen; **180,** Ontario Ministry of Agriculture and Food; **181 (top),** Birgitte Nielsen; **181 (bottom),** CANAPRESS; **183,** Birgitte Nielsen; **185,** S.S.C. Photo Centre; **186,** Department of Regional Industrial Expansion; **187,** Birgitte Nielsen; **189, 190 (top, bottom), 191 (top),** Ontario Ministry of Agriculture and Food; **191 (bottom), 193, 194,** Birgitte Nielsen; **196, 198, 201,** Ontario Ministry of Agriculture and Food; **202,** Don Boufford/Ontario Ministry of Natural Resources, Orono Provincial Forest Station; **206, 207, 208,** Birgitte Nielsen; **211 (left),** Ontario Ministry of Agriculture and Food; **211 (right),** S.S.C. Photo Centre; **212 (top),** Dr. W. Aubrey Crich; **212 (centre, bottom),** Ontario Ministry of Agriculture and Food; **216,** Dr. W. Aubrey Crich; **219 (left),** Ontario Ministry of Agriculture and Food; **219 (right),** J.A. Kraulis/MASTERFILE; **220,** Ron Watts/MASTERFILE; **223, 224,** Ontario Ministry of Agriculture and Food; **225,** Department of Regional Industrial Expansion; **226,** Birgitte Nielsen.

Chapter 5 Heat and Temperature

230, Henry Georgi/MILLER COMSTOCK INC.; **232,** Department of Regional Industrial Expansion; **237,** New York Academy of Medicine Library; **238, 240 (top, bottom), 244,** Birgitte Nielsen; **245,** Ontario Hydro; **246 (top),** Birgitte Nielsen; **246 (bottom),** Bill Ivy; **247,** Ontario Hydro; **248 (left, right),** Department of Regional Industrial Expansion; **249,** Ontario Hydro; **250 (top, bottom), 252,** Birgitte Nielsen; **254,** Consumers Gas Association; **257,** Department of Regional Industrial Expansion; **259,** Birgitte Nielsen; **262 (left, right),** Department of Regional Industrial Expansion; **265,** Birgitte Nielsen, **270 (bottom),** Department of Regional Industrial Expansion; **270 (top),** John Jacquemain/MILLER COMSTOCK INC.; **271 (top, bottom),** Birgitte Nielsen; **274,** Ontario Hydro; **275,** Irwin Barrett/VALAN PHOTOS; **277,** CANAPRESS; **282,** Birgitte Nielsen; **283,** Pollution Probe; **284,** S.S.C. Photo Centre; **285,** Ontario Hydro; **286,** Birgitte Nielsen.

Chapter 6 Adaptations

290, Tyrrell Museum of Palaeontology; **293 (left),** Karl Weidmann/VALAN PHOTOS; **293 (right),** S.J. Kraseman/VALAN PHOTOS; **294, 295 (all),** Bill Ivy; **298 (left),** Province of British Columbia; **298 (right),** Fred Bruemmer/ VALAN PHOTOS; **300 (top),** J.A. Wilkinson/VALAN PHOTOS; **300 (bottom),** Metro Toronto Zoo; **301 (top),** Birgitte Nielsen;